ELECTRICITY
For
Engineering Technology

THE ALLYN AND BACON
SERIES IN ELECTRICAL TECHNOLOGY
UNDER THE CONSULTING EDITORSHIP OF GLADE WILCOX

ELECTRICITY
For
Engineering Technology

Glade Wilcox
and
Cassius A. Hesselberth

Department of Engineering Technology
Western Michigan University

Allyn and Bacon, Inc.   Boston

Library of Congress Catalog Card Number: 69–11371

Printed in the United States of America

Table of Contents

Preface

Because of present-day emphasis on automation and control, there is an increasing need for knowledge concerning electrical principles in all of the technical areas. It is the purpose of this book to present electrical theory on a level which lies between that of oversimplified technology and advanced engineering. It is intended not only for the electrical or electronics majors but for all engineering technologists in areas where a knowledge of electrical principles is essential.

The contents of the first two sections of *Electricity for Engineering Technology* are organized for use in technical institute, junior college, community college, and college courses in electricity. The material may also be used in industrial training courses. It assumes a basic knowledge of algebra, elementary trigonometry, and elementary physics as prerequisite tools. Although a few derivatives and integrals appear in the text, the treatment is such that calculus is not a prerequisite.

Section I deals with the fundamentals of d-c circuits. In addition to the usual branch current method of circuit analysis, there is a presentation of the more useful methods of mesh current and node voltage analysis. A number of practical circuit theorems are also presented in this section. Capacitors and inductors are introduced and their transient behavior discussed in the last two chapters.

Section II treats the analysis of steady state sinusoidal a-c circuits. Here emphasis is placed on the use of phasors, which are expressed in the form of complex numbers as well as illustrated graphically. The appendix contains a section on the use of complex numbers for those who have not been exposed to them in previous algebra courses.

Section III is a reference section planned to supplement the theory and laboratory work. It is unique in its treatment of applications. Instead of many pages of detailed explanations, the applications selected are shown by line drawings and related formulas with only the necessary phrases to relate the applications to principles discussed in Sections I and II.

Many examples and illustrations are given throughout to help the students' understanding. The rationalized mks system of units is used except for certain examples and problems in areas where it is felt that the student should be exposed to other commonly used systems. A summary, as well as programmed questions and problems, appears at the end of each chapter. Line drawings are selected to help with the understanding of word descriptions. These features, together with a table of contents based on teaching units that may be covered in one week, are intended to make the content more meaningful.

The authors wish to express their sincere appreciation to their associates and students whose comments and suggestions are reflected in *Electricity for Engineering Technology*. They are also especially grateful to Mrs. Erika G. Hesselberth, who typed the entire manuscript.

Glade Wilcox
Cassius A. Hesselberth

1

Physical Basis of Electricity

As early as 600 B.C., Thales, the Greek philosopher, wrote of the attraction of bits of chaff to a piece of amber (elektron) that had been rubbed by fur. This was the first written record of man's conception of electricity. Nearly two thousand years later Sir William Gilbert, who was court physician to Queen Elizabeth I, found that substances other than amber could be *electrified* and in 1600 published his treatise *De Magnete*. The relationship between magnetism and electricity, however, was not suspected by Gilbert.

It was Hans Christian Oersted, in 1820, who discovered that a magnetic needle was deflected when placed beneath a wire carrying an electric current. A few years later, Faraday and Henry, working independently, both showed in 1832 that a current could be produced in a loop of wire by passing a magnet through the loop.

By the year 1837 a number of workable motors and generators had been developed and electricity was being thought of in terms of its practical application. In 1844, Samuel F. B. Morse demonstrated his telegraph system. Although Morse's telegraph marked the first practical use of electricity, the extensive use of electric power did not come about until the initial development of the electric light and power industry, around 1880. The latter is generally credited to the work of Thomas A. Edison.

While these early experimenters and inventors established certain basic principles and concepts concerning the behavior of electricity, modern man, without the additional knowledge of the physical structure of matter, could not have developed many of the electrical devices in use today. Correlating

1

experimental results with the modern theories of physical science, scientists have now verified the electrical nature of nearly all matter.

1.1   ATOMIC STRUCTURE

A *chemical element* is a substance that cannot be decomposed to form simpler substances by any chemical means. The smallest part into which such an element can be divided without losing its physical and chemical properties is called an *atom*. Each different kind of atom is therefore the basis for a different element. At the present time there are over one hundred different chemical elements known to man.

Atoms are made up of negatively charged particles called *electrons*, positively charged particles called *protons*, and electrically neutral particles called *neutrons*. The protons and neutrons are approximately equal in mass (1.67×10^{-27} kilograms) and are located in a concentrated central region of the atom called the *nucleus*. The number of protons, all of which are identical, is given by the *atomic number* of an element, which is written as a subscript in front of the letter symbol of a particular element. (See Figure 1-1.)

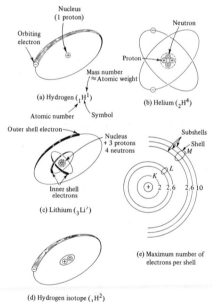

(a) Hydrogen ($_1H^1$)

(b) Helium ($_2H^4$)

(c) Lithium ($_3Li'$)

(d) Hydrogen isotope ($_1H^2$)

(e) Maximum number of electrons per shell

Figure 1-1

All electrons are identical and have the same magnitude of electric charge as protons. For an atom in the *normal state*, the number of electrons is equal to the number of protons. The mass of the electron, however, is $\frac{1}{1840}$ the mass of the proton, i.e., 9.11×10^{-31} kilograms.

Electrons often behave as if they were particles moving in elliptical orbits around the nucleus. These orbits are referred to as *shells* and *subshells*. Each shell is divided into *n* subshells and may contain a maximum of $2n^2$ electrons, where *n* is the shell number as counted from the nucleus. Thus, the innermost shell may have a maximum of two electrons. The second shell may have up to eight electrons, two in the first subshell and six in the second subshell. Likewise, the third shell cannot have more than eighteen electrons, two in the first subshell, six in the second subshell and ten in the third subshell. The heaviest atoms known today have a total of seven shells.

Figure 1-1 shows planar diagrams for hydrogen (a), helium (b), and lithium (c). The superscripts designate the total number of neutrons and protons in the nucleus. This number (called the *mass number*) represents the approximate *atomic weight* of an element. Atoms of the same element which differ in their total number of neutrons have different mass numbers and are called *isotopes*. Although the isotopes of a given element differ in mass, they have similar electrical and chemical properties.

1.2 ENERGY LEVELS

According to modern theories, electrons often behave as discrete electromagnetic waves. Such behavior means that electrons in an atom can possess only certain discrete amounts of energy, and therefore must move around the nucleus in certain predetermined paths or *energy levels*. The group of energy levels associated with a particular shell is referred to as an *energy band*, or a distribution of energy levels. Between energy levels are *forbidden gaps* where electrons cannot remain. The energy levels of the electrons within a shell tend to be nearly the same, since their distance from the nucleus is about the same. Figure 1-2 illustrates these energy levels and bands in terms of the electron volt, a unit of energy measurement. To move an electron from the lowest energy level through the forbidden gap to the next permissible band (from the first shell to next shell out) requires 9.7 electron volts. This energy must be acquired from outside the atom. Conversely, for an electron to move toward the nucleus within the atomic structure of a single atom means that the electron must give up 9.7 electron volts of energy.

The electrons that are in an unfilled outer shell of an atom are called *valence electrons*. It is these electrons that determine the electrical and chemical properties of an element. Valence may be thought of as an expression of the affinity of an atom for combinations with other atoms to form crystals and chemical compounds. In water, for example, two hydrogen atoms share their electrons with oxygen, which has six electrons in an unfilled outer second orbit that could hold eight electrons. Thus, oxygen has a valence of plus two and when combined with two hydrogen atoms each of which has a valence of minus one forms the compound H_2O. The

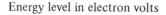

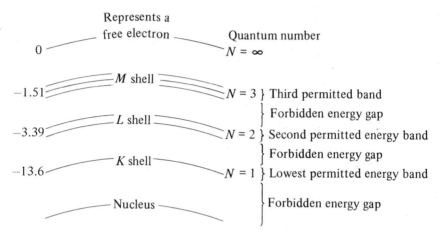

Figure 1-2

outermost or valence-shell electrons behave differently, depending on the environment in which the atom is found. The valence electrons have less force holding them to the atom than the inner shell electrons and therefore may be more easily removed from the atom. That is to say, they have higher energy levels and therefore need less energy to break away.

In metals and other crystalline solids the atoms are held close together. In these solids the paths of the valence electrons overlap each other extensively and the individual electrons are no longer associated with a specific atom. The valence electrons in these solids are shared by all of the atoms within the domain occupied by the electron cloud.

1.3   CONDUCTORS

The name *conductor* is given to those materials which, by the nature of their atomic structure, do not excessively impede the movement of electrons throughout their volume. The solids vary widely in their ability to conduct electric current depending on the availability of free electrons and the ease with which they can move through the material. In general, the metals are the best conductors of electricity since they provide an abundance of free electrons.

In most metals the atoms are packed closely together to form a lattice (crystal structure) as shown in Figure 1-3. Normally, however, not all the valence electrons are involved in the cohesive process that holds the crystal

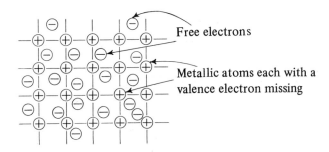

Free electrons

Metallic atoms each with a
valence electron missing

Figure 1-3

together. In fact, on the average, about one electron per atom breaks free
from its parent atom and is then able to move about inside the crystal.

Ordinarily, the movement of these free electrons is completely random
unless they are subjected to an electric force field. In the latter case, the free
electrons tend to drift in the direction of the force, and an electric current is
said to exist in the conductor. However, because the atoms are packed so
tightly together, the electrons are continually colliding with the atoms, thus
retarding the directional movements. Furthermore, heat causes the atoms in
the lattice to vibrate about their average positions, thus causing the collisions
to be more frequent. This means that increasing the temperature of a conductor increases its resistance to electric current flow. At zero degrees Kelvin
the vibrations of the atoms are small and most metals are almost perfect
conductors.

1.4 SEMICONDUCTORS

There is an important class of materials called *semiconductors*, in which
the density of free electrons is much lower than in the conductor and which
display, in addition to electron conduction, a phenomenon called *hole conduction*. Such materials do not conduct electricity as well as conductors.

Most important of the semiconductors are silicon and germanium,
both of which are used in the manufacture of transistors. Silicon has a
total of 14 electrons and germanium a total of 32 electrons. Both, however,
have only 4 electrons in the outer shell. In their solid state these elements
form a lattice in which the 4 valence electrons bind the semiconductor
in a uniform crystal as shown in Figure 1-4. At zero degrees Kelvin electrons
are not free to move from atom to atom. As a result, the semiconductor
would not be able to conduct electric current at the temperature of absolute
zero. Raising the temperature, however, causes thermal agitation and frees
some of the electrons from their bonds in the lattice.

Whenever an electron is freed, a *hole* in the lattice results as shown in
Figure 1-5. The charge existing at the hole is equal and opposite to that of

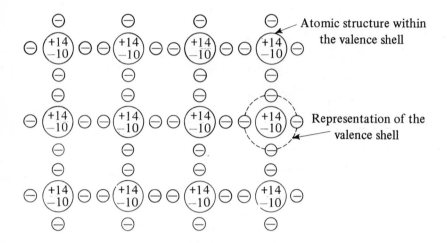

Figure 1-4

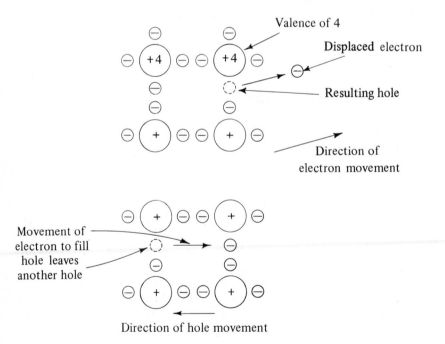

Figure 1-5

6

the electron. Thus, an electron from a neighboring bond may easily move into the vacancy, leaving behind a hole at that electron's original position. The new hole may then steal an electron from another nearby bond leaving another hole. In this way the hole is mobile and a charge carrier in the same manner as an electron.

The movement of holes, however, is not the same as that of free electrons, for the energy associated with the hole is equal to the energy of the electron in its valence band. The free electron, on the other hand, is in the conduction band and has a greater energy associated with it.

When impurity atoms are added to an *intrinsic* (*pure*) semiconductor it is called an *extrinsic* (*impure*) semiconductor. Figure 1-6 shows the effect

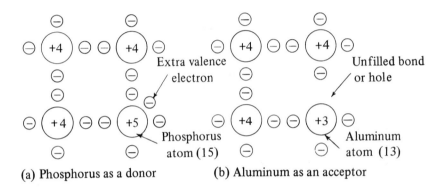

(a) Phosphorus as a donor   (b) Aluminum as an acceptor

Figure 1-6

of impurities in a semiconductor. In Figure 1-6, silicon has been "doped" with a very small amount of phosphorus.[1] Phosphorus atoms are about the same size as silicon atoms but have five valence electrons in the outer shell. As a result of the doping, a phosphorus impurity atom has taken a regular place in the crystal lattice, using four of its valence electrons and leaving one electron which can easily be freed to wander through the material. This extra or free electron from the *donor* atom results in a negative charge carrier and the semiconductor is called an *N-type* semiconductor. An intrinsic semiconductor always has the same number of holes as electrons. The *N*-type, however, has more electrons than hole carriers since the donor atoms contribute only electrons.

Aluminum atoms with a valence of three may also be used to dope the semiconductor. These impurity atoms are called *acceptors*, as they result in unfilled bonds or holes as shown in Figure 1-6b. Semiconductors which are doped with acceptor materials have more hole carriers than electron car-

---

[1] Doping is a man-made process of adding controlled amounts of impurities in the semiconductor's crystal development.

riers and are called *P-type* semiconductors. Combinations of *P-* and *N*-type semiconductors are used to form the many solid state devices so important in electronics today.

1.5   INSULATORS

Materials that do not readily permit the movement of free electrons are called *insulators*. This means a good insulator must have a low free-electron density. An expression of the value of an insulator is in the amount of energy needed to free electrons from their orbital bonds. Some comparative values are given below in Table 1-1.

Table 1-1

Material	Energy Units/Unit thickness
Dry air	3×10^3
Porcelain	5×10^3
Bakelite	10 to 30×10^3
Rubber	15×10^3
Glass	20 to 60×10^3
Mica	50 to 220×10^3

As shown in Figure 1-7, the forbidden energy gap between the valence band and the free electron band increases in height, moving from conductors to semiconductors to insulators.

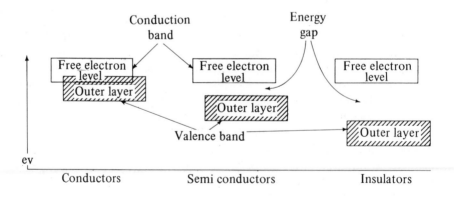

Figure 1-7

1.6   IONIZATION

Electron movements in liquids and gases may be the same as in solids or may be different, depending on the structure of the liquid or gas.

If a free electron with sufficient force strikes a gas molecule it may displace one or more electrons of the gas molecule. As a result the gas molecule is positively charged and it is now a gas *ion*. If the gas ion is free to move, it will be attracted toward any negatively charged area and the free electrons will tend to move toward a positive area. However, the positive ion, being more massive than an electron, will move more slowly.

It is common in gaseous ionization for a stream of positive ions to move in one direction, intermingling with a stream of electrons moving more rapidly in the other direction, with the stream of both taken together being almost electrically neutral. This stream is then called a *plasma*.

Ionization of gas molecules is usually accompanied by the emission of light. This occurs because some of the electrons which have received energy from collisions have been bombarded into orbits farther from their nuclei and when they fall back to their original position in a lower energy level they give up their new energy in the form of light. It should be understood that this effect is not ionization, since the electron is not knocked free of the structure, but usually accompanies ionization.

In liquids another effect, called *disassociation*, often takes place. Liquids in either the atomic or molecular form may group themselves naturally into positive or negative ions. For instance, sodium chloride when dissolved in water forms a sodium ion lacking an electron and a chloride ion with an extra electron. These ions move within the liquid to areas of opposite charge. It is this later action that explains electroplating, electrochemical reduction, charging and discharging of storage cells, and other similar actions.

1.7 ELECTRON SPIN

Studies of the behavior of electrons in electromagnetic fields indicate that their movement contains a spinning action. This action results in a force directed perpendicular to the plane of the electron orbit. The effect of this force is to cause the electron orbit to take up definite positions in space with respect to a magnetic field. Any field, no matter how weak it may be, will provide a space orientation for the electron orbit. (See Figure 1-8.)

It is further known that a spinning electron in a magnetic field will experience a force. This force acts in such a way as to cause the total spin moment[2] to be either parallel or antiparallel (stretching or moving in parallel lines but 180° out of phase, i.e., in opposite directions) to the direction of the applied magnetic field.

Since the spins are either parallel or antiparallel, the spin moments either add or subtract from each other. In some materials the net *spin magnetic moment* is zero because there are equal numbers of electrons spinning in

---

[2] Moment is a physical quantity that measures the tendency of a system to produce rotation.

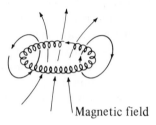

Magnetic field

Figure 1-8

opposite directions. In other materials the net spin magnetic moment does not equal zero and the atom is a small permanent magnet.

1.8 MAGNETIC PROPERTIES OF MATTER

In Section 1.7 it was indicated that electrons in atoms have two movements, an orbital motion in which the electrons revolve around a nucleus and a spinning motion. These movements are the important factor in determining the magnetic character of a given material.

When a substance is brought within a magnetic field, the force exerted on the electrons of the substance is of the same type as the force setting up the magnetic field alignment. Three effects are present.

The *diamagnetic effect* is found in all substances. The orbiting electrons in the presence of a magnetic field take up a motion much like the precession[3] of a spinning top. This diamagnetic effect is due to the fact that a spinning electron moving in an orbit acts like a gyroscope and the induced alignment (magnetic field) produces the precession, called the *Larmor action*. The diamagnetic effect reduces the magnetic field a very small amount and is present in all substances independent of temperature.

Acting oppositely to diamagnetism is the *paramagnetic effect*. This effect occurs when an atom has one or more moving electrons whose magnetic effect is not cancelled by other electrons within the atom. The magnetic axis varies from atom to atom within a substance outside a magnetic field. Within a magnetic field the atomic magnets align themselves in such a direction that the strength of the magnetic field is increased slightly. The paramagnetic effect is reduced as the thermal motion of the electrons increases with heat. In paramagnetic materials the paramagnetic effect overwhelms the diamagnetic effect, which is always present. While paramagnetic and diamagnetic effects are not large they are important in instrumentation and solid state electronics.

[3] Precession is a change in the orientation of the axis of a rotating body, such as a gyroscope, the effect of which is to rotate the axis of spin about a line perpendicular to its original direction and to the axis of torque of the movement producing the change.

Ferromagnetism constitutes the third and most important magnetic effect. In ferromagnetic materials, such as iron, cobalt and nickel, the atomic magnets exert forces of alignment on each other, and entire crystals of these substances are pulled into line. The crystals form *magnetic domains* or volumes of alignment. In each domain, the magnetically polarized atoms are lined up together and tend to remain in this alignment unless some external forces are applied to force them out of their magnetized state.

As the field applied to a ferromagnetic substance is increased, the alignment of the domains increases until all of the crystals are aligned. The substance is then said to be *saturated*. Additional magnetizing force does not alter the alignment. (See Figure 1-9, point *a*.) When the magnetizing force

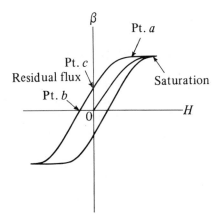

Figure 1-9

is removed, a measure of residual magnetism (point *c*) remains in a ferromagnetic material. A return to the unmagnetized state (point *b*) is obtained only by reversing the external magnetizing force. The graph in Figure 1-9 is called the *hysteresis loop* for the ferromagnetic material. Its shape is a determining factor in the use of various ferromagnetic materials.

When the temperature of a ferromagnetic substance is raised beyond a value called the *Curie temperature*, the thermal agitation destroys the magnetic alignment and the material is no longer ferromagnetic. Some substances are heated beyond their Curie temperature and cooled through their Curie point in a magnetic field strong enough to saturate the alignment. They are then permanent magnets.

1.9 SUMMARY

The discovery of the physical basis of electricity began about 600 B.C. and continues into the present. Electricity today is one of the physical sciences, based on the properties of the atom.

The *atom* is the smallest part into which a chemical element can be divided without losing its physical and chemical properties. Atoms are made up of negatively charged *electrons* revolving about a nucleus containing positively charged *protons* and electrically neutral *neutrons*.

Electrons in an atom possess discrete *energy levels* depending on their distance from the nucleus. The electrons in the outermost shell have the highest energy level and are called *valence electrons*. These valence electrons determine the chemical and electrical properties of an element.

Conductors are materials whose atomic structure and crystalline nature provide the abundance of free electrons necessary for the conduction of electric current. Metals are the best conductors because they require only a small amount of energy to bring their valence electrons into the free state.

Insulators are materials that do not provide an abundance of free electrons and therefore cannot readily conduct electric current. Good insulators require very large amounts of energy to bring their valence electrons into the free state.

Semiconductors are between conductors and insulators in ability to conduct electric current. Conduction in semiconductors is due to both electron and hole movement. A *hole* is the absence of an electron in the bond between two atoms in the lattice structure of the semiconductor and acts as a positive charge carrier.

Extrinsic semiconductors are formed by adding to elements with four electrons in their outer shell very small amounts of elements having either three or five electrons in their outer shell. When semiconductors are doped with elements having five valence electrons they are called *N-type* semiconductors and the majority of current carriers are electrons. When semiconductors are doped with elements having only three valence electrons they are called *P-type* semiconductors and the majority of current carriers are holes.

In liquids and gases electric current may be due to the movement of both electrons and ions. *Ions* are atoms or molecules that have an excess or deficiency of electrons. A natural grouping of positive and negative ions when a compound is dissolved in a liquid is termed *disassociation*.

Diamagnetism, while in small amount, is present in all substances and is due to a precessional movement of the spinning electrons in an atom. Its effect is to oppose an external magnetizing force.

Paramagnetism occurs when an atom has one or more moving electrons whose magnetic effect is not cancelled by other electrons within the atom. Its effect is to aid an external magnetizing force slightly.

Ferromagnetism is the most important type of magnetism, in which entire *domains* of magnetically polarized atoms line up together and tend to retain their alignment (i.e., become permanent magnets) unless some demagnetizing force is applied. Iron, cobalt and nickel are examples of ferromagnetic materials. At temperatures beyond the *Curie temperature* thermal agitation destroys the magnetic alignment in ferromagnetic materials.

1.10   QUESTIONS AND PROBLEMS

Questions

1. Define an atom.   (1.1)
2. Consult a periodic chart of elements to determine how many different chemical elements there are.   (Chemistry book)
3. Define the atomic number of an element?   (1.1)
4. Describe the structure of an atom.   (1.1)
5. Which electrons determine the electrical and chemical properties of an atom?   (1.1)
6. What is the relation between the mass of an electron and that of a proton and of a neutron?   (1.1)
7. What is an isotope?   (1.1)
8. Explain what is meant by valence electrons.   (1.2)
9. What is the valence of each of the following: H, O, Na, Cl, Ge, Śi, and Ne? (Chemistry book)
10. Are the valence electrons at a high- or low-energy level compared to electrons in the shell nearest the nucleus?   (1.2)
11. When an electron moves from an outer shell to one closer to the nucleus, does it give up energy or must it take on energy?   (1.2)
12. What is an electrical conductor?   (1.3)
13. List several good conductors of electricity.   (1.3)
14. What are free electrons?   (1.3)
15. How does temperature affect an electrical conductor?   (1.3)
16. Why are most metals better conductors at low temperatures?   (1.3)
17. How does the conduction of electrical current in a semiconductor differ from the conduction of current in a conductor?   (1.4)
18. Does a semiconductor conduct current better at high or low temperature?   Explain.   (1.4)
19. Name the two most used semiconductor materials.   (1.4)
20. What is a hole?   (1.4)
21. Is the energy associated with a hole the same as the energy associated with a free electron?   Explain.   (1.4)
22. What is an *N*-type semiconductor?   (1.4)
23. What is a *P*-type semiconductor?   (1.4)
24. List some acceptor elements.   (1.4)
25. List some donor elements.   (1.4)
26. What is an insulator?   (1.5)
27. What is a good way to measure the value of a material as a good insulator?   (1.5)
28. How is the quality of an insulator affected by temperature?   (1.5)
29. What is an ion?   (1.6)
30. What is a plasma?   (1.6)
31. Explain why ionization of gas molecules is usually accompanied by light emission.   (1.6)
32. What is disassociation?   (1.6)
33. What is meant by electron spin?   (1.7)

34. Do all electrons of a given atom spin in the same direction?   (1.7)
35. What is the diamagnetic effect?   (1.8)
36. What would happen if you brought a diamagnetic material into the field of a permanent magnet? Would it be attracted or repelled?   (1.8)
37. Apply Question 36 to a paramagnetic material.   (1.8)
38. What is ferromagnetism?   (1.8)
39. What is a magnetic domain?   (1.8)
40. Sketch the magnetizing curve for a ferromagnetic material.   (1.8)
41. What is the Curie temperature?   (1.8)

Section I

Direct-Current Fundamentals

The directional movement of electrons through a conductor constitutes an electric current. When the direction of this movement of charge does not change with respect to time, the current is called direct current, abbreviated d-c. If, in addition, the magnitude of the current does not vary with respect to time, the current is called steady d-c. Most of the circuit analysis in this section deals with steady d-c.

2

Electrical Quantities and Units

Concepts and relations in the sciences are more easily understood and properly processed if they are systematized and represented numerically. Systems are made up of quantities, either measured or calculated. Furthermore, certain measurable quantities are fundamental to every system; that is, all other quantities can be expressed in terms of the fundamental quantities. For example, the force of a newton may be defined in terms of the movement of a mass of one kilogram with an acceleration of one meter per second each second. Here the measurements of mass, length, and time are necessary. They are the basic quantities for the system of mechanics. For electricity, however, it is necessary to have one more basic quantity, that of charge. All other electrical quantities can then be expressed in terms of mass, length, time and charge.

2.1 INTERRELATIONSHIPS

In 1948, a new system of standards, called the mks system, was generally accepted. These standards were established by the International Committee of Weights and Measures and made possible the interrelationships between systems of measurement on a practical basis. Table 2-1 lists important quantities along with their units in the mks system. For a complete discussion of the interrelationships between systems, the student should consult a physics textbook.

The expression of an interrelationship in words alone is cumbersome.

17

Table 2-1   Units and Symbols

Quantity	Symbol	mks unit
acceleration	a	meter/sec/sec
admittance	Y	mho
angular frequency	ω	radian/second
area	A	square meter
capacitance	C	farad
capacitivity	ϵ	farad/meter
charge	Q	coulomb
conductance	G	mho
conductivity	σ	mho/meter
elastance	S	daraf
electric current	I	ampere
electric field intensity	$\mathscr{E}$	volt/meter or newton/coulomb
electromotive force	E	volt
energy	W	joule
force	F	newton
frequency	f	cycle/second or hertz
impedance	Z	ohm
inductance	L	henry
length	l	meter
magnetic flux	ϕ	weber
magnetic flux density	β	weber/meter
magnetic intensity	H	ampere-turn/meter
magnetomotive force	F	ampere-turn
mass	M	kilogram
permeability	μ	henry/meter
power	P	watt
reactance	X	ohm
resistance	R	ohm
resistivity	ρ	ohm-meter
susceptance	B	mho
temperature	T	degree
time	t	second
velocity	v	meter/sec
voltage drop	V	volt
volume	v	cubic meter

To simplify things, symbols are used for the various quantities. For example, average velocity is equal to distance divided by time. In symbolic form we write the formula

$$v = d/t$$

where

$$d = \text{distance in feet}$$

t = time in seconds

v = velocity in feet per second

If, for example, an object travels 88 feet in 11 seconds, its average velocity is

$$v = (88 \text{ ft})/(11 \text{ sec})$$

$$v = 8 \text{ ft/sec}$$

Since the units can be treated like algebraic symbols, it is convenient to carry them along with the quantities.

To save writing extremely large numbers or very small numbers, unit prefixes are sometimes used. The prefixes in Table 2-2 are often used in expressing electrical quantities.

Table 2-2   Unit Prefixes

Prefix	Symbol	Meaning
tera	T	10^{12}
giga	G	10^{9}
mega	M	10^{6}
kilo	K	10^{3}
milli	m	10^{-3}
micro	μ	10^{-6}
nano	n	10^{-9}
pico	p	10^{-12}

2.2 ELECTRIC CHARGE

The basic quantity of electric substance is called *charge*. Although electric charges cannot be seen they can be identified by the forces they exert on each other. While little is known of how these forces are produced, it is known that they are dependent on the magnitude and relative position of the charges. It is also known that like charges repel each other and unlike charges attract each other.

All electrons and protons are known to have the same magnitude of charge. However, electron charge and proton charge are found to be opposite in kind. Electron charge is assigned a negative (−) sign and proton charge a positive (+) sign.

The basic unit of charge is the *coulomb*, which is defined as the charge on 6.28×10^{18} electrons. An electron, therefore, has a charge of 1.6×10^{-19} coulomb. The symbol for charge is Q.

2.3 COULOMB'S LAW

Coulomb's experiments on forces between charged bodies, made in 1785, show that:

1. Charges of the same sign repel while those of unlike signs attract.

2. The magnitude of the force between two charges is directly proportional to the product of the charges.

3. The magnitude of the force between two charges is inversely proportional to the square of the distance between the charges.

4. The force between two charges is along a straight line joining the charges.

Mathematically, this can be expressed as

$$F \propto \frac{Q_1 Q_2}{d_2}$$

where

F = force

Q_1, Q_2 = the charges

d = the distance between the charges

and is known as *Coulomb's law*. The proportion can be changed to an equation by multiplying the right-hand side by a constant. The value of this proportionality constant depends on the system of units and the medium. For the mks rationalized system

$$F = \left(\frac{1}{4\pi\epsilon}\right)\frac{Q_1 Q_2}{d^2} \qquad (2.1)$$

where

F = the force in newtons

ϵ = permittivity of the medium (8.85×10^{-12}) for free space

Q_1 = the charge in coulombs on one body

Q_2 = the charge in coulombs on the second body

d = the distance between the charges in meters

If Q_1 and Q_2 have like signs, the force is one of repulsion. If these charges have unlike signs, the force is one of attraction.

Example (2.1):
    What is the force between two electrons separated by one meter?

Solution:
    Using Equation 2.1 and the charge on an electron as 1.6×10^{-19} coulomb, we obtain

$$F = \left(\frac{1}{4\pi\epsilon}\right)\frac{Q_1 Q_2}{d_2}$$

$$= \left(\frac{1}{4\pi(8.85 \times 10^{-12})}\right) \frac{(1.6 \times 10^{-19})(1.6 \times 10^{-19})}{(1)^2}$$

$$= 2.3 \times 10^{-28} \text{ newton}$$

This is a force of repulsion since the charges are of like sign.

2.4 THE ELECTRIC FIELD

Any region in which a stationary charge is acted upon by a force is called an *electric field*. Consider a point charge (i.e., a charge concentrated at a single point) Q_1 held fixed at some point in space, and a test charge Q_2 (also a point charge) which can be moved about in space. From Coulomb's law we know that Q_2 experiences a force due to the presence of Q_1 and that this force is inversely proportional to the square of the distance between the charges. If, at any point, we divide the force on the test charge Q_2 by the charge Q_2 we obtain what is known as the *electric field intensity* ($\mathscr{E}$) at the point of Q_2 due to the charge Q_1. Mathematically,

$$\mathscr{E} = \frac{F}{Q_2} \tag{2.2}$$

Using Equation 2.1 in Equation 2.2, we obtain

$$\mathscr{E} = \frac{Q_1}{4\pi\varepsilon d^2} \tag{2.3}$$

where, for the mks system of units

$\mathscr{E}$ = electric field intensity in newtons/coulomb
  or volts/meter

F = force in newtons

Q_1 = fixed charge in coulombs

Q_2 = test charge in coulombs

d = distance from Q_1 to Q_2 in meters

Note that the magnitude of the electric field is dependent only on the charge Q_1 and the distance from Q_1. It is entirely independent of the charge on Q_2.

The electric field intensity is a vector quantity. This means it has direction as well as magnitude. The direction of the $\mathscr{E}$ field at a point is always considered as the direction of the force on a positive charge placed at that point in the field.

It is often convenient to visualize the electric field as being composed of invisible *lines of force* which are paths along which a positive charge would move when introduced into the field. Such lines must always originate at a positive charge and terminate at a negative charge. Furthermore,

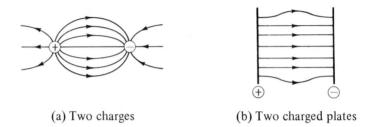

(a) Two charges   (b) Two charged plates

Figure 2-1

they may never cross each other. Figure 2-1 illustrates some simple field patterns.

If there is more than one charge fixed in space, the electric field due to each charge can be computed separately and the results added together vectorially to give the resultant electric field due to all the charges. The force on any charge Q_x at the point where the field is known is then given by the product of the resultant field and the charge on Q_x.

When charges are in motion, another kind of field exists. This is called the *magnetic field*, which is then pictured as exerting additional forces on any charge that is in motion. Magnetic fields are discussed in Chapter 6.

Example (2.2):
    What is the electric field intensity at a distance of one meter from an isolated electron?

Solution:
    If we use Equation 2.3 and the charge on an electron, the magnitude of the electric field is

$$\mathscr{E} = \frac{Q_1}{4\pi\epsilon d^2}$$

$$= \frac{1.6 \times 10^{-19}}{4\pi(8.85 \times 10^{-12})(1)^2}$$

$$= 1.44 \times 10^{-9} \text{ newtons/coulomb}$$

The direction of the field is along a straight line from the point toward the charge.

2.5   ENERGY AND POTENTIAL

Whenever a force is used in moving an object through some distance we say *work* is being done. For example, when a constant force of one newton is used to move an object a distance of one meter, we say the work is equal to one newton-meter, or one *joule*. *Energy* is the ability to do work and must, therefore, be the same quantity as work. The symbol for work or energy is W.

The *electric potential* or *voltage* at a point is defined as the work required to bring a unit charge from infinity to that point within the field. The *potential difference* between two points is the work required to move a unit charge from one point to the other. Potential difference exists between any two points of a current-carrying circuit provided one point in the circuit has an excess of electrons with respect to the other point.

Potential difference is measured in volts. The *volt* is the basic unit of potential difference. It is defined as the potential difference between two points in an electric circuit when the energy involved in moving one coulomb from one point to the other is one joule. Expressed mathematically

$$V = \frac{W}{Q} \qquad (2.4)$$

where

V = potential in volts between any two points

W = work in joules

Q = charge in coulombs

Example (2.3):
Find the voltage across a device that passes five coulombs and releases ten joules of heat energy in a given amount of time.

Solution:
From Equation (2.4)

$$V = \frac{W}{Q}$$

$$= \frac{10 \text{ joules}}{5 \text{ coulombs}}$$

$$= 2 \text{ volts}$$

Energy may be expressed in electron volts. If the charge moved is an electron (1.602×10^{-19} coulomb) and it is moved through a potential difference of one volt, an *electron volt* of energy is expended. From Equation 2.4 we see that 6.24×10^{18} electron volts are equivalent to a joule.

Devices that convert some other form of energy to displace electrons unequally at two terminals are called *electromotive force sources*, and the potential difference between their two terminals is referred to as *electromotive force*, abbreviated emf. A battery is a source of emf, as its chemical action produces the potential difference needed to cause electrons to drift through a conductor. The symbol used for source voltage is E.

All of the various kinds of energy can be used to obtain an electromotive force. Table 2-3 lists the common emf-producing devices which are illustrated in Chapter 15.

Table 2-3   Energy Sources

Energy Source	*Device*
Chemical	Cells and batteries
Heat	Thermocouples, thermopyles, and electrothermodynamics
Mechanical	Generators
Light	Solar cells
Pressure	Piezoelectric cells

2.6   ELECTRIC CURRENT

It was pointed out in Chapter 1 that electrons in the highest energy levels were in the outermost shell and in a conductor little additional energy is needed to free them from their parent atom. Once free, electrons will move in random directions unless an electric field is present to influence the movement. When subjected to an electric field, the electrons will *drift* along the lines of force toward the more positive part of the field and an electric current is said to be present.

Electron drift is not the same drift as experienced by a free balloon in air but more like the continuous directed movement of billiard balls on a table hitting one another and moving on. Electric current is propagated along a conductor at the speed of light (186,282 miles/sec) or 2.99792×10^{10} cm/sec $= 3 \times 10^8$ m/sec, whereas the average drift velocity of electrons through a conductor is very slow.

Current is defined as the time rate of flow of charge. If this time rate of flow is constant, the current is referred to as direct current (d-c) and

$$I = \frac{Q}{t} \tag{2.5}$$

where

$$I = \text{current in amperes}$$

$$Q = \text{charge in coulombs}$$

$$t = \text{time in seconds}$$

In a metallic conductor the electrons are the charge-carriers.

The *ampere* is basic in the study of electric circuits and may be defined in several ways. When 6.28×10^{18} electrons (one coulomb) pass a given point in one second, an electric current of one ampere is said to flow. The ampere may also be defined as the current necessary to cause a force of 2×10^{-7} newton per meter of length between two parallel conductors of infinite length spaced one meter apart. By the electrochemical electrolysis method the ampere is defined as the steady current which deposits silver from a silver nitrate solution at the rate of 0.00111800 gram per second with certain specified apparatus under standard conditions.

Example (2.4):
> What is the average current when 3.744×10^{20} atoms of copper are deposited on a plate in one minute?

Solution:
> Each copper ion has a charge equal to that of one electron. Therefore, the total charge transported is

$$Q = 3.744 \times 10^{20} \times 6.24 \times 10^{-18} = 60 \text{ coulombs}$$

and from Equation 2.5

$$I = \frac{Q}{t}$$

$$= \frac{60}{60}$$

$$= 1 \frac{\text{coulomb}}{\text{second}} = 1 \text{ ampere}$$

2.7 POWER

Power is defined as the time rate of transferring or transforming energy. In electrical systems the basic unit of power is the *watt*. If the rate of doing work is constant over any certain period of time

$$P = \frac{W}{t} \tag{2.6}$$

where

$$P = \text{power in watts or joules/sec}$$

$$W = \text{energy in joules}$$

$$t = \text{time in seconds}$$

In mechanics, in the English system of units, energy is expressed in foot-pounds. Since 1 ft-lb = 1.356 joules, Equation 2.6 becomes

$$P = (1.356) \frac{W}{t} \tag{2.7}$$

Example (2.5):
> How much power is required to lift 1000 pounds 44.25 feet in one minute?

Solution:
> Using Equation 2.7 yields

$$P = \frac{(1.356)\,(\text{ft-lb})}{t}$$

$$= \frac{(1.356)\,(1000 \times 44.25)}{60}$$

$$= 1000 \text{ watts or 1 kilowatt (kw)}$$

The power in a d-c circuit can be obtained by combining Equations 2.4 and 2.5.

$$P = VI \qquad (2.8)$$

where

$$P = \text{power in watts}$$
$$I = \text{current in amperes}$$
$$V = \text{potential difference in volts}$$

Example (2.6):

A 120 volt d-c motor is used to lift 1000 lb 44.25 ft in one minute. How much current is needed if the motor is 100% efficient?

Solution:

From Equation 2.8

$$I = \frac{P}{V}$$

$$= \frac{1000 \text{ watts}}{120 \text{ volts}}$$

$$= 8.33 \text{ amperes}$$

In the English system of measurements, power is often expressed in units of horsepower. One horsepower is 33,000 ft-lb per minute or 550 ft-lb per sec and since 1 ft-lb = 1.356 joules,

$$1 \text{ hp} = 550 \text{ ft-lb/sec} \times 1.356$$

$$= 746 \text{ joules/sec}$$

$$= 746 \text{ watts}$$

Kilowatt-hours are commonly used to measure electric energy. This work unit (kwh) is found by multiplying the power P in kilowatts by the time in hours.

$$\text{kwh} = Pt \qquad (2.9)$$

The kilowatt-hour is a more practical unit than the joule. One kilowatt-hour is equivalent to 3.6×10^6 joules.

Example (2.7):

An electric iron consumes 1000 watts. At $0.025 per kwh, how much does it cost to operate the iron continuously from 8 A.M. to 12 noon? Assume the thermostat does not cut off the current when the iron reaches its operating temperature.

Solution:

$$1 \text{ kwh} \times \$0.025 \times 4 \text{ hours} = \$0.10$$

2.8 RESISTANCE

The *resistance* of a conductor is a measure of the ability of that conductor to retard electric current. At temperatures above absolute zero all conductors have some resistance. The value of this resistance is given by the equation

$$R = \frac{\rho l}{A} \tag{2.10}$$

where

$R =$ the resistance in ohms

$\rho =$ the *resistivity* of the material in ohms per cubic centimeters

$l =$ the length of the conductor in cm

$A =$ the cross-sectional area of the conductor in square centimeters

The *resistivity* of a material is the resistance of a specimen of that material having unit length and cross-sectional area. It is a constant dependent only on the type of material and the temperature. The value most frequently given in tables is at 20°C. If the resistance is desired at some other temperature, Equation 2.10 is used in conjunction with Equation 2.11.

Example (2.8):

The Bureau of Standards lists the resistivity of silver at 1.629×10^{-6} ohm per cm^3 at 20°C. What is the resistance of a 20-ft bar of silver 4 in by 1/4 in?

Solution:

First determine the length in centimeters and the area in square centimeters.

$$l = (20 \text{ ft}) (30.48 \text{ cm/ft})$$

$$= 609.6 \text{ cm} \approx 610$$

$$A = (4 \text{ in}) (1/4 \text{ in}) (6.425 \text{ sq cm/sq in})$$

$$= 6.452 \text{ cm}^2 \approx 6.45 \text{ cm}^2$$

From Equation 2.11

$$R = \frac{\rho l}{A}$$

$$= (1.629 \times 10^{-6}) \frac{610}{6.45}$$

$$= 1.54 \times 10^{-4} \; \Omega$$

The resistance R is expressed in ohms, indicated by the Greek letter Ω (omega).

The examination of a wire table will show that the diameter of electrical conductors is given in *mils*. A mil is 0.001 inch. The area of copper conductors as given in a wire table is in *circular mils*. This is *not* the area $\pi d^2/4$, but it is merely the diameter of the wire in thousandths of an inch (a mil) squared. (See Figure 2-2.)

The areas of copper bus bars are given in *square mils*. Square mils are

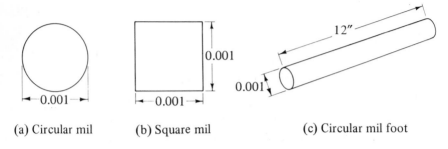

(a) Circular mil   (b) Square mil   (c) Circular mil foot

Figure 2-2

found in wire by using the $\pi d^2/4$ expression. To change from square mils to circular mils multiply square mils by $4/\pi$.

Example (2.9):
How many square mils in a wire whose diameter is 0.10 in (a No. 10 wire)? To how many circular mils does this correspond?

Solution:

$$0.1 \text{ in} = 100 \text{ mils}$$

$$\frac{\pi d^2}{4} = \frac{(3.14)(100)^2}{4}$$

$$= 7850 \text{ mils}^2$$

To change to circular mils

$$7.85 \times 10^3 \times 4/\pi = 9.97 \times 10^3$$

An examination of a wire table will show that there are 10,380 circular mils in a No. 10 wire with 101.9 mil diameter.

A *circular-mil-foot* is the measure of a wire whose cross section is 1 mil in diameter and whose length is 1 foot. For convenience, the resistivity p is usually given in ohms/circular-mil-foot as shown in Table 2-4.

Table 2-4   Resistivity of Some Common Conductors

Material	Ohms/cir-mil-ft
Annealed copper	10.37
Hard drawn copper	10.78
Hard drawn aluminum	17.00
Iron (electrolytic)	58
Nichrome (Ni-Fe-Cr alloy)	660
Manganin (Cu 84, Mn 12, Ni 4)	319

Table 2-5 shows the diameter, area, weight, and resistance for copper wire from size 0000 through size 40. Note that: (1) a No. 10 wire has a diameter of approximately 100 mils and a resistance of 1 ohm/1000 ft; (2) as the wire decreases in gauge number by 3, the area and weight are approximately doubled while the resistance is nearly halved.

Table 2-5   Resistance of Annealed Copper Wire

SIZE B & S or AWG	DIAMETER Mils	AREA Cir Mils	Lbs per 1000 ft	Ohms per 1000 ft @20°C
0000	460	211,600	641	0.049
000	410	167,800	508	0.0618
00	365	133,100	403	0.0779
0	325	105,500	320	0.0983
1	289	83,700	253	0.1239
2	258	66,400	201	0.1563
4	204	41,700	126	0.2485
6	162	26,250	79.5	0.395
8	128.5	16,510	50.0	0.628
10	101.9	10,380	31.4	1.000
12	80.8	6,530	19.8	1.588
14	64.1	4,110	12.4	2.525
16	50.8	2,580	7.82	4.02
18	40.3	1,624	4.92	6.38
20	32.0	1,022	3.09	10.15
22	25.3	642	1.95	16.14
24	20.1	404	1.22	25.67
26	15.9	254	0.769	40.8
28	12.6	160	0.484	64.9
30	10.0	100	0.304	103.2
32	8.0	63.2	0.191	164
34	6.3	39.8	0.12	261
36	5.0	25.0	0.0757	415
38	4.0	15.7	0.0476	660
40	3.1	9.9	0.0299	1,015

2.9   TEMPERATURE AND RESISTANCE

As indicated in Chapter 1, the resistance of most conductors increases with an increase in temperature. (See Figure 2-3a.) These conductors, mostly metals, are said to have a *positive temperature coefficient of resistance* and their resistance change is almost linear over the normal operating range of temperatures. Substances which decrease in resistance with an increase in temperature (semiconductors have this property) are said to have a *negative temperature coefficient of resistance*. As shown in Figure 2-3b, the variation in resistance of these substances is ordinarily not linear over any large range of temperatures.

The *temperature coefficient of resistance* of a conductor is defined as the change in resistance per ohm per degree change in temperature at the initial

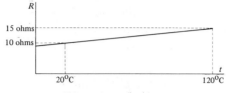

(a) Linear change in no. 20 copper wire

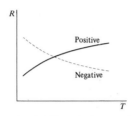

(b) Non-linear change of semiconductors

Figure 2-3

standard temperature (20°C). Thus

$$R_t = R_i\,(1 + \alpha\Delta T) \tag{2.11}$$

where

R_t = resistance at any specified temperature
R_i = resistance at 20°C
α = temperature coefficient of resistance (at 20°C)
ΔT = difference in temperature ($\pm$°C) between
the specified temperature and 20°C

Table 2-6 gives some temperature coefficients of resistance for some common materials.

Table 2-6   Temperature Coefficients at 20°C

Material	Temperature Coefficient
Aluminum	3.9×10^{-3}
Carbon	-5×10^{-4} to -3×10^{-3}
Copper	3.9×10^{-3}
Iron	5×10^{-3}
Manganin	6×10^{-6}
Nickel	6×10^{-3}

Example (2.10):
What is the resistance of a conductor at 120°C whose temperature coefficient is 0.00427, and whose initial resistance at 20°C is 100 ohms?

Solution:
From Equation 2.12

$$R_t = R_i\,(1 + \alpha\Delta T)$$

$$= (100)[1 + 0.00427(120° - 20°)]$$
$$= 100 (1.427)$$
$$= 142.7 \text{ ohms}$$

Example (2.11):

What is the resistance of 1000 ft of No. 10 annealed copper wire at 50°C?

Solution:

For No. 10 annealed copper wire

$$p = 10.37 \text{ ohms/cir-mil-ft at } 20°C$$
$$l = 1000 \text{ ft}$$
$$A = 102^2 \text{ cir. mils}$$

Using Equation 2.10, we find the resistance at 20°C is

$$R = \frac{pl}{A}$$
$$= \frac{(10.37) (1000)}{(100) (100)}$$
$$= \frac{10,370}{10,000}$$

From Equation 2.11

$$R_t = R_i (1 + \alpha\Delta T)$$
$$= 1.0[1 + (3.9 \times 10^{-3}) (50 - 20°C)]$$
$$= 1.117 \text{ ohms}$$

When the resistance changes nonlinearly with temperature, Equation 2.11 is not applicable. It is then necessary to refer to a graph. This phenomenon occurs in tungsten filaments, thyrite, and thermistors. Other materials such as constantan, which is used for precision resistors, have a temperature coefficient of resistance of near zero. Mercury vapor gas also has a zero temperature coefficient of resistance in its normal operating range.

2.10 CONDUCTANCE

The reciprocal of resistance is *conductance*.

$$G = \frac{1}{R} \tag{2.12}$$

where

$$G = \text{conductance in mhos}$$
$$R = \text{resistance in ohms}$$

Whereas resistance represents the ability to retard current, conductance expresses the ability to pass current. Conductance is convenient to use when solving parallel circuit problems. (See Section 3.6.) This is particularly true when using a slide rule, as the inverted scale permits direct conversion from conductance to resistance or vice versa.

The reciprocal of resistivity is called *conductivity*.

$$\sigma = \frac{1}{\rho} \tag{2.13}$$

where

$$\sigma = \text{conductivity in mhos/cir-mil-ft}$$

$$\rho = \text{resistivity in ohms/cir-mil-ft}$$

Electrical conductivity is analogous to the conductivity in steady state heat conduction. The same free electrons which contribute to electrical conduction play an important role in the conduction of heat. Metals which are good electrical conductors are also good conductors of heat.

2.11 SUMMARY

Certain quantities are fundamental to every system of measurement. These quantities are mass, length, time, and charge. All other quantities can be expressed in terms of these.

The *coulomb* is the basic unit of electric charge and is defined as the charge of 6.28×10^{18} electrons.

Coulomb's law states that the force between two charges is directly proportional to the product of the charges and inversely proportional to the square of the distance between them.

$$F = \left(\frac{1}{4\pi\epsilon}\right)\frac{Q_1 Q_2}{d^2} \tag{2.1}$$

An *electric field* exists in the neighborhood of an electric charge. The *electric field intensity* is defined as force per unit charge and is measured in newtons per coulomb or volts per meter.

$$\mathscr{E} = \frac{F}{Q_2} \tag{2.2}$$

An *electric potential* (*voltage*) at a point is defined as the work required to bring a unit charge from infinity to that point. Thus, *potential difference* exists between two points when they are at different work levels. Potential V is measured in volts and is given by

$$V = \frac{W}{Q} \tag{2.4}$$

Sources of potential difference such as generators and batteries are referred to as *electromotive force* (emf) sources.

Electric current is defined as charge per unit time.

$$I = \frac{Q}{t} \tag{2.5}$$

A current of one *ampere* exists when 6.28×10^{18} electrons (one coulomb) pass a given point in one second.

Power is the time rate of doing work. It is measured in *watts*. One watt equals one joule per second.

$$P = \frac{W}{t} \tag{2.6}$$

Where current and voltage are constant, power is given by

$$P = VI \tag{2.8}$$

Energy is the product of power times time. Electrical energy is often measured as kilowatt-hours (kwh).

Resistance is a measure of opposition to current. The resistance of a conductor is directly proportional to its length and inversely proportional to its cross-sectional area. Resistance is measured in ohms.

$$R = \frac{\rho L}{A} \tag{2.10}$$

where ρ is the *resistivity* of the material.

Areas of circular conductors are often measured in circular mils. A circular mil is the measure of the diameter of a conductor in thousandths of an inch squared.

If the resistance of a given material increases with an increase in temperature it is said to have a *positive temperature coefficient of resistance*. If the resistance decreases when temperature increases the material has a *negative temperature coefficient of resistance*.

Conductance is the reciprocal of resistance and is measured in mhos.

$$G = \frac{1}{R} \tag{2.12}$$

2.12   QUESTIONS AND PROBLEMS

Questions

1. What are the four basic quantities in every system?   (Introduction)
2. What is the mks system?   (2.1)
3. How are units treated as algebraic symbols?   (2.1)
4. What is the basic unit of charge?   (2.2)
5. How are electric charges identified?   (2.2)
6. What is Coulomb's law?   (2.3)
7. What is an electric field?   (2.4)
8. What is meant by electric field intensity?   (2.4)
9. How does the electric field intensity vary with distance from a charge?   (2.4)
10. What units are used for electric field intensity?   (2.4)
11. What is a vector?   (2.4)
12. What is the direction of the electric field originating from a positive charge? a negative charge?   (2.4)

13. How does one find the electric field intensity at a given point when the point is surrounded by several charges? (2.4)
14. Charges in motion set up another type of field. What is this field called? (2.4)
15. What is meant by electric potential? (2.5)
16. What is the difference between "the potential at a point" and "the potential difference" between two points? (2.5)
17. What is electromotive force? (2.5)
18. List some sources of emf. (2.5)
19. What is a volt? (2.5)
20. What is an electron volt? (2.5)
21. Define electric current. (2.6)
22. Define the ampere in terms of a certain number of electrons and time. (2.6)
23. At what speed do electrical impulses travel? (2.6)
24. How can electrical impulses travel so fast while the electron drift in a conductor is so slow? (2.6)
25. What is the relationship between power and energy? (2.7)
26. In electricity, what units are commonly used to measure power? (2.7)
27. What is a kilowatt-hour and how is it related to energy and power? (2.7)
28. What is horsepower? (2.7)
29. Define resistance. (2.8)
30. What is a mil? (2.8)
31. What is the difference between resistance and resistivity? (2.8)
32. What is a circular mil? (2.8)
33. Why are circular mils used instead of square mils? (2.8)
34. What is a circular-mil-foot? (2.8)
35. What is meant by a positive temperature coefficient of resistance? a negative temperature coefficient? (2.9)
36. What materials generally have a positive temperature coefficient? a negative temperature coefficient? (2.9)
37. Define conductance. Why is it useful? (2.10)
38. What is the difference between conductance and conductivity? (2.10)

Problems

1. One megohm equals how many ohms? (2.1)
2. A millisecond is how many microseconds? (2.1)
3. A kiloton is equal to how many tons? (2.1)
4. How many megohms is 10^5 ohms? (2.1)
5. One millivolt equals how many picovolts? (2.1)
6. A nanosecond is equal to how many microseconds? (2.1)
7. A charge of 8×10^{-19} coulomb is equivalent to the charge on how many electrons? (2.2)
8. What is the total charge on 3.14×10^{18} electrons? (2.2)
9. What is the force exerted between 2 electrons separated by a distance of 1 centimeter? (2.3)
10. How close together would a proton and an electron have to be in order that the force between them would be 1 newton? (2.3)
11. Find the electric field intensity at a distance of 1 centimeter from an isolated electron. (2.4)

12. If the distance from a given charge is doubled, how will the electric field intensity change? (2.4)

13. If the force on a unit charge is 1 newton, what is the field intensity at the point where the unit charge is stationed? (2.4)

14. One joule of work is required to move a charge of 10^{-6} coulomb from infinity to a given point. What is the potential at that point? (2.5)

15. One joule of work is required to move an electron from one point to another. What is the potential difference between the two points? (2.5)

16. How many joules are required to move an electron through a potential difference of 10 volts? How many electron volts is this? (2.5)

17. How much work is done in moving an electron from a point where the potential is 5 volts to a point where the potential is 3 volts? (2.5)

18. The potential across a certain device is 5 joules. What is the current in the device? (2.5)

19. If 5 joules of work are done in moving a charge through a potential difference of 100 volts, what is the charge? (2.5)

20. In order that a current of 5 amperes exist in a conductor, a charge of 1 coulomb must flow past a given point in _____ seconds. (2.6)

21. A current of 10 amperes flows for 1 hour. How much charge is transported past a given point during this 1-hour period? (2.6)

22. If 1 electron passes a given point in 1 second, how much current flows? (2.6)

23. If 1 coulomb is moved through a potential difference of 5 volts in 1 microsecond, what is the rate of energy transformation in watts? (2.7)

24. How much energy is used in 1 hour in a heater element rated at 1500 watts? (2.7)

25. If the current in Problem 24 is 15 amperes, what is the voltage? (2.7)

26. How many ft-lbs of energy are used in 1 hour in a device rated at 3000 watts? (2.7)

27. A 120 volt d-c motor lifts 1 ton 50 feet in 2 minutes. How much current is needed if the motor is 100% efficient? What is the horsepower of the motor? (2.7)

28. The burner on a certain electric stove has a 2500-watt element. If the burner is used continuously for 5 hours, how many kilowatt-hours of energy are used? (2.7)

29. A 100 watt light bulb burns for 48 hours. How many kwh is this? (2.7)

30. A 100 watt light bulb is made to operate at 115 volts. How much current will it draw? (2.7)

31. A $7\frac{1}{2}$-horsepower motor is 100% efficient. It is rated at 230 volts d-c. How much current will it draw if it is delivering its full output? (2.7)

32. Find the resistance of a copper wire 10 feet long and 1 mil in diameter. (2.8)

33. A certain wire has a resistance of 30 ohms. If the length is doubled, what is the resistance? If the area is doubled, what is the resistance? If both the length and area are doubled, what is the resistance? (2.8)

34. A certain copper wire has a resistance of 40 ohms. If the same-sized piece of aluminum wire is used, what is the resistance? (2.8)

35. At 20°C, a certain piece of silver wire has a resistance of 0.5 ohm. If the material is changed to copper, the area reduced to one-half its previous value and the length doubled, what is the new value of resistance? (2.8)

36. A copper conductor has a resistance of 8 ohms and is 1 foot long. What is the diameter in mils? What is the area in circular mils? What is the area in square mils? (2.8)

37. The area of a circular conductor is 0.5 in². What is the area in circular mils? (2.8)

38. A certain piece of wire has a resistance of 24 ohms and is 6 ft long. The cross-sectional area is 15 circular mils. What material is the wire made from? (2.8)

39. What is the resistance of 1000 ft of No. 12 wire at 0°C? (2.9)

40. What is the temperature coefficient of a certain material whose resistance changes from 20 ohms at 20°C to 100 ohms at 200°C? (2.9)

41. A copper wire has a resistance of 0.1 ohm at 80°C. What is the resistance at 20°C (2.9)

42. What is the temperature coefficient of a certain material whose resistance changes from 10 ohms at 20°C to 5 ohms at 30°C?   (2.9)

43. A copper wire has a resistance of 1 ohm at 50°C. What is the resistance at 100°C? (2.9)

44. What is the conductance of a resistor of 10 ohms?   (2.10)

45. A certain element has a conductance of 0.2 mho. What is the resistance?   (2.10)

46. Express the resistance of a conductor in terms of conductivity, length, and area. (2.10),   (2.8)

47. Express the conductance of a conductor in terms of conductivity, length, and area (2.10),   (2.8)

3

Series and Parallel Circuit Analysis

The first step in analyzing any electrical network or device is to determine its equivalent circuit in terms of ideal electrical elements. Once this is done, all the currents and voltages can be found by applying three fundamental laws of circuits. These are known as Ohm's law, Kirchhoff's voltage law, and Kirchhoff's current law. In this chapter, the above laws are used to solve series, parallel, and series-parallel electrical circuits.

3.1 CIRCUIT ELEMENTS

The elements used in circuit analysis are classified as either active or passive. *Active elements* are sources of energy while *passive elements* are those elements which are not energy sources.

The active elements used here are either voltage sources or current sources. An *ideal voltage source* (sometimes referred to as a constant voltage source) will produce on demand any amount of current without a change in its output voltage. It has no internal resistance. An *ideal current source* (sometimes referred to as a constant current source) will produce on demand any voltage across its terminals without a change in its output current. It has an infinite internal resistance. Figure 3-1 shows the symbols used to represent ideal sources.

Passive elements include such elements as resistors, capacitors, and inductors.[1] Resistors are electrical components used to place resistance in a

---

[1] Capacitors and inductors are considered in Chapters 7 and 8.

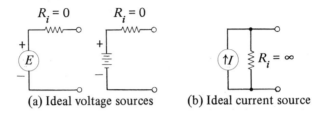

(a) Ideal voltage sources   (b) Ideal current source

Figure 3-1

circuit. They are usually constructed of resistive carbons, metals, or semiconductors. An ideal resistor is always considered to have no electrical properties other than resistance. In addition, it is always considered to be a *linear* element; that is, an element whose value is independent of current or voltage. Symbols and names for several functional types of resistors are given in Figure 3-2.

	Radio and Television Mfg. Assoc.	American Standards Assoc.
Fixed resistor	—/\/\/—	—[Value]—
Tapped resistor	—/\/\/—	—[Value]—
Rheostat	—/\/\— —/\/\/—	—[Value]—
Potentiometer	—/\/\/—	—[Value]—

Figure 3-2

3.2 SERIES CIRCUITS

The simplest d-c circuit is made up of three basic elements: an ideal voltage source, an ideal resistor in which electrical energy is expended (referred to as a *load*), and perfect conductors connecting the source to the resistor. A fourth element, the control element or switch, may also be included if desired, but will be left out in this chapter since it is not necessary in explaining the actions to be described.

Consider the simple d-c circuit in Figure 3-3. The battery generating the energy to force the electrons through the conductors and load is said to create a *rise* (+ to −) in potential when one considers electron flow moving through the source. On the other hand, the electrons flowing from the

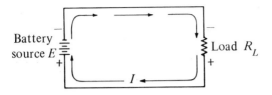

Figure 3-3

negative terminal of the source and through the load resistor produce a *drop* or *fall* (− to +) in potential. A voltage drop (− to +) is always considered) the negative of a voltage rise (+ to −). The letter E is used to represent source voltage and the letter V is used to represent voltage drops across passive elements.

In order that the source may raise the potential, electrons leaving the negative terminal of the source must be replaced by an equal number of electrons returning to the positive terminal of the source. Therefore, if there is only one external current path between the terminals of the source, the current must be the same anywhere along that path. Such a circuit consisting of only one path for the current is called a *series circuit*.

3.3 KIRCHHOFF'S VOLTAGE LAW

Kirchhoff in the 1840's, after repeated observations, announced two very important laws that bear his name. They are known as Kirchhoff's voltage law and Kirchhoff's current law. Both can be derived from the principle of conservation of energy.

According to Kirchhoff's voltage law, the *algebraic sum of all the voltage drops around any closed loop is equal to zero*. (Voltage rises are considered negative voltage drops.) The law holds regardless of whether or not the circuit elements are linear.

Considered clockwise around the circuit in Figure 3-4, Kirchhoff's law is written as

$$E_t - V_1 - V_2 - V_3 - V_4 = 0$$

Or, considered counterclockwise around the circuit

$$-E_t + V_1 + V_2 + V_3 + V_4 = 0$$

Note that the two equations are equivalent since the last equation can be made identical to the first by multiplying through by −1. It is, therefore, immaterial in which direction one moves around the loop in writing the equation.

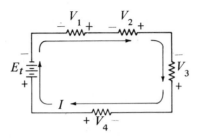

Figure 3-4

Example (3.1):

In the circuit shown in Figure 3-5, if $V_1 = 1.5$ volts, $V_2 = 3$ volts and $V_3 = 4.5$ volts, what is the emf of the source?

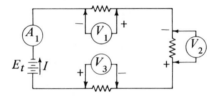

Figure 3-5

Solution:

$$E_t - V_1 - V_2 - V_3 = 0$$
$$E_t = V_1 + V_2 + V_3$$
$$E_t = 1.5 \text{ volts} + 3 \text{ volts} + 4.5 \text{ volts}$$
$$= 9 \text{ volts}$$

3.4   CURRENT IN A SERIES CIRCUIT

The current in a simple series circuit is a function of the applied voltage and the circuit resistance. That is $I = f(E, R)$. George Simon Ohm (1789–1854) discovered that current was directly proportional to the applied voltage and inversely proportional to the circuit resistance. This relation, known as Ohm's law, is written as

$$I = \frac{E}{R} \text{ or} \tag{3.1}$$

$$I = \frac{V}{R}$$

where

$$I = \text{current in amperes}$$
$$E = \text{applied voltage in volts}$$
$$R = \text{resistance in ohms}$$

Example (3.2):

A 4.5 volt battery supplies current to the simple circuit in Figure 3-3. The resistance is 9 ohms. How much current flows?

Solution:

From Ohm's law

$$I = \frac{E}{R} = \frac{4.5}{9} = 0.5 \text{ amp}$$
$$= 500 \text{ ma}$$

Example (3.3):

In Figure 3-5, voltmeter V_2 reads 6 volts and ammeter A_1 reads 600 milliamperes. What is the value of the resistance between the voltmeter leads?

Solution:

Change 600 ma to 0.6 amp. From Ohm's law,

$$R = \frac{V}{I}$$
$$= \frac{6 \text{ volts}}{0.6 \text{ ampere}}$$
$$= 10 \text{ volts/ampere}$$
$$= 10 \text{ ohms}$$

3.5 EQUIVALENT RESISTANCE IN A SERIES CIRCUIT

Since the same current passes through each resistor in a series circuit, and since the sum of the voltage drops equals the source voltage, the sum of the individual resistances must equal the total resistance. Mathematically, for a circuit with n series resistors, the total voltage is

$$E_t = V_1 + V_2 + V_3 + \ldots + V_n$$

From Ohm's law

$$V_1 = IR_1, V_2 = IR_2 \text{ etc. and } E_t = IR_t$$

so

$$IR_t = IR_1 + IR_2 + IR_3 + \ldots + IR_n$$

and

$$R_t = R_1 + R_2 + R_3 + \ldots + R_n \qquad (3.2)$$

where R_t = total circuit resistance in ohms and subscript n refers to the last resistor in the series.

Example (3.4):

What is the total or equivalent resistance of the circuit in Figure 3-6?

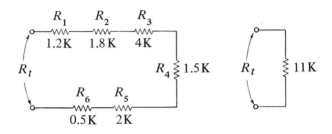

Figure 3-6

Solution:

$$R_t = R_1 + R_2 + R_3 + R_4 + R_5 + R_6$$
$$= (1.2 \times 10^3) + (1.8 \times 10^3) + (4 \times 10^3)$$
$$+ (1.5 \times 10^3) + (2 \times 10^3) + (0.5 \times 10^3)$$
$$= (1.2 + 1.8 + 2 + 4 + 1.5 + 0.5) \times 10^3$$
$$= 11 \times 10^3 \text{ ohms}$$
$$= 11 \text{ k}\Omega$$

Example (3.5):

In Figure 3-7, determine the current in each resistor and the voltage drop across each resistor.

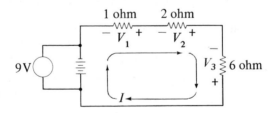

Figure 3-7

Solution:

The equivalent resistance is

$$R_t = 1 + 2 + 6 = 9 \text{ ohms}$$

From Ohm's law

$$I = \frac{E}{R_t} = \frac{9}{9} = 1 \text{ amp}$$

and

$$V_1 = IR_1 = (1)(1) = 1 \text{ volt}$$
$$V_2 = IR_2 = (1)(2) = 2 \text{ volts}$$
$$V_3 = IR_3 = (1)(6) = 6 \text{ volts}$$

3.6 PARALLEL CIRCUITS

When circuit elements are connected *across* the same two terminals they are said to be in parallel and form a parallel circuit as shown in Figure 3-8. Because the elements are connected across the same terminals, each one has

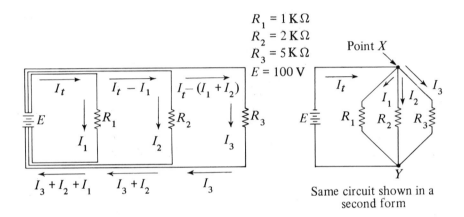

$R_1 = 1 \text{ K}\Omega$
$R_2 = 2 \text{ K}\Omega$
$R_3 = 5 \text{ K}\Omega$
$E = 100 \text{ V}$

Point X

Same circuit shown in a second form

Figure 3-8

the same voltage drop across it. The total current from the source, however, divides at the negative terminal of the battery and recombines to return to the positive terminal of the battery. Figure 3-8 shows that the top connections of resistors R_1, R_2, and R_3 form a junction with the negative terminal of the battery. Current divides at this point (point X) with part of it going through R_1, part through R_2, and the remainder through R_3. All of the individual currents recombine at point Y and return to the positive terminal of the source.

3.7 KIRCHHOFF'S CURRENT LAW

Kirchhoff's current law states that *the sum of the currents leaving a junction equals the sum of the currents entering the junction.*

By Ohm's law, the intensity of current in any circuit containing resistance only is a function of the total circuit resistance and the value of the source emf. To illustrate, in Figure 3-8 the same voltage is applied across each branch of the parallel circuit. By Ohm's law, the current in each branch is determined as follows:

$$I_1 = \frac{E_1}{R_1}$$

$$I_1 = \frac{100}{1000} = 0.1 \text{ amp}$$

where I_1 = current through R_1.

$$I_2 = \frac{E_2}{R_2}$$

$$= \frac{100}{2000} = 0.05 \text{ amp}$$

where I_2 = current through R_2.

$$I_3 = \frac{E_3}{R_3}$$

$$= \frac{100}{5000} = 0.02 \text{ amp}$$

where I_3 = current through R_3.

Then, from Kirchhoff's current law, the sum of $I_1 + I_2 + I_3$ (currents away from point X) should equal I_t (the current into point X).

$$I_t = I_1 + I_2 + I_3$$

$$I_t = 0.1 + 0.05 + 0.02$$

$$I_t = 0.17 \text{ amp}$$

3.8 EQUIVALENT RESISTANCE IN A PARALLEL CIRCUIT

It was shown that the current flow through R_1 in Figure 3-8 was 0.1 amp. If R_1 were the only resistance in the circuit the total resistance would be 1000 ohms. If, however, R_2 were then added in parallel with R_1, the total current I_t would increase to 0.15 amp and, by Ohm's law, the total resistance R_t would be

$$R_t = \frac{E}{I_t}$$

$$= \frac{100}{0.15} = 666.66 \text{ ohms}$$

Thus, the increase in current with additional parallel paths indicates the total effective resistance has decreased. From this it follows that the total resistance of a parallel circuit is less than the resistance of the lowest individual branch.

Again referring to Figure 3-8, the total resistance (three resistors) would be

$$R_t = \frac{E}{I_t}$$

$$= \frac{100}{0.17}$$

$$= 588 \text{ ohms}$$

This value of resistance (588 ohms) is smaller than any one of the individual resistors (1000, 2000, and 5000 ohms).

To find the total resistance of a parallel circuit, consider

$$I_t = I_1 + I_2 + I_3 + \ldots + I_n$$

By substitution,

$$I_t = \frac{E_t}{R_t}, \ I_1 = \frac{E_t}{R_1}, \ I_2 = \frac{E_t}{R_2} \text{ etc.}$$

$$\frac{E_t}{R_t} = \frac{E_t}{R_1} + \frac{E_t}{R_2} + \frac{E_t}{R_3} + \ldots + \frac{E_t}{R_n}$$

Dividing by E_t yields

$$\frac{I}{R_t} = \frac{1}{R_1} = \frac{1}{R_2} + \frac{1}{R_3} + \ldots + \frac{1}{R_n} \tag{3.3}$$

or

$$G_t = G_1 + G_2 + G_3 + \ldots + G_n \tag{3.4}$$

where G = conductance, i.e., $1/R$.

Equation 3.4 is convenient for slide-rule solution of parallel-circuit problems as one merely adds the conductances and then converts back to resistance by taking the reciprocal of G_t.

Example (3.6):

In Figure 3-9 assume resistors R_1, R_2, R_3, R_4, and R_5 are each 200 ohms. What is the total equivalent resistance?

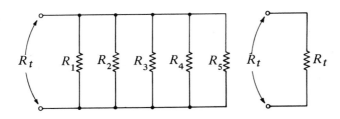

Figure 3-9

Solution:

The reciprocal of 200 is $1/200 = 0.005$.

$$G_t = 0.005 + 0.005 + 0.005 + 0.005 + 0.005$$

$$= 0.025 \text{ mho}$$

To convert the conductance to resistance, find its reciprocal

$$R_t = \frac{1}{0.025 \text{ mho}}$$

$$= 40 \text{ ohms}$$

This example points out another principle of parallel-circuit resistance. Whenever all of the resistors in a parallel group are equal, the total resistance is equal to the resistance of one resistor divided by the number of resistors in the parallel group, that is,

$$R_t = \frac{R}{N_r} \tag{3.5}$$

where N_r = number of equal value resistors in parallel.

In the above example,

$$R_t = \frac{200}{5}$$

$$= 40 \text{ ohms}$$

Another technique for solving for total resistance in a parallel circuit is the lowest-common-denominator (LCD) technique. Inasmuch as

$$\frac{1}{R_t} = \frac{1}{R_1} + \frac{1}{R_2} + \frac{1}{R_3} + \ldots + \frac{1}{R_n}$$

$$= \frac{\dfrac{LCD}{R_1} + \dfrac{LCD}{R_2} + \dfrac{LCD}{R_3} + \ldots + \dfrac{LCD}{R_n}}{LCD}$$

$$R_t = \frac{LCD}{\dfrac{LCD}{R_1} + \dfrac{LCD}{R_2} + \dfrac{LCD}{R_3} + \ldots + \dfrac{LCD}{R_n}} \tag{3.6}$$

With the values as given in the previous example, the lowest common denominator is 200, thus

$$R_t = \frac{200}{\dfrac{200}{200} + \dfrac{200}{200} + \dfrac{200}{200} + \dfrac{200}{200} + \dfrac{200}{200}}$$

$$= \frac{200}{5}$$

$$= 40 \text{ ohms}$$

Example (3.7):

In Figure 3-9 let $R_1 = 20$ ohms, $R_2 = 40$ ohms, $R_3 = 25$ ohms, $R_4 = 10$ ohms, $R_5 = 50$ ohms. Find the total resistance.

Solution:

By the conductance method

$$G_t = \frac{1}{20} + \frac{1}{40} + \frac{1}{25} + \frac{1}{10} + \frac{1}{50}$$

$$= 0.05 + 0.025 + 0.04 + 0.1 + 0.02$$

$$= 0.235 \text{ mho}$$

$$R_t = \frac{1}{G_t}$$

$$= \frac{1}{0.235}$$

$$= 4.25 \text{ ohms}$$

By the *LCD* method

$$R_t = \frac{200}{\dfrac{200}{20} + \dfrac{200}{40} + \dfrac{200}{25} + \dfrac{200}{10} + \dfrac{200}{50}}$$

$$= \frac{200}{47}$$

$$= 4.25 \text{ ohms}$$

Another method of determining equivalent resistance is to assume a voltage that is divisible by each of the resistors an even number of times. In the previous example, 400 volts will do.

$$I_t = I_1 + I_2 + I_3 + I_4 + I_5$$

$$= \frac{400}{20} + \frac{400}{40} + \frac{400}{25} + \frac{400}{10} + \frac{400}{50}$$

$$= 20 + 10 + 16 + 40 + 8$$

$$= 94 \text{ amp}$$

$$R_t = \frac{E}{I_t} = \frac{400}{94}$$

$$= 4.25 \text{ ohms}$$

Whenever there are *only two resistors* in a parallel circuit it is convenient to use the following equation:

$$R_t = \frac{(R_1)(R_2)}{R_1 + R_2} \tag{3.7}$$

This relationship is derived from Equation 3.3 as follows:

$$\frac{1}{R_t} = \frac{1}{R_1} + \frac{1}{R_2}$$

$$= \frac{R_1 + R_2}{(R_1)(R_2)}$$

or

$$R_t = \frac{(R_1)(R_2)}{R_1 + R_2}$$

3.9 SERIES-PARALLEL CIRCUIT ANALYSIS

The equivalent circuit of a series of resistors has been shown to be a single resistance which is equal in value to the sum of the individual resistors (Equation 3.2). The equivalent resistance of a group of resistors in parallel is given by Equation 3.3. Thus, to find the equivalent resistance of a combination series-parallel resistance circuit one needs only to reduce the series section to an equivalent resistance, the parallel section to an equivalent resistance, and then find the resistance equal to the sum of the two equivalents. This is shown in Figure 3-10, where R_1, R_2, and R_3 are equivalent to

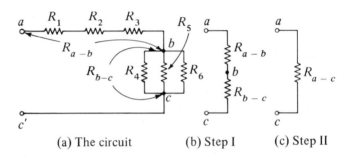

(a) The circuit   (b) Step I   (c) Step II

Figure 3-10

R_{a-b}, and R_4, R_5, and R_6 are equivalent to R_{b-c}. The resistance derived for the two equivalents in series is R_{a-c}.

Figure 3-11 illustrates a more complicated line of series, parallel, and parallel-series resistors. The solution to this line uses the same technique as was illustrated in Figure 3-10. Alternately change the series groups to their equivalents and change the parallel groups to their equivalents. Then total the equivalents that are now in series to determine the total resistance.

Example (3.8):

Using Figure 3-11, let

$$R_1 = 10\Omega, \quad R_2 = 30\Omega, \quad R_3 = 15\Omega, \quad R_4 = 10\Omega,$$
$$R_5 = 20\Omega, \quad R_6 = 10\Omega, \quad R_7 = 15\Omega, \quad R_8 = 15\Omega,$$
$$R_9 = 15\Omega, \quad R_{10} = 10\Omega, \quad R_{11} = 5\Omega.$$

Find the equivalent resistance.

Solution:

First add

$$R_5 \text{ and } R_6 = 20 + 10 = 30$$

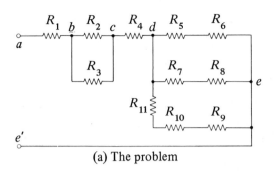

(a) The problem

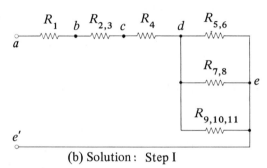

(b) Solution: Step I

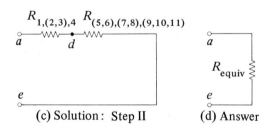

(c) Solution: Step II   (d) Answer

Figure 3-11

$$R_7 \text{ and } R_8 = 15 + 15 = 30$$

$$R_9, R_{10} \text{ and } R_{11} = 15 + 10 + 5 = 30$$

then

$$R_{5-6}, R_{7-8} \text{ and } R_{9-11} \text{ in parallel}$$

$$\frac{1}{\frac{1}{30} + \frac{1}{30} + \frac{1}{30}} = \frac{30}{3} = 10$$

and

$$R_2 \text{ and } R_3 \text{ in parallel} = \frac{(30)(15)}{30+15} = \frac{450}{45} = 10$$

Finally, combine the new series string

$$R_1 + R_{2-3} + R_4 + R_{5-11} = 10 + 10 + 10 + 10 = 40 \text{ ohms}$$

The equivalent (total) resistance is 40 ohms. That is, a single 40 ohm resistor will substitute for the series-parallel, parallel-series line in terms of resistance as shown in Figure 3-11.

3.10 POWER

In Chapter 2, power was defined as the rate of transferring or transforming energy and was shown to be equal to the product of voltage times current in Equation 2.9.

$$P = VI \tag{2.9}$$

For the power of a source substitute E for V.

Example (3.9):

A 1.5 volt dry cell is flash-tested and produces an instantaneous current of 8 amperes. What is its developed power?

Solution:

With Equation 2.9 and substituting E for V

$$P = EI$$

$$= (1.5 \text{ volts}) (8 \text{ amperes})$$

$$= 12 \text{ volt amperes} = 12 \text{ watts}$$

If V is replaced by $I \times R$ from Ohm's law, Equation 2.9 becomes

$$P = I^2 R \tag{3.8}$$

Thus, the power dissipated in a resistor is directly proportional to the square of the current through the resistor. If the current is doubled, the power goes up by a factor of four times.

Example (3.10):

A battery of 6 volts is connected in series with 2 resistors of 5 ohms and 1 ohm. How much power is dissipated in each resistor and what is the total power delivered by the battery?

Solution:

The current in both resistors is

$$I = \frac{E}{R_t}$$

$$= \frac{6}{5 + 1}$$

$$= 1 \text{ amp}$$

The power in the 5 ohm resistor is

$$P_1 = I^2 R_1$$

$$= (1)^2 \, 5$$

$$= 5 \text{ watts}$$

while the power in the 1 ohm resistor is

$$P_2 = I^2 R_2$$
$$= (1)^2 \, (1)$$
$$= 1 \text{ watt}$$

The total power P_t delivered by the battery is the sum of all the power dissipated in the resistors and is given by

$$P_t = P_1 + P_2$$
$$= 5 + 1$$
$$= 6 \text{ watts}$$
$$P_t = EI$$
$$= (6) \, (1)$$
$$= 6 \text{ watts}$$

If I is replaced by V/R in Equation 2.9, we have

$$P = V^2/R \qquad\qquad (3.9)$$

The power dissipated in a resistor, therefore, is also directly proportional to the square of the voltage across the resistor.

Example (3.11):
A 12 volt battery is connected in parallel with a 3 ohm resistor and a 4 ohm resistor. How much power is dissipated in the resistances and what is the total power delivered by the battery?

Solution:
The power dissipated in the 3 ohm resistor is

$$P_1 = \frac{V^2}{R_1}$$
$$= \frac{(12)^2}{3}$$
$$= 48 \text{ watts}$$

and the power dissipated in the 4 ohm resistor is

$$P_2 = \frac{V^2}{R_2}$$
$$= \frac{(12)^2}{4}$$
$$= 36 \text{ watts}$$

The total power dissipated, which equals the power delivered by the source is

$$P_t = P_1 + P_2$$
$$= 48 + 36$$
$$= 84 \text{ watts}$$

Resistors are often used to drop a given voltage to a lower value by connecting them in series with the load. Resistors used in this way are called *dropping resistors.*

All resistors have a power rating as well as an ohmic rating, for the resistor transforms electric energy to heat energy. It is common design practice to select a resistor $1\frac{1}{2}$ to 2 times the calculated wattage as a factor of safety.

Example (3.12):

A 6 volt light bulb which draws 300 ma of current is to be used with a 12 volt source. Calculate the size of the dropping resistor needed.

Solution:

The voltage dropped by the resistor is

$$V_R = E - V_1$$

$$= 12 - 6$$

$$= 6 \text{ volts}$$

The resistance is then given by

$$R = \frac{V_R}{I}$$

$$= \frac{6}{0.3}$$

$$= 20 \text{ ohms}$$

The power dissipated is

$$P = I^2 R$$

$$= (0.3)^2 \, 20$$

$$= 1.8 \text{ watts}$$

Using a safety factor of 2 gives the power rating

$$2 \times 1.8 = 3.6 \text{ watts}$$

The resistor selected should be one of 20 ohms and above 3.6 watts. A supplier's catalogue will show that 20 ohm resistors are available in $\frac{1}{8}$, $\frac{1}{4}$, $\frac{1}{3}$, $\frac{1}{2}$, 1, 2, 3, and 5 watt sizes. The 5 watt resistor is selected in this particular case.

3.11 SUMMARY

In analyzing any electrical circuit it is first necessary to determine an *equivalent circuit* using ideal electrical elements.

An *ideal voltage source* has the same voltage across its terminals regardless of the current it delivers. Its internal resistance is zero.

An *ideal current source* produces the same current ouput regardless of the voltage across its terminals. Its internal resistance is infinite.

Any element which is a source of energy is classified as an *active element,* while any element that is not a source of energy is classified as a *passive element.* Voltage and current generators are active elements while resistors, capacitors, and inductors are passive elements.

In reference to current due to electron flow, a *voltage rise* is encountered when moving through an element from + to − while a *voltage drop* occurs when moving through an element from − to +. A voltage rise is the negative of a voltage drop.

The current in each element of a *series circuit* is the same while the voltage divides among the various elements.

The voltage across each element of a *parallel circuit* is the same while the current divides among the various elements.

Ohm's law expresses the relation between voltage, current, and resistance.

$$I = \frac{E}{R} \quad \text{or} \quad I = \frac{V}{R} \tag{3.1}$$

Kirchhoff's voltage law says that the sum of all the voltage drops around *any* closed loop equals zero.

Kirchhoff's current law says that the total current entering a junction must equal the total current leaving that junction.

The *equivalent resistance* of a series circuit is the sum of all the resistance in the circuit.

$$R_t = R_1 + R_2 + R_3 + \ldots R_n \tag{3.2}$$

The equivalent resistance of a parallel circuit is given by

$$\frac{1}{R_t} = \frac{1}{R_1} + \frac{1}{R_2} + \frac{1}{R_3} + \ldots + \frac{1}{R_n} \tag{3.3}$$

When all the resistors in a parallel circuit are the same

$$R_t = \frac{R}{N_r} \tag{3.5}$$

When there are only two resistors in parallel, it is convenient to use

$$R_t = \frac{(R_1)(R_2)}{R_1 + R_2} \tag{3.7}$$

The equivalent resistance of *series-parallel* circuits is found by step-by-step reduction to simple series and parallel combinations.

The *power* dissipated in a resistor is given in terms of the resistance by

$$P = I^2 R \tag{3.8}$$

$$P = \frac{V^2}{R} \tag{3.9}$$

3.12   QUESTIONS AND PROBLEMS

Questions

1. What is meant by an active element? Give examples.   (3.1)
2. What is a passive element? Give an example.   (3.1)
3. What is an ideal voltage source?   (3.1)

4. What is an ideal current source?   (3.1)
5. What is the internal resistance of an ideal voltage source?   (3.1)
6. What is the internal resistance of an ideal current source?   (3.1)
7. What is a linear element?   (3.1)
8. Describe the simplest d-c circuit.   (3.2)
9. What is the difference between a voltage rise and a voltage drop?   (3.2)
10. Many textbooks use conventional current flow, which assumes positive current carriers. In this case, how would you define a voltage rise and a voltage drop?   (3.2)
11. Assuming electron flow, which terminal of a battery do electrons leave?   (3.2)
12. What is Kirchhoff's voltage law?   (3.3)
13. What is a series circuit?   (3.4)
14. Why is current the same in each element of a series circuit?   (3.4)
15. Can the voltage across every element of a series circuit ever be the same? If so, when?   (3.4)
16. What is Ohm's law?   (3.4)
17. What is meant by the equivalent resistance in a series circuit? How is it determined?   (3.5)
18. How is equivalent resistance useful?   (3.5)
19. What is a parallel circuit?   (3.6)
20. Why is the voltage across each of the elements the same in a parallel circuit?   (3.6)
21. Is the current always the same in each element of a parallel circuit?   (3.6)
22. What is Kirchhoff's current law?   (3.7)
23. How is the equivalent resistance of a parallel circuit found?   (3.8)
24. Explain the *LCD* method of finding equivalent resistance.   (3.8)
25. What is a series-parallel circuit?   (3.9)
26. What is the procedure for determining the equivalent resistance of a series-parallel circuit?   (3.9)
27. Are Kirchhoff's laws valid for a series-parallel circuit?   (3.9)
28. Give three equations for determining the power dissipated in a resistor.   (3.10)
29. What ratings are necessary in specifying a resistor?   (3.10)
30. What is the relationship between the power at the source and power dissipated in the rest of the circuit?   (3.10)

Problems

1. For the circuit in Figure 3-12, $E_1 = 10$ volts and $E^2 = 12$ volts. What is the voltage V_3?   (3.3)

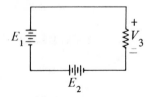

Figure 3-12

2. For the circuit shown in Figure 3-13, $E_1 = 6$ volts and $E_2 = 12$ volts. What is the voltage V_3? (3.3)

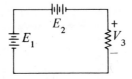

Figure 3-13

3. Find the voltage V_3 for the circuit shown in Figure 3-14. (3.3)

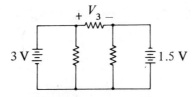

Figure 3-14

4. A 12 volt battery is connected directly across a resistor of 3 ohms. What is the current in the circuit? (3.4)

5. A 27 ohm resistor is connected directly across a battery. The current in the circuit is measured as 2 amperes. What is the voltage of the battery? (3.4)

6. The current in a resistor is measured as 3 amperes and the voltage across the resistor is measured as 15 volts. What is the resistance? (3.4)

7. Three resistors are connected in series. Their resistances are 27 ohms, 270 ohms, and 56 ohms. What is the total resistance of the combination? (3.5)

8. Three vacuum tubes have their heaters connected in series. The voltage drop across each heater is 6.3 volts and the current is 0.3 ampere. What is the total resistance of the three heaters in series? (3.5)

9. Find the voltage V_0 in the circuit of Figure 3-15.

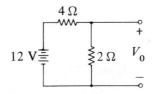

Figure 3-15

10. In Figure 3-16, determine the total resistance seen by the battery, the current I and the voltage V_0. (3.5)

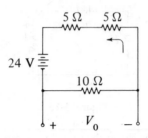

Figure 3-16

11. Determine the current in the circuit in Figure 3-17. Also, determine the voltage across each resistor. (3.5)

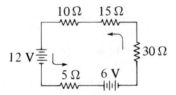

Figure 3-17

12. In Figure 3-18, determine the current I. (3.5)

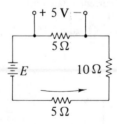

Figure 3-18

13. Find the battery voltage E in Figure 3-18. (3.5)
14. A series circuit contains 2 resistors, one 10 ohm resistor across which is measured

50 volts and another resistor which is unknown. The source voltage is 90 volts. What is the value of the unknown resistor?   (3.5)

15. A certain series circuit contains a 100 volt source and 5 series resistors. The voltage across one 5 ohm resistor is measured as 20 volts. What is the equivalent resistance of the entire series circuit?   (3.5)

16. A source E is connected in series with n resistors. Show that the voltage across the i'th resistor is given by

$$V_i = \frac{ER_i}{R_1 + R_2 + R_3 + \ldots + R_n}$$ (3.5)

17. A 350 ohm resistor and a 500 ohm resistor are connected in parallel. The voltage across the 500 ohm resistor is 24 volts. What is the voltage across the 350 ohm resistor?   (3.6)

18. Determine the current I in Figure 3-19.   (3.7)

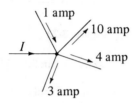

Figure 3-19

19. What is the magnitude of the current I in Figure 3-20? Is the current in the same direction as shown by the arrow?   Explain.   (3.7)

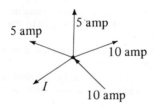

Figure 3-20

20. What is the current I in Figure 3-21?   (3.7)

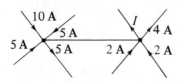

Figure 3-21

21. A 12 volt battery is connected in parallel with a 3 ohm resistor and a 4 ohm resistor. What are the currents in the resistors and the current delivered by the battery? (3.7)

22. Five resistors are connected in parallel across a 100 volt source. The resistors are 1, 2, 5, 10, and 20 ohms. What is the current in each resistor and the current from the source? (3.7)

23. A 4 ohm resistor and a 5 ohm resistor are connected in parallel. If the current in the 4 ohm resistor is 5 amperes, what is the current in the 5 ohm resistor? (3.7)

24. In Figure 3-22, what is the source current I? (3.7)

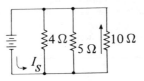

Figure 3-22

25. Two 100 ohm resistors are connected in parallel. What is the equivalent resistance of the combination? (3.8)

26. A 5 ohm resistor and a 20 ohm resistor are connected in parallel. What is the equivalent resistance of the combination? (3.8)

27. Fifteen 3000 ohm resistors are connected in parallel. What is the equivalent resistance of the combination? (3.8)

28. The equivalent resistance of two resistors connected in parallel is 500 ohms. One resistor is 1000 ohms. What is the value of the other resistor? (3.8)

29. A resistor R_x is connected in parallel with a 900 ohm resistor. If the equivalent resistance of the combination is 300 ohms, what is the value of R_x? (3.8)

30. A 20 ohm resistor and a 50 ohm resistor are connected in parallel. What value of resistance must be connected in parallel to make the equivalent resistance of the combination 10 ohms? (3.8)

31. Resistors of 10, 20, 25, and 50 ohms are connected in parallel. What is the equivalent resistance of the combination? (3.8)

32. A 100 ohm resistor and 2 other resistors are to be connected in parallel to obtain an equivalent resistance of 20 ohms. What are some possible values for the other 2 resistors? (3.8)

33. In Figure 3-23, determine the battery voltage E, the equivalent resistance seen by the battery, and the current in each of the resistors. (3.8)

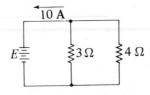

Figure 3-23

34. In Figure 3-24, determine the current in each resistor, the equivalent resistance seen by the battery, the total current I, and the battery voltage E. (3.8)

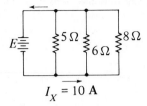

Figure 3-24

35. In the circuit in Figure 3-25, determine the value of the resistor R_a and the equivalent resistance seen by the battery.   (3.8)

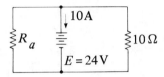

Figure 3-25

36. Find the equivalent resistance for the circuit in Figure 3-26.   (3.9)

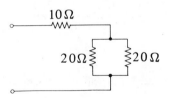

Figure 3-26

37. Find the equivalent resistance for the circuit in Figure 3-27.   (3.9)

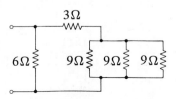

Figure 3-27

38. In Figure 3-28, the equivalent resistance is to be 5 ohms. What is the value of R_b?
   (3.9)

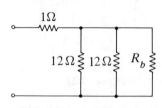

Figure 3-28

39. Find the equivalent resistance for the circuit in Figure 3-29.   (3.9)

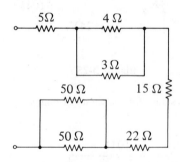

Figure 3-29

40. Find the equivalent resistance for the circuit in Figure 3-30.   (3.9)

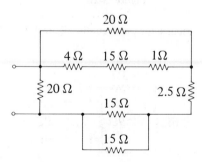

Figure 3-30

41. If 200 volts are applied to the circuit in Figure 3-26, what is the voltage across the two 20 ohm resistors and the current in each resistor? (3.9)

42. If 100 volts are applied to the circuit in Figure 3-27, what is the voltage across the 3 ohm resistor? (3.9)

43. If the current in one of the 9 ohm resistors in Figure 3-27 is 1 amp, what is the applied voltage at the terminals? (3.9)

44. In Figure 3-29, the voltage across the two 50 ohm resistors is 10 volts. What is the voltage across the 3 ohm resistor? (3.9)

45. In Figure 3-29, the current in the 4 ohm resistor is 1 ampere. What is the current in one of the 50 ohm resistors? (3.9)

46. What is the voltage applied to the terminals in problem 45? (3.9)

47. The current in the 1 ohm resistor of Figure 3-30 is 1 ampere. What is the current in the upper 20 ohm resistor? (3.9)

48. A voltage of 100 volts is applied to the circuit in Figure 3-30. What is the current in the 25 ohm resistor? (3.9)

49. If the voltage across the 20 ohm resistor in Figure 3-31 is 10 volts, what is the value of the resistor R_L? (3.9)

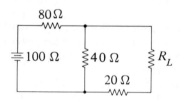

Figure 3-31

50. If the voltage across the 10 ohm resistor in Figure 3-32 is 16.67 volts, what is the value of the resistor R_d? (3.9)

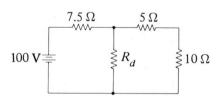

Figure 3-32

51. In Figure 3-33, what is the equivalent resistance sene by the battery? (3.9)

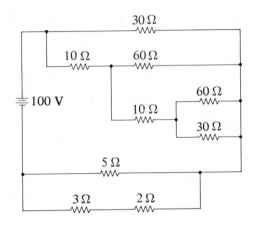

Figure 3-33

52. What is the current in the 2 ohm resistor in Figure 3-33? (3.9)
53. What is the total current from the source in Figure 3-33? (3.9)
54. The current in a certain resistor measures 10 amp and the voltage across the resistor measures 100 volts. What power is dissipated in the resistor? (3.10)
55. The current in a 500 ohm resistor is 10 ma. What power is dissipated in it? (3.10)
56. The voltage across a 200 ohm resistor is 100 volts. What is the power dissipated in the 200 ohm resistor? (3.10)
57. The power dissipated in a 100 ohm resistor is 2 watts. What is the current in the resistor and the voltage drop across the resistor? (3.10)
58. A certain device requires 100 watts at 50 volts. The only supply available is a 100 volt generator. Calculate the value of resistance for a dropping resistor and the power rating for the resistor. (3.10)
59. A certain device has a voltage of 60 volts across it. The device is connected to a 100 volt source through a dropping resistor. The dropping resistor dissipates 400 watts. What is the power used by the device? (3.10)
60. Determine the power dissipated in all the resistors of Figure 3-34 and the power delivered by the source. (3.10)

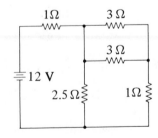

Figure 3-34

61. Determine the power dissipated in the resistor R_x of Figure 3-35, if the power delivered by the source is 1 kw. (3.10)

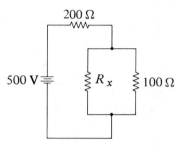

Figure 3-35

4

Analysis of More Complex Circuits

If there are two or more energy sources in different branches of an electric circuit, as shown in Figure 4-1, the circuit is said to be complex. Although the same basic laws described in the last chapter are used in solving complex circuits, it is now desirable to have some systematic method of applying these laws toward the solution of a given problem. This chapter deals with just such methods. It begins with the so-called branch current method and progresses to the more useful methods of mesh analysis and nodal analysis. In addition, there are sections on the analysis of some of the more common electrical networks such as voltage dividers and ladder networks.

4.1 BRANCH CURRENTS

In complex electric circuits it is not always possible to determine the direction of the unknown currents or voltages by inspection. It is, therefore, essential that one assign reference directions to these unknowns. The choice of these reference directions is purely arbitrary and will not affect the correctness of the final solution. Assignment of reference directions should be the first step in solving any complex circuit problem.

A *node* can be defined as the junction of three or more current paths while a *branch* is a path between any two nodes. A branch may include more than one element. For example, the circuit in Figure 4-1 consists of two nodes and three branches. The nodes are indicated as node 1 and node 2 on the figure. One branch consists of R_1 and E_1, another of R_2, and the third of

E_2 and R_3.

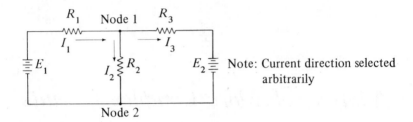

Figure 4-1

A *branch voltage* is merely the voltage between the terminating nodes of the branch while a *branch current* is defined as the current through the branch. In Figure 4-1 there are three branch currents, I_1, I_2, and I_3. The branches are connected to the same two points so that there is only one branch voltage.

To solve a circuit by the branch current method one must:

1. Arbitrarily indicate a reference current in each branch.

2. Write Kirchhoff's current equation at $(n - 1)$ nodes where n is the total number of nodes.

3. Write Kirchhoff's voltage equations around $b - n + 1$ loops where b is the number of branches and n is the number of nodes. Be sure that each equation contains at least one new element. In general, it is safe if one writes a voltage equation for each window[1] of the circuit.

4. Solve the above simultaneous equations.

As an example, again consider Figure 4-1 with the currents assigned arbitrarily as shown. Kirchhoff's current equation is

$$I_1 = I_2 + I_3$$

Kirchhoff's voltage equations around the inside windows in the clockwise direction are

$$-E_1 - I_1 R_1 - I_2 R_2 = 0$$
$$I_2 R_2 - I_3 R_3 + E_2 = 0$$

These three equations can then be solved to find the branch currents I_1, I_2, and I_3. Note the equations were obtained by going around the loops in the

---

[1]   A window as used here is an area enclosed by a continuous loop of circuit elements.

clockwise direction. It should be clear, however, that the direction the equations are written is not important. In other words, one could be written clockwise and the other counterclockwise or both counterclockwise.

Example (4.1):

In Figure 4-1, $E_1 = 10$ volts, $E_2 = 20$ volts, $R_1 = 10$ ohms, $R_2 = 20$ ohms, and $R_3 = 5$ ohms. What are the currents I_1, I_2, and I_3?

Solution:

Kirchhoff's equations are

$$I_1 = I_2 + I_3$$
$$-10 - I_1(10) - I_2(20) = 0$$
$$I_2(20) - I_3(5) + 20 = 0$$

These equations may be solved by substitution, subtraction, or addition or a combination of these methods. However, a more orderly technique might be the use of determinants. To use determinants, one should rewrite the above equations as follows:

$$0 = I_1 - I_2 - I_3$$
$$10 = 10I_1 - 20I_2 + 0$$
$$-20 = 0 + 20I_2 - 5I_3$$

By Cramer's rule[2]

$$I_1 = \frac{\begin{vmatrix} 0 & -1 & -1 \\ 10 & -20 & 0 \\ -20 & 20 & -5 \end{vmatrix}}{\begin{vmatrix} 1 & -1 & -1 \\ 10 & -20 & 0 \\ 0 & 20 & -5 \end{vmatrix}} = -1A. \quad I_2 = \frac{\begin{vmatrix} 1 & 0 & -1 \\ 10 & 10 & 0 \\ 0 & -20 & -5 \end{vmatrix}}{\begin{vmatrix} 1 & -1 & -1 \\ 10 & -20 & 0 \\ 0 & 20 & -5 \end{vmatrix}} = -1A.$$

$$I_3 = \frac{\begin{vmatrix} 1 & -1 & 0 \\ 10 & -20 & 10 \\ 0 & 20 & -20 \end{vmatrix}}{\begin{vmatrix} 1 & -1 & -1 \\ 10 & -20 & 0 \\ 0 & 20 & -5 \end{vmatrix}} = 0$$

Thus, the current I_1 is 1 ampere in a counterclockwise direction, I_2 is 1 ampere in the same direction, and no current exists in R_3.

4.2 MESH ANALYSIS

The branch current method has the disadvantage of requiring the solution of a relatively large number of simultaneous equations, as compared

---

[2] Cramer, a professor of Geneva, in 1750 used Leibnitz's method of determinants and is given credit for the development of the subject.

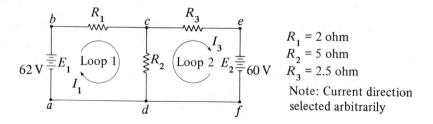

R_1 = 2 ohm
R_2 = 5 ohm
R_3 = 2.5 ohm

Note: Current direction selected arbitrarily

Figure 4-2

with the methods of mesh currents or node voltages. Figure 4-2 is the same circuit as the one used in the previous section except that two loop or mesh currents are used instead of the three branch currents. The current I_1 is now thought of as flowing around the first loop through E_1, R_1, and R_2, while the current I_3 is thought of as flowing around the entire second loop through R_2, R_3, and E_2. Note that I_1 and I_3 both flow through the resistor R_2. The current through R_2 was previously I_2 and that current is now given by Kirchhoff's current law as $I_1 - I_3$.

To solve a circuit by mesh currents one must first indicate the directions of $b - n + 1$ loop currents and then proceed as in steps 3 and 4 of Section 4.1. For Figure 4-2, starting at point d and writing equations clockwise around both loops, we have

$$-E_1 - I_1 R_1 - I_1 R_2 + I_3 R_2 = 0$$

$$-I_3 R_2 + I_1 R_2 - I_3 R_3 + E_2 = 0$$

Note there are only two equations here. The current equation which we had in the branch current method is already substituted in the voltage equations in the proper manner. The terms $-I_1 R_2 + I_3 R_2$ and $I_1 R_2 - I_3 R_2$ are equal to $-I_2 R_2$ and $I_2 R_2$ respectively. Of course, the solution of the two above equations will only give us I_1 and I_3, but once we have these currents, the current through R_2 is easily found by

$$I_2 = I_1 - I_3$$

Example (4.2):
   Using the circuit parameters in Figure 4-2, determine the current in each resistor.

Solution:
   The first mesh equation is established by starting at point a and tracing clockwise around circuit $a b c d$. The first voltage equation is

$$-E_1 - R_1 I_1 - I_1 R_2 + I_3 R_2 = 0$$

$$-62 - (2I_1) - (5I_1) + (5I_3) = 0$$
$$-7I_1 + 5I_3 - 62 = 0$$

The second mesh equation is established by starting at point d and tracing around circuit $d\ c\ e\ f$. Thus,

$$-R_2 I_3 + R_2 I_1 - R_3 I_3 + E_2 = 0$$
$$-5I_3 + 5I_1 - 2.5I_3 + 60 = 0$$
$$5I_1 - 7.5I_3 + 60 = 0$$

Multiplying each side of the first equation by 1.5 gives

$$-10.5I_1 + 7.5I_3 - 93 = 0$$
$$5I_1 - 7.5I_3 + 60 = 0$$

Adding the two equations gives

$$-5.5I_1 - 33 = 0$$
$$5.5I_1 = -33$$
$$I_1 = \frac{-33}{5.5} = -6.0 \text{ amp}$$

With I_1 equal to -6.0 amp, the first equation becomes

$$-7(-6.0) + 5I_3 - 62 = 0$$
$$5I_3 = 62 + 42$$
$$5I_3 = 20$$
$$I_3 = 4.0 \text{ amp}$$

The total current in R_2 is

$$I_2 = I_1 - I_3 = -6.0 - 4.0 = -10.0 \text{ amp}$$

The voltage source E_1 supplies 4.0 amperes and the voltage source E_2 supplies 6.0 amperes. The voltage across R_2 is equal to the voltage developed across terminals c and d which is

$$V_{cd} = I_2 R_2$$
$$= (-10)(5) = -50 \text{ volts}$$

4.3 NODAL ANALYSIS

Another popular method of circuit analysis is the nodal technique. In some cases a circuit may be solved more readily by this method while in other cases the mesh current method may prove easier. The number of equations necessary in the node voltage method is $n - 1$ where n is the total number of nodes.

To solve a circuit by the node voltage method one must first select one of the nodes as reference. All other nodes then have a voltage with respect to the reference node. The voltages at these nodes should be labeled as V_1, V_2, V_3, etc.

At each of the nodes except the reference node a current equation is written in terms of the node voltages, source voltages, and the resistances. It is convenient to assume all nodes except the reference node as negative and write the sum of all currents away from the node equal to zero, or to assume all the nodes except the reference node as positive and thus assume all the currents flowing toward the node equal to zero. The procedure is best illustrated by an example.

Example (4.3):

Write the equations for the nodal currents, using Kirchhoff's laws for Figure 4-3.

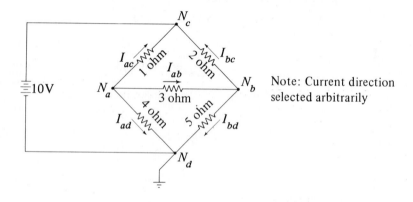

Note: Current direction selected arbitrarily

Figure 4-3

Solution:

Arbitrarily N_d is chosen as the reference and it is grounded. At node N_a the sum of the currents equals zero, thus,

$$I_{ad} + I_{ab} + I_{ac} = 0$$

and at node N_b

$$I_{bd} + I_{ba} + I_{bc} = 0$$

Rewriting the currents in terms of voltage and resistance, we have

$$\frac{V_{ad}}{4} + \frac{V_{ad} - V_{bd}}{3} + \frac{V_{ad} - 10}{1} = 0$$

$$\frac{V_{bd}}{5} + \frac{V_{bd} - V_{ad}}{3} + \frac{V_{bd} - 10}{2} = 0$$

Clearing fractions yields

$(LCD = 12)$:

$$3V_{ad} + 4V_{ad} - 4V_{bd} + 12V_{ad} - 120 = 0$$

$(LCD = 30)$:

$$6V_{bd} + 10V_{bd} + 10V_{ad} + 15V_{bd} - 150 = 0$$
$$19V_{ad} - 4V_{bd} = 120$$
$$-10V_{ad} + 31V_{bd} = 150$$

Multiplying the first equation by 31 and the second by 4, we can eliminate V_{bd}. Likewise, by multiplying the first equation by 10 and the second by 19, we can eliminate V_{ad}.

$$(31) \quad 589V_{ad} - 124V_{bd} = 3720$$
$$(4) \quad -40V_{ad} + 124V_{bd} = 600$$

$$549V_{ad} \phantom{- 124V_{bd}} = 4320$$
$$V_{ad} \phantom{- 124V_{bd}} = 7.87$$

$$(10) \quad 190V_{ad} - 40V_{bd} = 1200$$
$$(19) \quad -190V_{ad} + 589V_{bd} = 2850$$

$$549V_{bd} = 4050$$
$$V_{bd} = 7.38$$

Thus, the node voltages are 7.87 and 7.38. Current flows from the higher potential (node N_a) to the lower (node N_b) and the potential difference between nodes (N_a and N_b) is

$$7.87 - 7.38 = 0.49 \text{ volt}$$

The current flowing through this 3 ohm path is $0.49/3 = 0.16$ amp.

4.4 VOLTAGE DIVIDERS

A voltage divider is used to supply two or more voltages from a single source. A typical circuit is shown in Figure 4-4. This divider, as an ex-

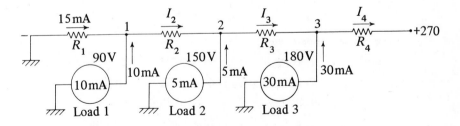

Figure 4-4

ample, is connected across a 270 volt source and supplies three loads simultaneously: 10 ma at 90 volts between terminal 1 and ground; 5 ma at 150 volts between terminal 2 and ground; and 30 ma at 180 volts between terminal 3 and ground. The current in resistor R_1 is 15 ma and is referred to as the bleeder current.

Example (4.4):
    Determine the resistance and the power dissipated in the four resistors in the voltage divider network shown in Figure 4-4.

Solution:
    Kirchhoff's law of currents applied to terminal 1 indicates that the current in resistor R_2 is equal to the sum of 15 ma from resistor R_1 and 10 ma from load 1. Thus,

$$I_2 = 15 + 10 = 25 \text{ ma}$$

Similarly

$$I_3 = 25 + 5 = 30 \text{ ma}$$
$$I_4 = 30 + 30 = 60 \text{ ma}$$

The voltage across R_1 is 90 volts. They voltage across R_2 is found by subtracting the voltage from terminal 1 to ground from the voltage from terminal 2 to ground.

$$V_2 = 150 - 90 = 60 \text{ volts}$$

The voltage across R_3 is

$$V_3 = 180 - 150 = 30 \text{ volts}$$

and the voltage across R_4 is

$$V_4 = 270 - 180 = 90 \text{ volts}$$

Since the currents given are in milliamperes, this network may best be solved for resistance in kilohms.

$$R_1 = \frac{V_1}{I_1} = \frac{90}{15} = 6 \text{ k}\Omega$$

$$R_2 = \frac{V_2}{I_2} = \frac{60}{25} = 2.4 \text{ k}\Omega$$

$$R_3 = \frac{30}{30} = 1 \text{ k}\Omega$$

$$R_4 = \frac{90}{60} = 1.5 \text{ k}\Omega$$

The power dissipated in

$$R_1 \text{ is } P_1 = V_1 I_1 = 90 \times 0.015 = 1.35 \text{ watts}$$
$$R_2 \text{ is } P_2 = V_2 I_2 = 60 \times 0.025 = 1.5 \text{ watts}$$
$$R_3 \text{ is } P_3 = V_3 I_3 = 30 \times 0.030 = 0.90 \text{ watt}$$
$$R_4 \text{ is } P_4 = V_4 I_4 = 90 \times 0.060 = 5.40 \text{ watts}$$

The total power dissipated by the network is

$$1.35 + 1.50 + 0.90 + 5.40 = 9.15 \text{ watts}$$

The power dissipated by the loads are as follows:

Load 1 $P = 90 \times 0.010 = 0.90 \text{ watt}$

Load 2 $P = 150 \times 0.005 = 0.75 \text{ watt}$

Load 3 $P = 180 \times 0.030 = 5.4 \text{ watts}$

The total power consumed by the loads is

$$0.90 + 0.75 + 5.4 = 7.05 \text{ watts}$$

The total power supplied to the circuit is

$$9.15 + 7.05 = 16.2 \text{ watts}$$

The value can be checked as follows:

$$P_t = E_t \times I_t = 270 \times 0.060 = 16.2 \text{ watts}$$

4.5   ATTENUATOR PADS

Attenuator pads are 4-terminal resistive networks for varying the voltage applied to a load while maintaining a constant resistance at one or both pairs of its terminals. Pads have extensive use in audio circuits. The *L*-pad attenuator maintains a constant resistance at one pair of terminals for any setting, while the *T*-pad attenuator maintains a constant resistance at both pairs of terminals for any setting. Figure 4-5 illustrates typical examples of these circuits.

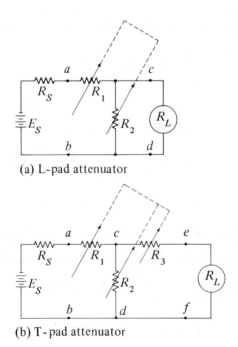

(a) L-pad attenuator

(b) T-pad attenuator

Figure 4-5

The schematic of an *L*-pad attenuator is shown in Figure 4-5a. The resistance R_s is the internal resistance of the generator. The input resistance is usually made equal to this resistance.

Since the input resistance is to remain constant, R_1 and R_2 must be varied such that

$$R_1 + \frac{R_2 R_L}{R_2 + R_L} = \text{a constant}$$

Constant input resistance also implies that the load voltage can be changed while maintaining the source current constant. The example below indicates how R_1 and R_2 are determined for a fixed value of attenuation.

Example (4.5):
  Assume R_s (Figure 4-5a) to be 100 ohms, $E_s = 20$ volts, and $R_L = 100$ ohms. Find R_1 and R_2 if the load voltage is to be 5 volts.

Solution:
  Before the attenuator is inserted, the source current is

$$I_s = \frac{E_s}{R_L + R_s} = \frac{20}{100 + 100} = 0.1 \text{ amp}$$

and the load voltage is

$$V_L = I_s R_L = 0.1 \times 100 = 10 \text{ volts}$$

To reduce the load voltage from its present value of 10 volts to 5 volts, an L-pad is to be inserted. The new load current is

$$I_L = \frac{V_L}{R_L} = \frac{5}{100} = 0.05 \text{ amp}$$

$$V_1 = E_s - I_s R_s - V_L$$
$$= 20 - (.1)(100)\, 5 = 5 \text{ volts}$$

$$R_1 = \frac{E_1}{I_s} = \frac{5}{0.1} = 50 \text{ ohms}$$

$$I_2 = I_s - I_L = 0.1 - 0.05 = 0.05 \text{ amp}$$

$$V_2 = V_L = 5 \text{ volts}$$

$$R_2 = \frac{V_2}{I_2} = \frac{5}{0.05} = 100 \text{ ohms}$$

Thus, an L-pad of $R_1 = 50$ ohms and $R_2 = 100$ ohms maintains the load voltage at 5 volts and the source current at 0.1 amp. To compute the range for an L-pad attenuator, the range of load voltages must be known.

For a T-pad attenuator (refer to Figure 4-5b), the input resistance is again made equal to the generator resistance.

$$R_s = R_1 + \frac{R_2(R_3 + R_L)}{R_2 + R_3 + R_L}$$

In addition, the resistance looking back into the load terminals e and f is made equal to the load resistance.

$$R_L = R_3 + \frac{R_2(R_1 + R_s)}{R_2 + R_1 + R_s}$$

If $R_s = R_L$, then $R_1 = R_3$, and the load and source are interchangeable; that is, the resistance to the flow of current through terminals a and b is equal to the resistance offered to the flow of current through e and f.

Example (4.6):

In Figure 4-5b, $R_s = 600$ ohms, $R_L = 600$ ohms and $E_s = 120$ volts. What are the values of R_1, R_2, and R_3 when the voltage across terminals e and f is 30 volts?

Solution:

Before the attenuator is inserted, the load current is

$$I_L = \frac{E_s}{R_s + R_L}$$

$$= \frac{120}{600 + 600} = 0.1 \text{ amp}$$

and the load voltage

$$V_L = I_L R_L$$

$$= (0.1)(600) = 60 \text{ volts}$$

With the T pad in the circuit, the load current is

$$I_L = \frac{V_L}{R_L}$$

$$= \frac{30}{600} = 0.05 \text{ amp}$$

Since the total current must remain 0.1 amp, the current through R_2 is

$$I_2 = I_s - I_L$$

$$= 0.1 - 0.05 = 0.05 \text{ amp}$$

Summing the voltage drops around $d\ c\ e\ f\ d$, we have

$$I_2 R_2 - I_L R_3 - V_L = 0$$

$$0.05 R_2 - 0.05 R_3 - 30 = 0$$

and since

$$R_3 = R_1$$

$$0.05 R_2 - 0.05 R_1 - 30 = 0$$

The voltage drops around loop $b\ a\ c\ d\ b$ equal

$$E_s - I_s R_s - I_s R_1 - I_2 R_2 = 0$$

$$120 - (0.1 \times 600) - 0.1 R_1 - 0.05 R_2 = 0$$

$$0.05 R_2 + 0.1 R_1 = 60$$

and adding both equations, we obtain

$$0.05 R_2 + 0.1\ R_1 = \quad 60$$

$$-0.05 R_2 + 0.05 R_1 = -30$$

$$\overline{\quad 0 \quad + 0.15 R_1 = \quad 30}$$

Thus,
$$R_1 = 200 \text{ ohms} = R_3$$
and substituting for R_1 yields
$$0.05R_2 - 0.05\,(200) = 30$$
$$0.05R_2 = 40$$
and
$$R_2 = 800 \text{ ohms}$$

4.6   LADDER NETWORKS

Ladders (Figure 4-6) are 4-terminal networks made up of alternate series and parallel resistors. They often represent parallel loads along a line with

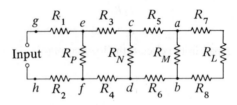

Figure 4-6

appreciable line resistance or they can be an attenuator with tapped output voltages.

To find the resistance as you look into a ladder network, it is convenient to start with the load resistance and work toward the source. In the simple network shown in Figure 4-6, if R_7, R_8, and R_L are disconnected at ab, the equivalent resistance of the combination is
$$R_{ab} = R_7 + R_L + R_8$$
At cd,
$$R_{cd} = R_5 + \frac{R_{ab} \times R_m}{R_{ab} + R_m} + R_6$$
and at ef,
$$R_{ef} = R_3 + \frac{R_{cd} \times R_n}{R_{cd} + R_n} + R_4$$
Then, at gh, the total resistance of the network
$$R_T = R_1 + \frac{R_{ef} \times R_p}{R_{ef} + R_p} + R_2$$

Example (4.7):

Let R_1, R_2, R_3, and R_4 be sections of a line with 0.5 ohm each, R_5 and

R_6 another section with 0.2 ohm each, and R_7 and R_8 a fourth section of longer length with 3 ohms each. Let R_L, R_m, R_n, and R_p be motors of 2 ohms each. Find the voltage across R_L when 6 volts are applied to the network.

Solution:

First determine the total resistance; then determine the total current.

$$R_{ab} = R_7 + R_L + R_8$$

$$= 3 + 2 + 3 = 8 \text{ ohms}$$

$$R_{cd} = R_5 + \frac{R_{ab}R_m}{R_{ab} + R_m} + R_6$$

$$= 0.2 + \frac{(8)(2)}{8 + 2} + 0.2$$

$$= 2 \text{ ohms}$$

$$R_{ef} = R_3 + \frac{R_{cd}R_n}{R_{cd} + R_n} + R_4$$

$$= 0.5 + \frac{(2)(2)}{2 + 2} + 0.5$$

$$= 2 \text{ ohms}$$

$$R_T = R_1 + \frac{R_{ef}R_p}{R_{ef} + R_p} + R_2$$

$$= 0.5 + \frac{(2)(2)}{2 + 2} + 0.5$$

$$= 2 \text{ ohms}$$

The total current

$$I_T = \frac{E_T}{R_T} = \frac{6}{2} = 3 \text{ amp}$$

R_1 and R_2 carry 3 amp, thus,

$$V_{ef} = E - (I_T R_1 + I_T R_2)$$

$$= 6 - [3(5) + 3(0.5)] = 3 \text{ volts}$$

$$I_{Rp} = \frac{V_{ef}}{R_p} = \frac{3}{2} = 1.5 \text{ amp}$$

$$I_{R_3} = I_T - I_{Rp}$$

$$= 3 - 1.5 = 1.5 \text{ amp}$$

$$V_{cd} = V_{ef} - [I_{R_3}R_3 + I_{R_4}R_4]$$

$$= 3 - [1.5(0.5) + 1.5(0.5)]$$

$$= 1.5 \text{ volts}$$

$$I_{R_n} = \frac{V_{R_n}}{R_n} = \frac{1.5}{2} = 0.75 \text{ amp}$$

$$I_{R_5} = I_{R_3} - I_{R_n}$$

$$= 1.5 - 0.75 = 0.75 \text{ amp}$$

$$V_{ab} = V_{cd} - [I_{R_5}R_5 + I_{R_6}R_6]$$
$$= 1.5 - [0.75\,(0.2) + 0.75\,(0.2)]$$
$$= 1.2 \text{ volts}$$

$$I_{R_m} = \frac{V_{R_m}}{R_m} = \frac{1.2}{2} = 0.6 \text{ amp}$$

$$I_{R_7} = I_{R_5} - I_{R_m}$$
$$= 0.75 - 0.6 = 0.15 \text{ amp}$$

$$V_{R_L} = V_{ab} - [I_{R_7}R_7 + I_{R_8}R_8]$$
$$= 1.2 - [0.15\,(3) + 0.15\,(3)]$$
$$= 0.3 \text{ volt}$$

4.7 SUMMARY

Nodes are junctions of three or more current paths.

A *branch* is a path between any two nodes.

A circuit is said to be *complex* when there are two or more energy sources in different branches of the circuit. Complex circuits may be solved by using the *branch current* method. However, the *mesh current* and *node voltage* methods are preferred since they result in fewer equations.

To solve a circuit by the method of mesh currents:

1. Arbitrarily assign current directions to $b - n + 1$ loops making sure to include one new element each time.

2. Write Kirchhoff's voltage equations around the $b - n + 1$ loops in terms of the mesh currents and resistances.

3. Solve the $b - n + 1$ equations for the mesh currents.

To solve a circuit by the method of node voltages:

1. Select one node as a reference node.

2. Write Kirchhoff's current equations in terms of node voltages, source voltages, and resistances at all nodes except the reference. ($n - 1$ nodes)

3. Solve the set of nodal equations for the node voltages.

For some circuits there will be fewer equations with use of the mesh current method, while for others there will be fewer equations if the node voltage method is used.

Voltage dividers are resistive networks used to obtain two or more voltages from the same source.

An *L-pad attenuator* is a 4-terminal resistive network used for varying the voltage across a load while maintaining a constant resistance at its input terminals.

A *T-pad attenuator* is a 4-terminal resistive network used for varying the voltage across a load while maintaining a constant resistance at both the source terminals and the load terminals.

Ladder networks are 4-terminal networks made up of alternate series and parallel elements.

4.8 QUESTIONS AND PROBLEMS

Questions

1. What is meant by a complex circuit? (Introduction)
2. Why is it necessary to assign reference directions to the unknowns in complex circuits? (4.1)
3. What is a node? (4.1)
4. What is a branch? (4.1)
5. What is a branch voltage? (4.1)
6. What is a branch current? (4.1)
7. What is the branch current method of solution? (4.1)
8. How many current equations are needed with the branch current method? (4.1)
9. How many voltage equations are necessary in the branch current method? (4.1)
10. What is the total number of necessary equations needed in the branch current method? (4.1)
11. Why must one be sure to include a new element each time another voltage equation is written? (4.1)
12. How can Kirchhoff's voltage equations be written around a loop in either direction and still be correct? (4.1)
13. What is a mesh current? (4.2)
14. What is the advantage of the mesh current method? (4.2)
15. How many equations are required in the mesh current method? (4.2)
16. Are mesh current equations voltage equations or current equations? Explain. (4.2)
17. Why are the node voltage and mesh current methods preferable to the branch current methods? (4.2)
18. What is a node voltage? (4.3)
19. What is the node voltage method? (4.3)
20. Are node voltage equations really voltage equations or current equations? Explain. (4.3)
21. How many equations are necessary in the node voltage method? (4.3)
22. Is there ever any advantage to the node voltage method over the mesh current method, or vice versa? (4.3)
23. What is a reference node? Can one choose any node as reference? (4.3)
24. What is a voltage divider? (4.4)
25. What is an *L*-pad attenuator? (4.5)
26. What is a *T*-pad attenuator? (4.5)
27. What is a ladder network? (4.6)

Problems

1. For the circuit shown in Figure 4-7, determine
   a) the number of nodes
   b) the number of branches
   c) the number of branch current equations necessary to solve the circuit.   (4.1)

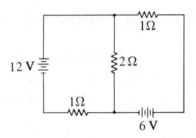

Figure 4-7

2. Write a set of branch current equations for Figure 4-7. Solve the equations for all the currents. Be sure to put in all the reference directions for your currents.   (4.1)

3. Repeat Problem 1 for Figure 4-8.   (4.1)

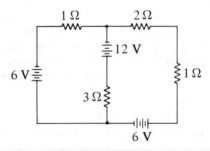

Figure 4-8

4. Repeat Problem 2 for Figure 4-8.   (4.1)

5. How many equations are necessary to solve the circuits in Figure 4-7 and Figure 4-8 by the mesh current method?   (4.2)

6. Write mesh current equations for the circuit in Figure 4-8 and solve for these currents. (4.2)

7. Repeat Problem 6 for Figure 4-9.   (4.2)

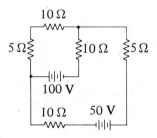

Figure 4-9

8. Solve for all the unknown currents and voltages in the circuit of Figure 4-10 using the mesh current method.   (4.2)

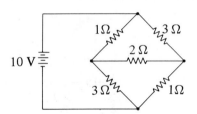

Figure 4-10

9. Use the mesh current method to solve for all the currents in Figure 4-11.   (4.2)

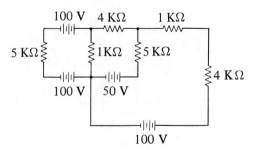

Figure 4-11

10. Write a complete set of mesh current equations for the circuit in Figure 4-12.   (4.2)

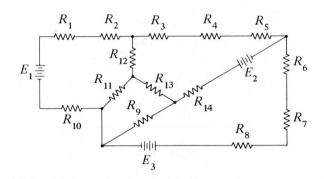

Figure 4-12

11. Repeat Problem 10 for Figure 4-13.   (4.2)

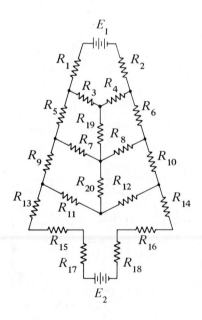

Figure 4-13

12. Repeat Problem 10 for Figure 4-14.   (4.2)

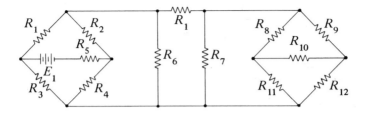

Figure 4-14

13. How many nodal equations are necessary to solve the circuits in Figure 4-7 and Figure 4-8? (4.3)

14. How many nodal equations are necessary to solve the circuits in Figure 4-13 and Figure 4-14? Is it easier to solve these circuits by the mesh or nodal method? (4.3)

15. Write a set of node voltage equations and solve for these voltages in the circuit of Figure 4-8. (4.3)

16. Repeat Problem 15 for Figure 4-9. (4.3)

17. Use the method of node voltages and solve for all of the currents and voltages in the circuit of Figure 4-10. (4.3)

18. Write a complete set of node voltage equations for the circuit in Figure 4-12. (4.3)

19. Repeat Problem 18 for Figure 4-13. (4.3)

20. Repeat Problem 18 for Figure 4-14. (4.3)

21. A voltage divider is to be used to obtain 90 volts from a 270 volt source. The 90 volt load takes 9 ma. With the load connected, the total current drawn by the divider and the load is 18 ma. Sketch the voltage divider network and give the appropriate values of resistors. (4.4)

22. A voltage divider is connected across a 300 volt source and supplies 2 loads simultaneously. One load draws 10 ma at 30 volts and the other draws 20 ma at 60 volts. The current in the resistor which parallels the 30 volt load is also 10 ma. Sketch the voltage divider and give the appropriate values of resistors. (4.4)

23. Given the voltage divider circuit in Figure 4-15, find the voltages and currents at the loads. (4.4)

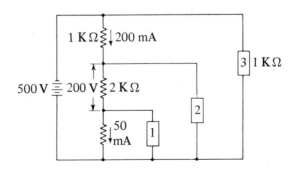

Figure 4-15

24. A voltage divider is connected across a 1000 volt source and supplies 4 loads. One load takes 1000 volts at 500 ma, another 500 volts at 50 ma, another 200 volts at 20 ma, and another 100 volts at 10 ma. The current through the divider with all loads disconnected is 50 ma. Sketch the divider circuit and determine the values of the resistors. (4.4)

25. An *L*-pad is inserted between a 16 ohm source and a 16 ohm load to reduce the voltage at the load to half the source voltage. Sketch the circuit and give the appropriate values of resistors. (4.5)

26. Repeat Problem 25 using a *T*-pad. (4.5)

27. An *L*-pad is inserted between a 600 ohm source and a 600 ohm load to reduce the load voltage to one-third the source voltage. Sketch the circuit and give the appropriate values of resistors. (4.5)

28. Repeat Problem 27 using a *T*-pad. (4.5)

29. For the network shown in Figure 4-16, determine the load voltage and the load current. (4.6)

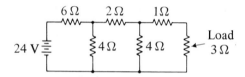

Figure 4-16

30. Find the source voltage in Figure 4-17. (4.6)

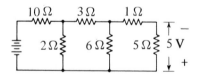

Figure 4-17

5

Network Theorems

The analysis of electrical circuits is sometimes simplified by the use of certain well-known network theorems. Many of these theorems indicate procedures for reducing a given network to a simpler form of equivalent circuit, which can then be solved more easily. Others deal with the conditions of maximum power transfer and methods of compensating for certain changes in circuitry.

5.1 INTERNAL RESISTANCE

To understand better some of the network theorems, the internal resistance of a source must be considered. This resistance occurs in all real sources of emf and may be represented as a resistor in series with the load and the ideal voltage source. Both the terminal voltage and the current and therefore the available power are affected by the internal resistance of the source. Unfortunately, this resistance is not always linear. For the present, however, to simplify things, only linear cases will be covered here.

Figure 5-1 shows the equivalent circuit for a dry cell. In Figure 5-1a the circuit is open and only the parallel resistance R_p is seen taking power from the internal source. This resistance R_p is a high value and is placed in parallel with the ideal battery to account for the "shelf life" of the cell. It is not considered as part of the source resistance. A voltmeter connected across the cell measures 1.5 volts. (The true value of the source when it was first manufactured as a dry cell was probably 1.58 volts.) This 1.5 volt

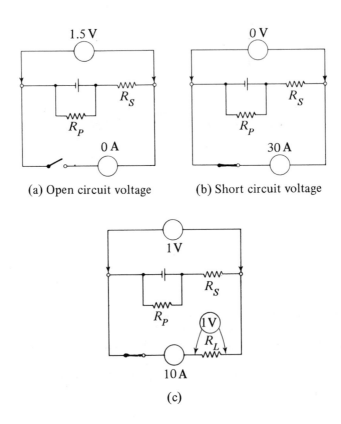

(a) Open circuit voltage   (b) Short circuit voltage

(c)

Figure 5-1

reading of Figure 5-1a is called the *"no-load"* voltage as there is no external load connected while the reading is being made.

In Figure 5-1a the cell is momentarily short-circuited through the ammeter, and a current of 30 amperes exists in the short. The series internal resistance (R_s) is therefore

$$R_s = \frac{E_{oc}}{I_{sc}} = \frac{1.5}{30} = 0.05 \text{ ohm}$$

If a load R_L of 0.10 ohm is connected to the circuit as shown in Figure 5-1c, the current I becomes

$$I = \frac{E_{oc}}{R_L + R_s} = \frac{1.5}{0.05 + 0.1} = \frac{1.5}{0.15} = 10 \text{ amp}$$

and the voltage available at the load is

$$V_L = IR_2 = 10 \times 0.1 = 1 \text{ volt}$$

The voltage drop across the internal resistance (R_s) of the cell is

$$IR_s = 10 \times 0.05 = 0.5 \text{ volt}$$

Thus, the effect of the series internal resistance is to decrease the terminal voltage from 1.5 volts to 1 volt when the cell delivers 10 amperes to the load.[1]

The series internal resistance that has been illustrated here is a characteristic of all realistic d-c voltage sources.

5.2   MAXIMUM POWER TRANSFER AND EFFICIENCY

If the load resistance R_L of Figure 5-2a is continuously increased from zero to 20 ohms, as indicated in Figure 5-2b, the current drawn from the source will continue to decrease from the short circuit current of 20 amperes to 4 amperes. At the same time the load voltage will continuously increase from 0 to 80 volts. On the other hand, the power increases from 0 to a maximum of 500 watts and then steadily decreases to 320 watts.

The *maximum power transfer theorem* states that *maximum power is transferred to a load when the equivalent load resistance equals the equivalent resistance of the source network*. Thus, in the circuit of Figure 5-2, with an internal resistance of 5 ohms, when the load resistance was 5 ohms, the maximum power of 500 watts was delivered to the load. No greater power can be transferred to the load unless the internal resistance can be lowered in some way.

The efficiency of power transfer (ratio of output power to input power) from the source to the load increases as the load resistance is increased and approaches 100 percent as the load resistance increases in value to infinity. Maximum power transfer always occurs at 50 percent efficiency.

The problem of high efficiency vs. maximum power transfer is resolved as a compromise. Where the amounts of power involved are large and the efficiency is important, the source resistance is made small relative to the load resistance. In that way losses are kept small and efficiency is high. where the problem of obtaining maximum power transfer to a load is more important than a high percentage of efficiency, the efficiency is decreased to 50 percent. The load is then said to be matched to the source. The latter is common in electronics where input devices and output devices are matched to electronic circuits.

---

[1]   The parallel resistance is insignificant in considering load voltage because it is parallel with the ideal source.

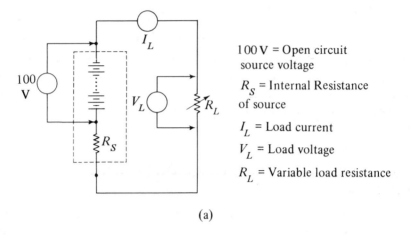

100 V = Open circuit
source voltage

R_S = Internal Resistance
of source

I_L = Load current

V_L = Load voltage

R_L = Variable load resistance

(a)

To find maximum power transfer: when R_S = 5 ohms

R_L	$R_L + R_S$	$I_L = \dfrac{E_S}{R_L + R_S}$	$V_L = I_L R_L$	$P_L = I_L V_L$
0	5	20	0	0
1	6	16.6	16.6	267.6
2	7	14.3	28.6	409
3	8	12.5	37.5	468.8
4	9	11.1	44.4	492.8
5	10	10	50	500
6	11	9.1	54.5	495.4
7	12	8.3	58.1	482.2
8	13	7.7	61.6	474.3
9	14	7.1	63.9	453.7
10	15	6.6	66	435.6
20	25	4	80	320

(b)

Figure 5-2

5.3 SUPERPOSITION THEOREM

The superposition theorem is useful *only* for circuits containing more than one voltage source and for determining the current in or voltage across *one* branch of these networks. The idea of superposition originated (in 1755) with the observation of the effect of water waves from more than one source. The original concept was that the transmission of one surface wave through water does not affect the transmission of other waves at the same time, and that the net disturbance of several waves together is equal to the sum of the disturbances of each wave taken one at a time.

Applying the same idea to electrical circuits, we have the following theorem called the *superposition theorem*.

In any electrical network consisting of only linear bilateral² elements and more than one generator, the current in any branch is the sum of the component currents (with due regard to signs) *which would flow if each voltage source is considered independently while the others are replaced in the network by their respective internal resistances.*

Example (5.1):

Find the current I_{ba} flowing from point *b* to *a* in Figure 5-3a.

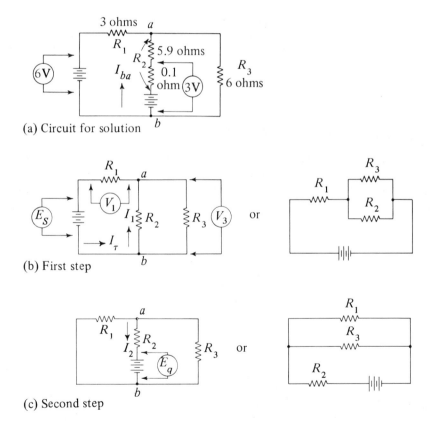

(a) Circuit for solution

(b) First step

(c) Second step

Figure 5-3

² A bilateral element is one that has the same relationship between current and voltage for current in either direction.

Solution:

First find the current I_1 flowing from b to a with the 3 volt source removed and replaced by its internal resistance of 0.1 ohm, as shown in Figure 5-3b.

$$I_T = \frac{E_S}{R^T} = \frac{6}{3 + \frac{(5.9 + 0.1)\,6}{(5.9 + 0.1) + 6}} = \frac{6}{6} = 1 \text{ amp}$$

$$V_1 = I_T R_1 = (1)\,(3) = 3 \text{ volts}$$

$$I_1 = \frac{E_S - V_1}{R_2} = \frac{6 - 3}{6} = \frac{3}{6} = 0.5 \text{ amp}$$

Second, find the current I_2 flowing from a to b with the 6 volt source replaced by its internal resistance of zero ohms (Figure 5-3c.)

$$I_2 = \frac{E_4}{R_T} = \frac{3}{(5.9 + 0.1) + \frac{(3)(6)}{3 + 6}} = \frac{3}{8} = 0.375 \text{ amp}$$

This current flows through R_2 from a to b, and is therefore negative with respect to I_1. Finally, the theorem states that the total current in any element is the algebraic sum of the component currents resulting from each source independently, thus

$$I_{ba} = I_1 + I_2 = 0.5 + (-0.375) = 0.125 \text{ amp}$$

A current of 0.125 ampere flows from b to a.

5.4 RECIPROCITY THEOREM

The reciprocity theorem states: *If a single source voltage E_A is acting in branch A of a linear bilateral network, producing a current I_B in branch B of the network, the same E_A acting in branch B will produce the same current I_B in branch A.* Figure 5-4 and the example below are used to illustrate this theorem.

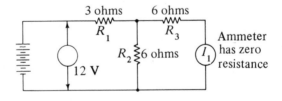

Figure 5-4

Example (5.2):

Find the current I_1 of Figure 5-4. Then interchange the 12 volt source and the ammeter to determine if the new current I_2 is equal to I_1.

Solution:

$$I_T = \frac{E_T}{R_T} = \frac{12}{3 + \frac{(6)(6)}{6 + 6}} = 2 \text{ amp}$$

$$I_1 = \frac{E_T - I_T R_1}{R_3} = \frac{12 - (3)(2)}{6} = 1 \text{ amp}$$

Interchanging E and I yields

$$I_T = \frac{E_T}{R_T} = \frac{12}{6 + \frac{(6)(3)}{6 + 3}} = 1.5 \text{ amp}$$

$$I_2 = \frac{E_T - I_T R_3}{R_1} = \frac{12 - (1.5)(6)}{3} = 1 \text{ amp}$$

From the example, it can be seen that a voltage source connected to either the input or output terminals of *any* 4-terminal network yields the same output current so long as the elements in the network are linear and bilateral.

5.5 THÉVENIN'S THEOREM

One of the most useful equivalent circuit theorems was first stated by Thévenin in 1887. Thévenin's technique can be used on any network composed of linear bilateral elements where one branch of the network can be thought of as a load and the rest of the network as a two-terminal "black box". The so-called "black box" is replaced by Thévenin's equivalent circuit, which consists of an ideal voltage source in series with a linear resistance. The theorem follows: *Any network made up of linear bilateral elements as viewed from any two terminals can be replaced by a single source of electromotive force E_t having a series internal resistance R_t. E_t is the potential difference between the two terminals of the network when open-circuited and R_t is the resistance between the two terminals of the network at open circuit with all the generators in the network replaced by only their internal resistance.*

The example below illustrates the use of Thévenin's theorem.

Example (5.3):

The network shown in Figure 5-5a has the following values: $E = 5$ volts, $R_1 = R_2 = R_3 = 10$ ohms, R_L is variable. The problem is to find how the current in R_L varies with its resistance.

Solution:

If we apply Thévenin's theorem, R_L is separated from the network as shown in Figure 5-5b, and points x and y become the terminals of an equivalent network with E_t and R_t (Figure 5-5c).

The potential difference of the terminals x and y of the "black box" is determined at open circuit to be 2.5 volts, as follows (Figure 5-5d). Since the circuit is open at x and y, no current flows in R_3; therefore

$$I = \frac{E}{R_1 + R_2} = \frac{5}{10 + 10} = 0.25 \text{ amp}$$

$$E_t = IR_2 = (0.25)(10) = 2.5 \text{ volts}$$

This value is now called Thévenin's equivalent voltage E_t.

To find the internal resistance R_t, consider the voltage source removed

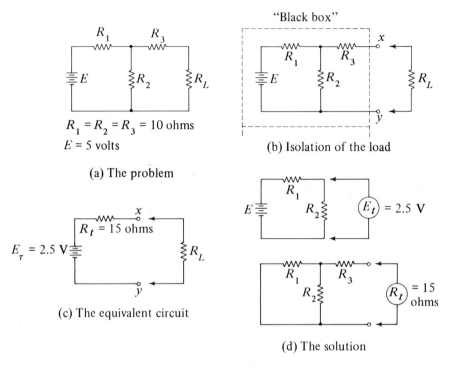

"Black box"

$R_1 = R_2 = R_3 = 10$ ohms
$E = 5$ volts

(a) The problem

(b) Isolation of the load

$E_T = 2.5$ V
$R_t = 15$ ohms

(c) The equivalent circuit

$E_t = 2.5$ V

$R_t = 15$ ohms

(d) The solution

Figure 5-5

and replaced by its internal resistance of zero ohms. Now R_1 and R_2 are in parallel, thus

$$R_t = \frac{R_1 R_2}{R_1 + R_2} + R_3 = \frac{(10)(10)}{10 + 10} + 10 = 15 \text{ ohms}$$

To find how the current in R_L will vary with its resistance

$$I_L = \frac{E_t}{R_t + R_L}$$

If a value of R_L is taken as 5 ohms

$$I_L = \frac{2.5}{15 + 5} = 0.125 \text{ amp}$$

Calculating for I_L directly from Figure 5-5a, we find the total resistance

$$R_T = R_1 + \frac{(R_3 + R_2)(R_2)}{R_3 + R_L + R_2}$$

$$= 10 + \frac{(10 + 5)(10)}{10 + 5 + 10} = 16 \text{ ohms}$$

$$I = \frac{E}{R_T} = \frac{5}{16} = 0.3125 \text{ amp}$$

$$V_1 = IR_1 = (0.3125)(10) = 3.125 \text{ volts}$$

$$V_2 = E - V_1$$

$$= 5 - 3.125 = 1.875 \text{ volts}$$

$$I_2 = \frac{V_2}{R_2} = \frac{1.875}{10} = 0.1875 \text{ amp}$$

$$I_L = I - I_2$$

$$= 0.3125 - 0.1875 = 0.125 \text{ amp}$$

Thévenin's theorem is particularly useful when one must calculate the current through a resistor for many different values of resistance.

5.6   NORTON'S THEOREM

Unlike Thévenin who reasoned that the internal resistance of the "black box" was a series resistance, Norton thought of it as a parallel resistance. Thus, Thévenin's equivalent circuit consists of a *constant-voltage source and a series resistor*, while Norton's equivalent circuit consists of a *constant-current source and a parallel resistor*.

Norton's theorem states: *Any network made up of linear bilateral elements, as viewed from any two terminals, can be replaced by a single constant-current source in parallel with a resistance R_p. The value of the constant-current source is equal to the current which flows between the two terminals when they are short-circuited, and R_p is the resistance between the two terminals of the network at open circuit with all the generators in the network replaced by their internal resistance.*

To obtain Norton's equivalent current source, the two terminals under consideration are shorted. The current I_n in the short circuit is then Norton's current. The Norton resistance R_p has the same value as Thévenin's resistance, and is, therefore, calculated in the same manner.

Example (5.4):

The network shown in Figure 5-6a has the following values:

$$E = 5 \text{ volts}, \; R_1 = R_2 = R_3 = 10 \text{ ohms}.$$

Find the load voltage for $R_L = 15$ ohms.

Solution:

With the terminals A and B shorted together, since $R_3 = R_2$, half the current is in R_3 and the other half in R_2. Thus,

$$I_n = \frac{1}{2} \left[\frac{E}{R_1 + \dfrac{R_2 R_3}{R_2 + R_3}} \right]$$

$$= \frac{1}{2} \left[\frac{5}{10 + \dfrac{(10)(10)}{10 + 10}} \right]$$

"Black box"

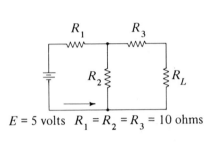

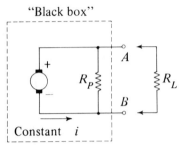

$E = 5$ volts $R_1 = R_2 = R_3 = 10$ ohms

(a) The problem

(b) The assumption
R_P is equivalent to $R_1, R_2,$ and R_3

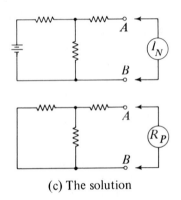

(c) The solution

Figure 5-6

$$= 0.165 \text{ amp}$$

With the source replaced by its internal resistance, the resistance between terminals A and B

$$R_p = R_3 + \frac{R_1 R_2}{R_1 + R_2}$$

$$= 10 + \frac{(10)(10)}{10 + 10} = 15 \text{ ohms}$$

$$I_L = 0.5 I_n = 0.5(0.165)$$

Now let $R_L = 15$ ohms. Then

$$V_L = I_L R_L = \frac{(0.165)(15)}{2} = 1.25 \text{ volts}$$

Using Figure 5-7, the equivalence between Thévenin's and Norton's

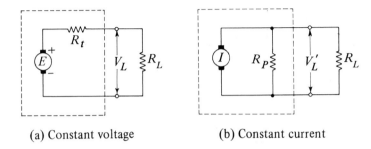

(a) Constant voltage   (b) Constant current

Figure 5-7

circuits may be illustrated. The terminal voltage of Thévenin's equivalent circuit (Figure 5-7a) with the load R_L connected is

$$V_L = \frac{E_t R_L}{R_t + R_L} \tag{5.1}$$

Likewise, the terminal voltage of Norton's equivalent circuit (Figure 5-7b) can be found as follows:

$$V_L' = I_L R_L = I_n \left[\frac{R_p R_L}{R_p + R_L} \right]$$

but

$$R_p = R_t \quad \text{and} \quad I_n = \frac{E_t}{R_t}, \text{ therefore}$$

$$V_L' = \frac{E_t R_L}{R_t + R_L} \tag{5.2}$$

Since V_L and V_L' are equal when the load resistances are equal, the two circuits are equivalent as seen from the load erminals.

5.7   COMPENSATION THEOREM

This theorem states: *Any change in the resistance* (ΔR) *of a branch of any network can be compensated for by placing a generator in the branch having zero internal resistance and a voltage equal to the change in resistance times the original current.*

To illustrate the use of the compensation theorem, consider the example below.

Example (5.5):

In Figure 5-8, the resistance R_3 is decreased 5 ohms from its original value of 10 ohms. Show that the new circuit can be restored to its original condition with a voltage source.

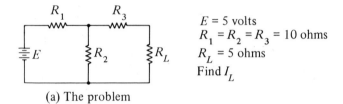

$E = 5$ volts
$R_1 = R_2 = R_3 = 10$ ohms
$R_L = 5$ ohms
Find I_L

(a) The problem

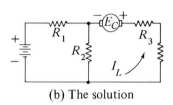

(b) The solution

Figure 5-8

Solution:

From the example on Thévenin's theorem

$$I_3 = 0.125 \text{ amp}$$

$$E_c = I_3(\Delta R_3) = (0.125)(5) = 0.625 \text{ volt}$$

By use of superposition

$$I_L = I'_L - I''_L \quad \text{where}$$

I'_L with E_c shorted

$$= \frac{R_3 - \Delta R_3}{R_3 - \Delta R_3 + R_L} \left[\frac{E}{R_L + \dfrac{R_2(R_3 - \Delta R_3)R_L}{R_3 - \Delta R_3 + R_L + R_2}} \right]$$

$$= \frac{10 - 5}{10 - 5 + 5} \left[\frac{5}{10 + \dfrac{10(10 - 5 + 5)}{10 - 5 + 5 + 10}} \right]$$

$$= 0.167 \text{ amp}$$

I''_L with E shorted

$$= \frac{E_c}{(R_3 - \Delta R_3) + R_L + \dfrac{R_1 R_2}{R_1 + R_2}}$$

$$= \frac{0.625}{10 - 5 + 5 + \dfrac{(10)(10)}{10 + 10}}$$

$$= 0.042 \text{ amp}$$

$$I_L = I'_L - I''_L = 0.167 - 0.042 = 0.125 \text{ amp}$$

Therefore, a correctly polarized ideal voltage generator of 1.25 volts may replace a resistor in a network whose voltage drop is 1.25 volts.

5.8   TRANSFORMATIONS   Δ-Y or π-T.

The equivalence of Delta-Pie (Δ-π) and Tee-Wye (T-Y) networks are apparent from Figures 5-9a, b, and e, f. The electrical equivalents of Δ

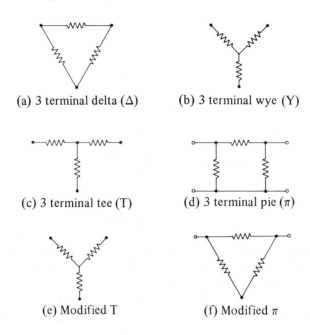

(a) 3 terminal delta (Δ)   (b) 3 terminal wye (Y)

(c) 3 terminal tee (T)   (d) 3 terminal pie (π)

(e) Modified T   (f) Modified π

Figure 5-9

or π networks in the form of a Y or T, however, are less apparent. Nevertheless, a transformation between the two forms is possible, and, in fact, is a very useful technique used for the purpose of simplification. Thus, we may obtain an equivalent Y from a Δ, or an equivalent Δ from a Y, whichever is easier to work with.

For the networks in Figure 5-10 to be equivalent, the resistance between any two terminals of one network must be equal to the resistance between the same two terminals of the other network. By finding the total resistance between *ab*, *ac*, and *cb* in one network, and equating these resistances to the corresponding resistances at the same terminals of the other network, the following equations are obtained. Looking into *ab*, we find

$$R_1 + R_3 = \frac{R_A(R_B + R_C)}{R_A + R_B + R_C} \qquad (5.3)$$

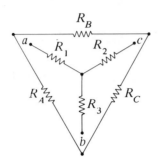

Figure 5-10

Looking into *ac*,

$$R_1 + R_2 = \frac{R_B(R_A + R_C)}{R_A + R_B + R_C} \qquad (5.4)$$

Looking into *cb*,

$$R_2 + R_3 = \frac{R_C(R_A + R_B)}{R_A + R_B + R_C} \qquad (5.5)$$

Equations 5.3, 5.4, and 5.5 may be solved for R_1, R_2, and R_3 in terms of R_A, R_B, and R_C in terms of R_1, R_2, and R_3. All three equations are needed inasmuch as there are three unknowns.

To solve for R_1, R_2, and R_3 in terms of R_A, R_B, and R_C let $R_A + R_B + R_C = S$, then solve for R_1 by subtracting Equation 5.5 from Equation 5.3 as follows:

$$R_1 - R_2 = \frac{R_A R_B + R_A R_C - R_B R_C - R_A R_C}{S}$$

$$R_1 - R_2 = \frac{R_A R_B - R_B R_C}{S} \qquad (5.6)$$

To Equation 5.6 add Equation 5.4

$$2R_1 = \frac{R_A R_B + R_B R_C + R_A R_B - R_B R_C}{S}$$

$$2R_1 = \frac{2R_A R_B}{S}$$

$$R_1 = \frac{R_A R_B}{S} = \frac{R_A R_B}{R_A + R_B + R_C} \qquad (5.7)$$

Using the same method and other combinations of Equations 5.3, 5.4, and 5.5, we find that

$$R_2 = \frac{R_B R_C}{S} = \frac{R_B R_C}{R_A + R_B + R_C} \tag{5.8}$$

and

$$R_3 = \frac{R_A R_C}{S} = \frac{R_A R_C}{R_A + R_B + R_C} \tag{5.9}$$

To obtain the equations for a Y to Δ transformation, multiply Equations 5.7 and 5.8, Equations 5.8 and 5.9, and Equations 5.7 and 5.9 as follows:

$$R_1 R_2 = \frac{R_A R_C R_B^2}{S^2}$$

$$R_2 R_3 = \frac{R_A R_B R_C^2}{S^2}$$

$$R_1 R_3 = \frac{R_B R_C R_A^2}{S^2}$$

Adding these three equations and factoring the right-hand side gives

$$R_1 R_2 + R_2 R_3 + R_1 R_3 = \frac{R_A R_C R_B^2 + R_A R_B R_C^2 + R_B R_C R_A^2}{S^2}$$

$$= \frac{R_A R_B R_C (R_A + R_B + R_C)}{S^2}$$

$$= \frac{R_A R_B R_C}{S} \tag{5.10}$$

Substituting Equation 5.8 into Equation 5.10 we have:

$$R_1 R_2 + R_2 R_3 + R_1 R_3 = R_2 R_A$$

Solving for R_A yields

$$R_A = \frac{R_1 R_2 + R_2 R_3 + R_1 R_3}{R_2} \tag{5.11}$$

In the same manner, with use of Equations 5.9 and 5.7, R_B and R_C are found.

$$R_B = \frac{R_1 R_3 + R_2 R_3 + R_1 R_3}{R_3} \tag{5.12}$$

$$R_C = \frac{R_1 R_2 + R_2 R_3 + R_1 R_3}{R_1} \tag{5.13}$$

With the results derived above, it is possible to make a transformation in either direction. The following example illustrates the use of these transformations.

Example (5.6):
In the network of resistors illustrated in Figure 5-11a (using the values indicated) find the resistance between points *A* and *B*.

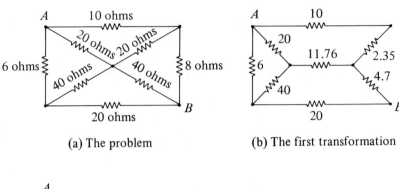

(a) The problem

(b) The first transformation

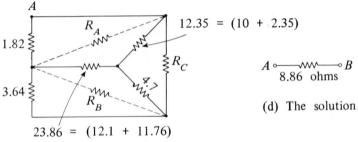

$12.35 = (10 + 2.35)$

$A \circ\!\!-\!\!\text{vvv}\!\!-\!\!\circ B$
8.86 ohms

(d) The solution

$23.86 = (12.1 + 11.76)$

(c) The second equivalent circuit

Figure 5-11

Solution:

There are several methods for solving this problem. The one that follows has fewer transformations or conversions than some of the others. First change the Δ network made up of 20, 40, and 8 ohms to a Y network as follows:

$$R_1 = \frac{R_A R_B}{R_A + R_B + R_C} = \frac{(20)(8)}{68} = 2.35 \text{ ohms}$$

$$R_2 = \frac{R_B R_C}{R_A + R_B + R_C} = \frac{(8)(40)}{68} = 4.7 \text{ ohms}$$

$$R_3 = \frac{R_A R_C}{R_A + R_B + R_C} = \frac{(20)(40)}{68} = 11.76 \text{ ohms}$$

The circuit shown in Figure 5-11b results. This equivalent circuit still does not lend itself to the immediate calculation of the resistance between points *A* and *B*. Therefore, transform the Δ network consisting of the 6, 40, and 20 ohm resistors into a Y network.

$$R_1 = \frac{R_A R_B}{R_A + R_B + R_C} = \frac{(6)(20)}{66} = 1.82 \text{ ohms}$$

$$R_2 = \frac{(6)(40)}{66} = 3.64 \text{ ohms}$$

$$R_3 = \frac{(20)(40)}{66} = 12.1 \text{ ohms}$$

The resulting equivalent circuit is shown in the solid lines of Figure 5-11c. The 12.1 ohms have been combined with the 11.76 ohms from Figure 5-11b to give 23.86 ohms.

To transform the Y network composed of 23.86, 12.35, and 4.7 ohms into a Δ network as shown in the dotted line Figure 5-11c

$$R_A = \frac{12.35(4.7) + 4.7(23.86) + 23.86(12.35)}{4.7}$$

$$= \frac{58 + 112.1 + 295}{4.7} = \frac{465.1}{4.7} = 99 \text{ ohms}$$

$$R_B = \frac{465.1}{12.35} = 37.7 \text{ ohms}$$

$$R_C = \frac{465.1}{23.86} = 19.5 \text{ ohms}$$

Combining 1.82 ohms and R_A, which are in parallel, yields 1.79 ohms. R_B parallels 23.64 ohms to give 14.5 ohms. These two parallel circuits are in series with each other and are also in parallel with R_C. Therefore

$$R_{AB} = \frac{(14.5 + 1.79) 19.5}{14.5 + 1.79 + 19.5}$$

$$= \frac{(16.29) 19.5}{35.79}$$

$$= 8.86 \text{ ohms}$$

5.9 SUMMARY

Internal source *resistance* causes an internal voltage drop and a power loss under load conditions. It is present in all real sources.

Maximum power is transferred from a source to a load when the equivalent load resistance equals the equivalent resistance of the source.

The *superposition* theorem states: In any electrical network consisting of only linear bilateral elements and more than one generator, the current existing in any branch is the sum of the component currents which would exist if each voltage source is considered independently while the others are replaced in the network by their internal resistance.

The *reciprocity* theorem states: If a single source voltage E_A is acting in branch A of a linear bilateral network, producing a current I_B in branch B of the network, the same E_A acting in branch B will produce the same current I_B in branch A.

Thévenin's theorem states: Any network made up of linear bilateral elements as viewed from any two terminals can be replaced by a single source E_t having a series internal resistance R_t. E_t is the potential difference between the two terminals of the network when open-circuited. R_t is the resistance between the two terminals of the network with the load removed and with all the generators in the network replaced by only their internal resistance.

Norton's theorem states: Any network made up of linear bilateral elements, as viewed from any two terminals, can be replaced by a single constant-current source in parallel with a resistance R_p. The value of the constant-current source is equal to the current which flows between the two terminals when they are short-circuited, and R_p is the resistance between the two terminals of the network at open circuit with all the generators in the network replaced by their internal resistance.

The *compensation* theorem states: Any change in the resistance of a branch of any network can be compensated for by placing a generator in the branch having zero internal resistance and a voltage equal to the change in resistance times the original current.

Δ-Y and Y-Δ *transformations* can be used to reduce certain networks containing Y and Δ combinations of resistors to simple series and parallel combinations.

To transform from Δ to Y

$$R_1 = \frac{R_A R_B}{R_A + R_B + R_C} \tag{5.7}$$

$$R_2 = \frac{R_B R_C}{R_A + R_B + R_C} \tag{5.8}$$

$$R_3 = \frac{R_A R_C}{R_A + R_B + R_C} \tag{5.9}$$

To transform from Y to Δ

$$R_A = \frac{R_1 R_2 + R_2 R_3 + R_1 R_3}{R_2} \tag{5.11}$$

$$R_B = \frac{R_1 R_2 + R_2 R_3 + R_1 R_3}{R_3} \tag{5.12}$$

$$R_C = \frac{R_1 R_2 + R_2 R_3 + R_1 R_3}{R_1} \tag{5.13}$$

5.10   QUESTIONS AND PROBLEMS

Questions

1. What is meant by the internal resistance of a source?   (5.1)
2. Why is the load voltage of a battery lower than its no-load voltage?   (5.1)
3. How do you determine the internal resistance of a battery?   (5.1)
4. What is the maximum power transfer theorem?   (5.2)
5. What is the efficiency of a system when maximum power transfer occurs?   (5.2)

6. Does one always strive toward maximum power transfer or maximum efficiency? Discuss. (5.2)
7. State the superposition theorem. (5.3)
8. Does the superposition theorem apply to circuits with nonlinear elements? Explain. (5.3)
9. What is the reciprocity theorem? (5.4)
10. Does the reciprocity theorem apply to circuits with nonlinear elements? Explain. (5.4)
11. What is Thévenin's theorem? (5.5)
12. How does Thévenin's theorem simplify circuit analysis? (5.6)
13. What is meant by open-circuit voltage? (5.6)
14. How do you determine Thévenin's resistance? (5.6)
15. In what way is Thévenin's circuit equivalent to the original circuit? (5.6)
16. What is Norton's equivalent circuit? (5.7)
17. How do you determine the current for Norton's circuit? (5.7)
18. How is the resistance for Norton's equivalent circuit calculated? (5.7)
19. What is the difference between the resistance for Thévenin's equivalent circuit and Norton's equivalent circuit? (5.7)
20. How can Thévenin's equivalent circuit be obtained from Norton's equivalent circuit? (.57)
21. What is the compensation theorem? (5.8)
22. How are Δ-Y and Y-Δ transformations useful? (5.9)
23. Is there any method of solving the circuit in Figure 5-11 other than using Δ-Y or Y-Δ transformations? (5.9)
24. Sketch a diagram which makes it easy to remember Δ-Y and Y-Δ transformations. Explain. (5.9)

Problems

1. The no-load voltage of a certain battery is 1.58 volts. The short-circuit current is 30 amperes. Assuming that the equivalent internal series resistance is linear, calculate its value. Sketch the equivalent circuit in terms of an ideal source and an ideal resistor. (5.1)
2. Repeat Problem 1 for an open-circuit voltage of 1.8 volts and a short-circuit current of 20 amperes. (5.1)
3. A certain battery has a no-load voltage of 12.8 volts. When it is connected to a given load it delivers 50 amperes at 12 volts. What is the equivalent internal series resistance of the battery? What is the load resistance? Sketch an equivalent circuit of the battery and the load. (5.1)
4. A certain battery delivers 6.3 volts at 5 amperes. When connected to another load it delivers 6 volts at 35 amperes. What is its equivalent series internal resistance? (5.1)
5. A certain battery has an internal resistance of 0.5 ohm. It is connected to a load which is matched for maximum power transfer. What is the load resistance? What is the efficiency of the system? (5.2)
6. A 90 volt generator has an internal resistance that is 1.5 ohms. It is connected to a load of 3 ohms. What is the power developed in the load? What is the efficiency? (5.2)
7. In Problem 6, a resistor of 1.5 ohms is added in series with the 1.5 ohm generator resistance and the 3 ohm load so that the maximum power theorem is satisfied. What is the power developed at the load? What is the efficiency? Compare the results with those of Problem 6. Explain. (5.2)

8. A certain source has an open-circuit voltage of 100 volts and a series internal resistance of 25 ohms. Plot a curve of the power in a load vs. the value of the load resistance. What does the curve show? (5.2)

9. Use the superposition theorem to calculate the current in R_3 of Figure 5-12. (5.3)

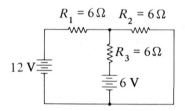

Figure 5-12

10. Use superposition to determine the current in R_2 of Figure 5-13. (5.3)

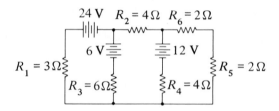

Figure 5-13

11. Using the superposition theorem, determine the voltage across R_3 in Figure 5-14. (5.3)

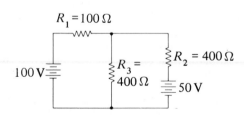

Figure 5-14

12. In Figure 5-15, calculate the current at point X. Next remove the source and place it at point X shorting out the circuit where the source was originally. What is the current at the point where the source was originally? (5.4)

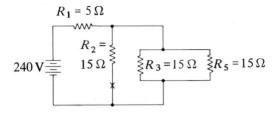

Figure 5-15

13. Repeat Problem 12 for the circuit in Figure 5-16. (5.4)

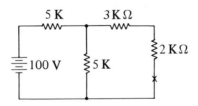

Figure 5-16

14. Determine Thévenin's equivalent circuit for Figure 5-17. Use the equivalent circuit to calculate the current in the load. (5.5)

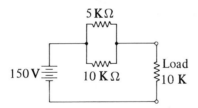

Figure 5-17

15. Repeat Problem 14 for the circuit in Figure 5-18. (5.5)

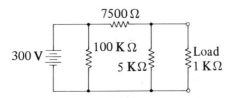

Figure 5-18

16. Repeat Problem 14 for the circuit in Figure 5-19.   (5.5)

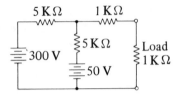

Figure 5-19

17. Using Thévenin's theorem and the maximum power transfer theorem, determine the value of R_L in Figure 5-20.   (5.5)   (5.2)

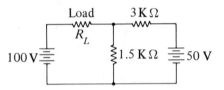

Figure 5-20

18. Apply Thévenin's theorem to the circuit in Figure 5-12 to determine the voltage across R_L for $R_L = 10, 15, 20$, and 25 ohms.   (5.5)

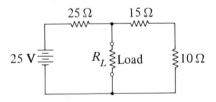

Figure 5-21

19. Obtain Norton's equivalent in terms of Thévenin's equivalent.   (5.6)
20. Determine Norton's equivalent circuit for Figure 5-17. Use the equivalent circuit to determine the current in the load.   (5.6)
21. Repeat Problem 20 for Figure 5-18.   (5.6)
22. Repeat Problem 20 for Figure 5-19.   (5.6)
23. Repeat Problem 18 using Norton's theorem.   (5.6)
24. In Figure 5-22, the resistance R_1 is reduced to one-half its present value. Use the compensation theorem to determine the new current.   (5.7)

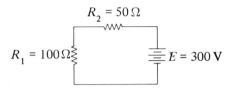

Figure   5-22

25. In Figure 5-23, the resistance R_2 is doubled. Use the compensation theorem to determine the new current.   (5.7)

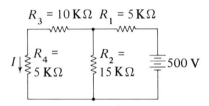

Figure   5-23

26. Find the equivalent resistance of the circuit in Figure 5-24.   (5.8)

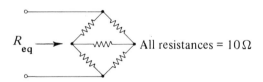

Figure   5-24

27. Repeat Problem 26 for Figure 5-25.   (5.8)

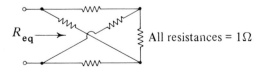

Figure   5-25

28. Repeat Problem 26 for Figure 5-26.   (5.8)

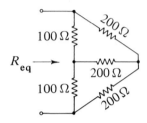

Figure 5-26

29. Repeat Problem 26 for Figure 5-27.   (5.8)

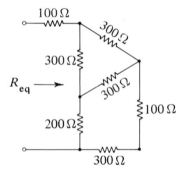

Figure 5-27

30. Determine the current in R_x of Figure 5-28.   (5.8)

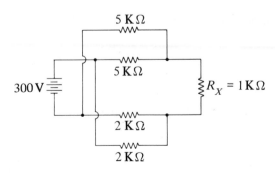

Figure 5-28

6

Electromagnetism

The discovery of magnets and the study of magnetism can be traced back to the early Greeks, for descriptions of many common magnetic effects appeared in their early writings. The first important use of magnetism was about 1100, when the Chinese constructed compasses from pieces of magnetic iron ore. However, it was not until many years later, in 1819, that Hans Christian Oersted showed that a magnetic field was always present in the vicinity of a conductor carrying electric current.

The importance of the study of magnetism in electricity is rather obvious if one considers that the operation of generators, motors, transformers, relays, loudspeakers, and many other electromagnetic devices is based on electromagnetism. In fact, almost every application of electricity involves magnetism. *A magnetic field is always present in the vicinity of a current-carrying conductor.*

6.1 THE MAGNETIC FIELD

A magnetic field can be defined as a region in which a *moving* charge experiences a force when all other force fields such as gravitational and electric fields are removed. The region surrounding a magnet or a conductor carrying an electric current is a magnetic field.

Two vector quantities (i.e., quantities having magnitude and direction) are used to describe the magnetic field. They are the *magnetic intensity* or **H** vector and the *flux density* or **β** vector. The flux density may be de-

109

fined in terms of the force on a charge moving through the magnetic field
by the equation

$$\mathbf{F} = q\mathbf{v} \times \boldsymbol{\beta} \tag{6.1}$$

where

$\mathbf{F}$ = force vector in newtons
q = charge in coulombs (including sign)
$\mathbf{v}$ = velocity vector of the charge in meters/second
$\boldsymbol{\beta}$ = flux density vector in webers/meter^2

$\mathbf{v} \times \boldsymbol{\beta}$ is known as the cross product of $\mathbf{v}$ and $\boldsymbol{\beta}$. The magnitude of the
resultant force vector is given by the product of the magnitudes of $\mathbf{v}$ and $\boldsymbol{\beta}$
times the sine of the angle between $\mathbf{v}$ and $\boldsymbol{\beta}$. The direction of the resultant
vector is the direction which a right-hand screw would move if rotated
through the acute angle from the velocity vector to the $\boldsymbol{\beta}$ vector. (See Figure
6-1.)

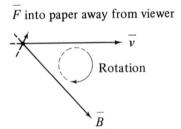

$\overline{F}$ into paper away from viewer

$\overline{v}$

Rotation

$\overline{B}$

Figure 6-1

A concept useful in describing and visualizing flux density is the use of
"lines" of flux. At each point of the magnetic field, the direction of the
$\boldsymbol{\beta}$ vector corresponds to the direction of the flux lines and the magnitude of
the vector is given by the line density. Thus, $\boldsymbol{\beta}$ is said to have so many
lines *per unit area* or so many webers per is unit area (1 weber = 10^8 lines).
The direction of the lines external to a magnetic source such as a magnet
is always considered as originating at the north pole and terminating at
the south pole. Each line is continuous and never crosses another line.
(See Figure 6-2.)

When the flux density is *uniform* over some cross-sectional area of a given
core, the *total flux* ϕ is determined by the product of the magnitude of the
flux density and the cross-sectional area.

$$\phi = \beta A \tag{6.2}$$

where

ϕ = flux in webers

β = magnitude of flux density in webers/meter^2

A = cross-sectional area in meters^2

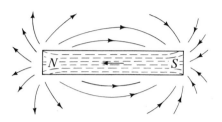

Figure 6-2

The *magnetic field intensity* **H** is a measure of the magnetizing force producing the field. It is measured in ampere-turns per meter and is related to flux density by the *permeability* μ of the magnetic material as shown in the following equation

$$\beta = \mu H \tag{6.3}$$

where

β = flux density in webers/meter^2

μ = permeability

H = magnetic intensity in ampere-turns/meter

The permeability is a function of the material in which the magnetic field is present. It is representative of the ability to set up a magnetic flux in a given material. The higher the permeability, the easier it is to set up a magnetic field in the material. Sometimes one speaks of the *relative permeability* of a substance. This is defined as the ratio of the permeability of that substance to the permeability of free space.

For most diamagnetic and paramagnetic[1] materials μ is a constant independent of β or **H**. However, for ferromagnetic materials μ is dependent on the magnetic intensity. In other words, the relation between β and **H** in ferromagnetic materials is nonlinear.

The curve showing the relationships between β and **H** is called the β **H** curve or magnetization curve. For air, μ is constant and the curve is a straight line. For ferromagnetic materials such as iron, however, the curve is as shown in Figure 1-9. This is often called the *hysteresis loop* for the material and its shape is dependent on the type of ferromagnetic material. The area of this loop is representative of an energy loss called the *hysteresis loss*.

In solving magnetic circuit problems, average magnetization curves, as shown in Figure 6-3, are used. These average curves are obtained by

[1]   See Chapter 1.

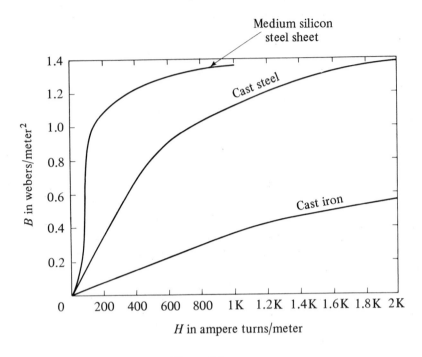

Figure 6-3

drawing a curve through the tips of a family of hysteresis loops, each loop having been taken with a different maximum magnetic intensity.

Note that as **H** is increased beyond a certain point, there is very little increase in the flux density for a large increase in magnetic intensity. That is, the slope is becoming less and less. When this slope is equal to the permeability of free space, the material is said to be *saturated*.

6.2 ELECTROMAGNETISM AND MAGNETOMOTIVE FORCE

When an electric current flows in a conductor, a magnetic field is set up around the conductor. The direction of the lines of force around the conductor are as shown in Figure 6-4. This direction can be found by placing the thumb of the left hand along the conductor in the direction of electron flow. The other fingers will then point in the direction of the magnetic lines about the conductor.

If a conductor is wound around a core to form a coil, the device is called an *electromagnet*. In this case, the direction of the magnetic field is found by wrapping the fingers of the left hand around the coil in the direction of

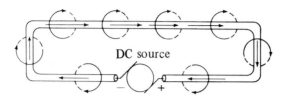

Figure 6-4

electron flow. The thumb then points in the direction of the north magnetic pole. (See Figure 6-5.) In this example the magnetic intensity within the core

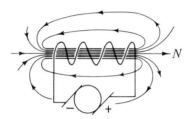

Figure 6-5

is directly proportional to both the current and the number of turns. The product of the number of turns times the current (NI) is known as the *magnetomotive force* and is analogous to the electromotive force in an electric circuit.

$$\mathscr{F} = NI \tag{6.4}$$

where

$\mathscr{F}$ = magnetomotive force in ampere-turns
N = total number of turns
I = current in amperes.

The drop in magnetic potential across a magnetic path is given by the product of the magnetic intensity H in the material times the length of the flux path in the material.

$$U = HL \tag{6.5}$$

where

U = magnetic potential drop in ampere-turns
H = magnetic intensity in ampere-turns/unit length
L = mean length of the flux path

For a given specimen it is sometimes convenient to plot the flux density β as a function of the potential drop. (See Figure 6-6.) Magnetic potential drop is analogous to the drop in voltage that appears across a resistance in an electrical circuit.

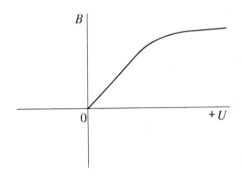

Figure 6-6

6.3 RELUCTANCE

The reluctance of a material is a measure of opposition to the setting up of magnetic flux in a material. It is analogous to resistance in an electric circuit. The following formula is used to determine the reluctance of a given material

$$\mathscr{R} = \frac{L}{\mu A}$$

(6.6)

where

$\mathscr{R}$ = the reluctance
L = the length in meters
μ = the permeability
A = the cross-sectional area in meters^2

(Note the similarity between the above equation and the equation for the resistance of a conductor.)

Due to the low permeability of the best magnetic substances there are no good magnetic insulators. The permeability of the best magnetic materials is only 10^4 times the permeability of air, while the conductivity of copper is 10^{18} times the conductivity of a good electrical insulator.

6.4 THE MAGNETIC CIRCUIT

A simple magnetic circuit is shown in Figure 6-7. The current through the coil of wire produces an mmf equal to the product NI. The core material acts as a reluctance path for the magnetic flux. This reluctance can be found from the above equation, 6.6. The total magnetic flux ϕ is determined by an equation analogous to Ohm's law

$$\phi = \frac{\mathscr{F}}{\mathscr{R}} \tag{6.7}$$

Note that ϕ is analogous to current in the electric circuit.

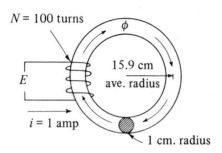

$N = 100$ turns

ϕ

15.9 cm
ave. radius

E

$i = 1$ amp

1 cm. radius

Figure 6-7

Since most of the useful magnetic circuits involve cores which are nonlinear, the equation above is not very useful in practice. In this case it is necessary to use Equation 6.6 along with magnetizing curves of the materials involved.

In solving magnetic circuits, we must make use of laws analogous to Kirchhoff's laws on electric circuits. These laws state that *the sum of the mmf drops around any closed loop equals zero* and that *all the magnetic flux entering a junction equals all the magnetic flux leaving the junction.*

The methods of solving simple series circuits are best illustrated by examples as given below.

Example (6.1):
A toroidal cast steel form is shown in Figure 6-7 with a core having a radius of 15.9 cm and a cross-sectional radius of 1 cm. It is wound with a 100 turn coil which carries one ampere. What is the flux?

Solution:
First determine the mean length.

$$L = 2\pi r$$

$$= (2)(3.1416)(0.159) \text{ meter}$$

$$\approx 1 \text{ meter}$$

From Equation 6.6 the magnetic intensity is

$$H = \frac{NI}{L}$$

$$= \frac{(100)(1)}{1}$$

$$= 100 \text{ ampere-turns/meter}$$

From the *BH* curve for cast steel (Figure 6-3), $H = 100$ ampere-turns/ meter gives $\beta = 0.20$ weber/meter². The cross-sectional area is

$$A = \pi r^2$$

$$= (3.14)(0.01)^2$$

$$= 3.14 \times 10^{-4} \text{ meter}^2$$

The total flux ϕ is then

$$\phi = \beta A$$

$$= (0.20)(3.14 \times 10^{-4})$$

$$= 6.28 \times 10^{-5} \text{ weber}$$

When solving for the total flux in a core given in inches, one can change inches to meters by multiplying by 2.54×10^{-2}. To change from lines/sq in to webers/sq m, multiply by 1.55×10^{-5}.

Example (6.2):
In Figure 6-8, dimensions *a*, *b*, and *e* are each 2 in. Dimension *c* is 20 in and dimension *d* is 10 in. The material is cast steel. How many ampere-turns are necessary to provide a total flux of 240 kilolines?

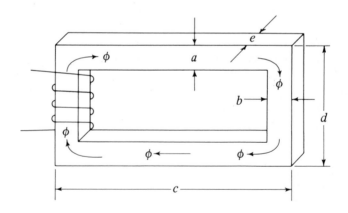

Figure 6-8

Solution:

$$B = \frac{\phi}{A}$$

$$= \frac{240}{(2)(2)}$$

$$= 60 \text{ kilolines/in}^2$$

Changing lines/in^2 to webers/meter^2

$$(60 \times 10^3)(1.55 \times 10^{-5}) = 93 \times 10^{-2} \text{ weber/meter}^2$$

From Figure 6-3, **H** in ampere turns/meter is 6000.

$$L = \text{average distance around the rectangle}$$
$$= 18 + 8 + 18 + 8$$
$$= 52 \text{ inches}$$

Changing inches to meters

$$(52 \times 2.54 \times 10^{-2})$$
$$L = 132.08 \times 10^{-2}$$
$$= 1.32 \text{ meters}$$
$$NI = HL$$
$$= (600)(1.32)$$
$$= 792 \text{ ampere-turns}$$

Therefore, 792 ampere-turns are required. With a magnetization curve graduated in ampere-turns/in and kilolines/in^2, 60 kilolines/in^2 yields 15.2 ampere-turns/in. Thus,

$$NI = 52 \times 15.2$$
$$= 790.4 \text{ ampere-turns}$$

In most magnetic circuits there is a gap through which the magnetic lines must pass before completing the circuit. These gaps are found in inductors, motors, relays, meters movements, loudspeakers, etc. Often the gap is air. Sometimes it is some nonmagnetic substance such as brass or copper which is used in inductors. Gaps are usually in series with some part of the magnetic path so that all of the magnetic lines of force pass through them. Because air has more reluctance to flux than the iron circuit, and because lines of force tend to repel one another, the magnetic lines of force tend to spread out as they pass through the gap. (See Figure 6-9a.)

This is called the *fringe effect*. The fringe effect causes the average flux density of the gap to be less than the flux density of the more permeable iron circuit. For practical purposes, if the gap is short (not more than approximately 0.2 inches or 0.5×10^{-2} meters) we assume that it has the same flux density as iron. For larger airgaps the area of a rectangular gap may be corrected by the following equation as illustrated in Figure 6-9:

$$A = (h + g)(d + g) \tag{6.8}$$

where

$A = $ the corrected area
h and $d = $ dimensions of the rectangular cross section
$g = $ length of air gap

For a circular cross section

$$A = \frac{\pi(D + g^2)}{4} \qquad\qquad (6.9)$$

where

A = the corrected area
D = diameter of the cross section
g = length of air gap

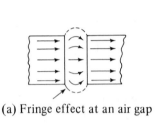

(a) Fringe effect at an air gap

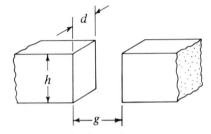

(b) Dimensions for finding correction factor for air gap

Figure 6-9

Example (6.3):

What magnetomotive force must be developed by the coil wound on the core of Figure 6-7 to develop a total flux of 4.71×10^{-5} weber when an air gap of 1 cm exists in the toroid?

Solution:

The cross-sectional area of the steel is

$$A_{\text{steel}} = \pi r^2$$

$$= 3.14 \times (0.01)^2$$

$$= 3.14 \times 10^{-4}$$

Correcting for fringing the equivalent area for air is

$$A_{\text{air}} = \frac{\pi(D + g)^2}{4}$$

$$= \frac{3.14(0.02 + 0.01)^2}{4}$$

$$= 7.06 \times 10^{-4}$$

$$\mathcal{R}_{\text{steel}} = \frac{L}{A}\left(\frac{1}{\mu}\right)$$

$$= \frac{2\pi r}{A}\left[\frac{1}{\mu_{\text{rel}}(4 \times 10^{-7})}\right]$$

Assuming the steel to have a relative permeability of 8000

$$\mathscr{R}_{\text{steel}} = \frac{(2)(3.14)(0.159)}{(3.14 \times 10^{-4})(8 \times 10^3)(4)(3.14)(10^{-7})}$$

$$= 1.26 \times 10^6$$

$$\mathscr{R}_{\text{air}} = \frac{1}{A}\left(\frac{1}{\mu}\right)$$

$$= \frac{0.01}{(3.14)(10^{-4})(1)(4)(3.14)(10^{-7})}$$

$$= 25.4 \times 10^6$$

$$\mathscr{R}_t = \mathscr{R}_{\text{air}} + \mathscr{R}_{\text{steel}}$$

$$= (25.4 \times 10^6) + (1.26 \times 10^6)$$

$$= 26.66 \times 10^6$$

$$U = \phi R$$

$$= (4.71 \times 10^{-5}) + (26.66 \times 10^6)$$

$$= 1.256 \times 10^3$$

$$NI = 1.256\text{K ampere-turns}$$

Thus, a 1 cm air gap in the toroidal cast steel form shown in Figure 6-7 would require 12 times as much current or 12 times as many turns to supply the flux density as without the gap.

6.5 PARALLEL AND SERIES-PARALLEL MAGNETIC CIRCUITS

Just as series magnetic circuits are handled like series electrical circuits, so are parallel and series-parallel magnetic circuits handled like electrical circuits.

In practice there are few true parallel magnetic circuits. Circuits that appear to be parallel are actually series-parallel magnetic circuits. This is true because the leg on which the coil is wound is in series with the parallel paths. (See Figure 6-10.)

Example (6.4):
In Figure 6-10, the leg on which the coil is wound measures 5 cm by 10 cm. The rest of the core measures 5 cm by 5 cm. The air gaps *a*, *b*, and *c* all measure 1 cm. There are 1000 turns on the coil and 5 amperes of current flow in the coil. What is the magnetic flux density in each air gap?

Solution:
Since the air gaps are relatively long, most of the magnetic potential is dropped across these gaps. The iron is acting as a magnetic conductor. The total mmf produced by the coil is

$$\mathscr{F} = NI$$

$$= (1 \times 10^3)(5)$$

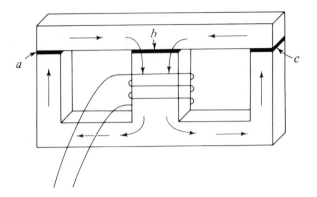

Figure 6-10

$$= 5 \times 10^3 \text{ amp-turns}$$

The reluctance of gaps a and c is

$$\mathscr{R}_c = \mathscr{R}_a = \frac{L}{\mu A}$$

$$= \frac{1 \times 10^{-2}}{(4 \times 10^{-7})(5 \times 10^{-2})^2}$$

$$= 1.59 \times 10^7 \text{ amp-turns/weber-meter}$$

The reluctance of gap b is one-half that of a since the area is twice as great. The total reluctance, assuming reluctance of iron small, is

$$\mathscr{R}_t = \mathscr{R}_b + \frac{\mathscr{R}_a \mathscr{R}_c}{\mathscr{R}_a + \mathscr{R}_c}$$

$$= 0.795 \times 10^7 + \frac{(1.59 \times 10^7)(1.59 \times 10^7)}{(1.59 \times 10^7) + (1.59 \times 10^7)}$$

$$= 1.59 \times 10^7 \text{ amp-turns/weber-meter}$$

The flux ϕ_a in gap b is

$$\phi_a = \frac{NI}{\mathscr{R}_t}$$

$$= \frac{5 \times 10^3}{1.59 \times 10^7}$$

$$= 1.57 \times 10^{-4} \text{ weber}$$

The flux in gaps a and c are only half as much, since the flux through gap a divides equally among the two other legs. The flux density at a and at c is

$$\beta_c = \beta_a = \frac{\phi_a}{A}$$

$$= \frac{1.57 \times 10^{-4}}{(5 \times 10^{-2})^2}$$

$$= 0.63 \text{ webers/meter}^2$$

At gap c the flux density β_c is

$$\beta_c = \frac{\phi_c}{A}$$

$$= \frac{3.14 \times 10^{-4}}{(5 \times 10^{-2})(10 \times 10^{-2})}$$

$$= 0.63 \text{ weber/meter}^2$$

6.6 MAGNETIC FORCE

When a direct current is applied to a magnetic circuit with a gap, a force exists between the faces of the gap tending to close the air gap. This force will depend on the number of lines of force across the gap.

$$F = \frac{\beta^2 A}{2\mu} \qquad (6.10)$$

where

$F =$ force in newtons
$\beta =$ magnitude flux density in webers/meter^2
$A =$ cross-sectional area in meters^2
$\mu =$ permeability of gap medium

When the gap is an air gap, μ becomes $4\pi \times 10^{-7}$. The equivalent equation for F in pounds, B in lines/in^2, and A in in^2 is

$$F = 1.4 \times 10^{-8} \beta^2 A \qquad (6.11)$$

Equation 6.11 is used in the design of solenoids, relays, and lifting magnets.

Example (6.5):
A certain relay has an air gap whose cross-sectional area is 1 in^2. The holding force is 2.8 lb. Find the necessary flux density.

Solution:
Rewriting Equation 6.11, we obtain

$$\beta = \sqrt{\frac{F}{1.4 \times 10^{-8} A}}$$

$$= \sqrt{\frac{2.8}{1.4 \times 10^{-8}}}$$

$$= 1.41 \times 10^{-4} \text{ line/in}^2$$

6.7 SUMMARY

A *magnetic field* is defined as a region in which a moving charge experiences a force when all other force fields are absent. It is described by two vector quantities known as the magnetic intensity **H** and the flux density $\boldsymbol{\beta}$.

The *flux density* $\boldsymbol{\beta}$ is defined by the equation

$$\mathbf{F} = q\mathbf{v} \times \boldsymbol{\beta} \tag{6.1}$$

If the flux density is uniform over a given area, the total *magnetic flux* ϕ is given by

$$\phi = \beta A \tag{6.2}$$

Magnetic *lines* of flux leave the north pole of a magnet or electromagnet and return to the south pole. They never cross each other.

Magnetic intensity $\mathbf{H}$ is a measure of the magnetizing creating the field. The relation between $\boldsymbol{\beta}$ and $\mathbf{H}$ is

$$\boldsymbol{\beta} = \mu\,\mathbf{H} \tag{6.3}$$

where μ is the permeability of the magnetic material.

The *permeability* of a material is a measure of ease with whice a magnetic flux can be set up in that material. For air μ is constant, but for ferromagnetic materials it depends upon the flux density. In the latter a *hysteresis loop* gives the relation between $\boldsymbol{\beta}$ and H.

The *relative permeability* of a substance is the ratio of the permeability of that substance to the permeability of air.

Magnetomotive force is analogous to electromotive force and is given by

$$\mathscr{F} = NI \tag{6.4}$$

Magnetic potential drop aiong a magnetic path is analogous to voltage drop in an electrical circuit and is given by

$$U = HL \tag{6.5}$$

Reluctance is analogous to resistance in an electric circuit and is given by

$$\mathscr{R} = \frac{L}{\mu A} \tag{6.6}$$

The equivalent of *Ohm's law* in magnetic circuits is

$$\phi = \frac{F}{R} \tag{6.7}$$

The equivalents of *Kirchhoff's laws* in magnetic circuits are

(a)   The sum of all the potential drops around any closed loop is equal to zero.

(b)   The total magnetic flux into a junction must equal the total flux leaving the junction.

Magnetic lines tend to spread out as they pass through an air gap. This is called *fringing* and causes the average flux density in the air gap to be lower than in the iron. To allow for the fringing, the cross-sectional areas are modified. For rectangular cross sections.

$$A = (h + g)(d + g) \tag{6.8}$$

and for circular cross sections

$$A = \frac{\pi (D + g)^2}{4} \tag{6.9}$$

The *magnetic force* exerted between two pole faces is

$$F = \frac{\beta^2 A}{2 \mu} \tag{6.10}$$

6.8 QUESTIONS AND PROBLEMS

Questions

1. When is a magnetic field always present? (Introduction)
2. Define a magnetic field. (6.1)
3. What is a vector? (6.1)
4. What is the cross product of two vectors? (6.1)
5. What is magnetic flux? What units is it measured in? (6.1)
6. What is magnetic flux density? What units is it measured in? (6.1)
7. What must be true of the flux density before Equation 6.2 can be used? (6.1)
8. What is magnetic intensity? What units is it measured in? (6.1)
9. What is permeability? What is relative permeability? (6.1)
10. Is the permeability for iron constant? Explain. (6.1)
11. What is a hysteresis loop? (6.1)
12. What is meant by an average magnetization curve? How is it obtained? (6.1)
13. Define saturation. (6.1)
14. How would you find the direction of the magnetic field around a current-carrying conductor? (6.2)
15. How would you find the direction of the magnetic field of an electromagnet? (6.2)
16. What is magnetomotive force? What units is it measured in? (6.2)
17. What is the relationship between magnetic intensity and magnetic potential drop? (6.2)
18. What is reluctance and in what units is it measured? (6.3)
19. Discuss the subject of magnetic insulators. (6.3)
20. Describe a magnetic circuit, pointing out all the analogies to electrical circuits. (6.4)
21. What is the equivalent of Ohm's law in magnetic circuits? (6.4)
22. What is the equivalent of Kirchhoff's voltage law in magnetic circuits? (6.4)
23. What is the equivalent of Kirchhoff's current law in magnetic circuits? (6.4)
24. Why is Equation 6.7 useful only in a few applications? (6.4)
25. What is fringing? How do we make corrections for it? (6.4)
26. In practice, why are there few parallel magnetic circuits? (6.5)
27. When can you neglect the reluctance in the iron in a magnetic circuit? (6.5)
28. How is the force between two pole faces dependent on flux density? (6.6)

Problems

1. An electron is moving to the right through a magnetic field which is directed into the paper. What is the direction of the force on the electron? (6.1)
2. If the flux density in Problem 1 is 3×10^{-4} weber/meter^2 and the velocity of the electron is 100 meters/sec, what is the magnitude of the force on the electron? (6.1)

3. An electron is moving at a velocity of 300 meters/sec as shown in Figure 6-11. The flux density is 3×10^{-4} weber/meter. What is the magnitude and direction of the force?   (6.1)

Figure 6-11

4. A toroid has 350 turns of wire and carries 2 amp. What is the magnetomotive force produced?   (6.2)

5. A toroid has 1000 turns of wire and carries 3 amp. If the magnetic intensity in the core is 30,000 amp-turns/meter, what is the mean length of the flux path?   (6.2)

6. A coil of 500 turns is required to produce an mmf of 5000 amp-turns. What current must the coil carry?   (6.2)

7. The magnetic intensity in a piece of iron is 15,000 amp-turns/meter and the mean length of the flux path is 0.1 meter. What is the drop in magnetic potential across the material?   (6.2)

8. What is the reluctance of a piece of cast iron 10 cm long and having a diameter of 1 cm when the flux density is 0.4 weber/meter^2? Use Figure 6-3.   (6.3)

9. What is the reluctance of a piece of cast steel whose length is 5 cm and whose cross-sectional area is 2 cm^2? The magnetic intensity is 1.2×10^3 amp-turns/meter.   (6.3)

10. Calculate the reluctance of an air gap whose length is 1 cm and whose cross-sectional area is 4 cm^2.   (6.3)

11. The drop in magnetic potential across a certain piece of material is 1400 amp-turns. The flux is 0.018 weber. What is the reluctance?   (6.4)

12. The reluctance of a certain toroid is 70×10^3 amp-turns/weber and the magnetic potential around the toroid is 1400 amp-turns. What is the flux?   (6.4)

13. The flux in a certain core is 0.05 weber. The reluctance is 50×10^3 amp-turns/weber. What is the drop in magnetic potential?   (6.4)

14. What is the flux ϕ_A in Figure 6-12?   (6.4)

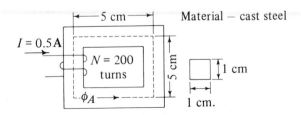

Figure 6-12

15. What is the flux ϕ_C in Figure 6-13?   (6.4)

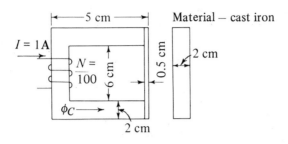

Figure 6-13

16. What is the drop in magnetic potential from *a* to *b* in Figure 6-14?   (6.4)

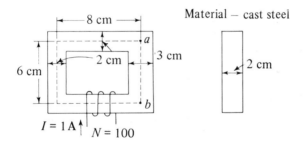

Figure 6-14

17. What is the current in the coil in Figure 6-15?   (6.4)

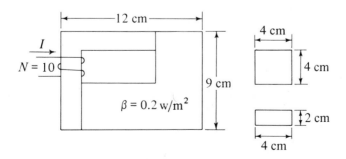

Figure 6-15

18. A toroidal cast steel core has a mean length of 10 cm and a diameter of 1 cm. The 50 turn coil carries a current of 2 amp. What is the flux density and the total flux? (6.4)

19. Determine the flux in the core of Figure 6-16.   (6.4)

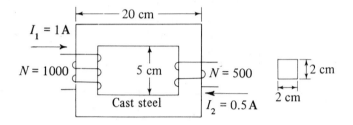

Figure 6-16

20. Determine the flux in the air gap of Figure 6-17.   (6.4)

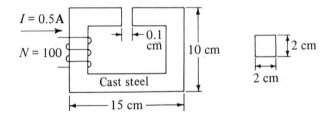

Figure 6-17

21. In Figure 6-18, determine the flux density in each section and in the air gap.   (6.4)

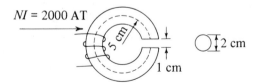

Figure 6-18

22. In Figure 6-19, determine the current I. (6.4)

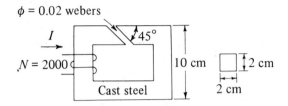

Figure 6-19

23. Determine the flux in the air gaps of Figure 6-20. (6.5)

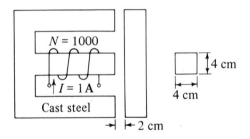

Figure 6-20

24. Determine the flux in each leg of Figure 6-21. (6.5)

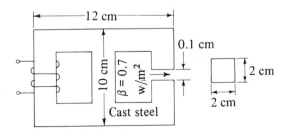

Figure 6-21

25. Repeat Problem 24 for Figure 6-22. (6.5)

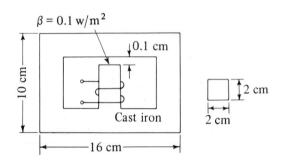

Figure 6-22

26. Determine the force between the pole faces of Figure 6-17. (6.6)
27. What is the flux density necessary to produce a force of 0.5 lb between pole face having a diameter of 0.25 in? (6.6)

7

Inductance and Inductors

The phenomenon known as electromagnetic induction was discovered by Michael Faraday in 1832. Faraday found that moving a conductor in a magnetic field produced an electromotive force in the conductor. He also noted that a changing magnetic field in the vicinity of a conductor produced an electromotive force in the conductor. Later, a scientist by the name of Heinrich Lenz found that the direction of the electromotive force was always such that it would oppose the cause producing it. The latter accounts for the fundamental property of a coil or inductor, that is, to oppose any change in current. This chapter deals with inductance in simple d-c circuits. The analysis of inductive a-c circuits will be considered in Section II.

7.1 FARADAY'S LAW

Also known as the "Law of Electromagnetic Induction," Faraday's law states that the magnitude of emf induced in a circuit linked by magnetic flux is proportional to the time rate of change of that portion of the magnetic flux that links the circuit. Expressed mathematically, the magnitude of the *instantaneous* voltage is

$$e = \frac{d\lambda}{dt} \tag{7.1}$$

where

e = the instantaneous induced voltage in volts
λ = the total flux linkage in webers

$\dfrac{d\lambda}{dt}$ = the derivative of linkage flux with respect to time. It denotes the rate of change of flux linkage with respect to time at any given instant of time.

The *average* induced voltage is found by taking the ratio of the total flux change and the corresponding change in time.

$$E = \frac{\Delta\lambda}{\Delta t} \tag{7.2}$$

Using a coil of N turns, each turn is linked by a common flux ϕ. Therefore, the total flux linkage is given by

$$\lambda = N\phi \tag{7.3}$$

where

λ = total flux linkage in webers

N = total number of turns

ϕ = all of the flux linking each turn

and Equations 7.1 and 7.2 become

$$e = N\frac{d\phi}{dt} \tag{7.4}$$

and

$$E = N\frac{\Delta\phi}{\Delta t} \tag{7.5}$$

Example (7.1):

In a coil of 250 turns the flux changes from 0.0025 weber to 0.0026 weber in 5 μ sec. What is the magnitude of the induced voltage?

Solution:

$$E = N\frac{\Delta\phi}{\Delta t}$$

$$= 250\frac{(0.0026 - 0.0025)}{5 \times 10^{-6}}$$

$$= 5000 \text{ volts}$$

7.2 LENZ'S LAW

Heinrich Lenz, a German scientist, in experimenting with electromagnetic induction observed that the direction of induced emf is always such that it opposes the cause producing it. This last statement is known as Lenz's law.

If the induced voltage is the result of moving a conductor in a magnetic field, it will be in such a direction as to cause an opposition to the motion.

If the induced voltage is caused by a changing flux, the current resulting is in such a direction as to oppose the change in flux. *It does not oppose the flux itself but the change in flux.*

7.3 SELF-INDUCTANCE

Consider a coil of wire wrapped around some core, as shown in Figure 7-1. A changing current in the coil will set up a changing flux which will

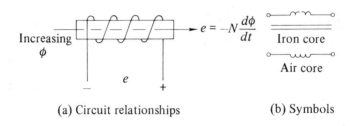

(a) Circuit relationships   (b) Symbols

Figure 7-1

in turn induce a voltage in the coil. The magnitude of the induced voltage at the terminals is given by Faraday's law and the direction by Lenz's law. Multiplying Equation 7.4 by di/di where i is the symbol for instantaneous current, we have

$$e = N\frac{d\phi}{dt}\frac{di}{di}$$

$$= N\frac{d\phi}{di}\frac{di}{dt}$$

The quantity $N(d\phi/di)$ is called the *self-inductance L* of the coil and is measured in units called *henrys*. It is the property of a conductor (usually wound in a coil) to produce within itself a flux change with current change. It is the rate of change of flux with respect to current. One *henry* equals one weber-turn per ampere or one volt-second per ampere. That is, when a change of one ampere in one second produces one volt, the coil is said to have one henry of inductance.

$$L = N\frac{d\phi}{di} \tag{7.6}$$

or

$$L_{avg} = N\frac{\Delta\phi}{\Delta i} \tag{7.7}$$

$$e = L\frac{di}{dt} \tag{7.8}$$

or

$$E = L\frac{\Delta i}{\Delta t} \tag{7.9}$$

A coil designed for the express purpose of having inductance is called an *inductor* or *choke*. Figure 7-2 shows several types of inductors.

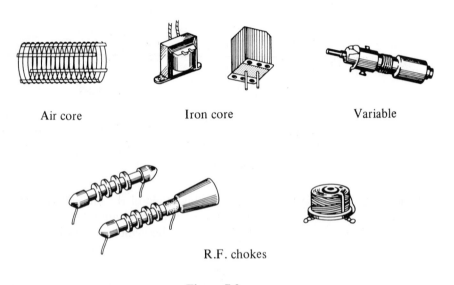

Air core   Iron core   Variable

R.F. chokes

Figure 7-2

Although we have been considering only coils as inductors, any length of wire has inductance. Likewise, no coil is purely inductive for it always has some resistance in the wire from which it is constructed, as well as capacitance between its turns and energy losses in its core.

To determine the inductance of a coil like that shown in Figure 7-3, we use Equation 7.7

$$L_{\mathrm{avg}} = N\frac{\Delta \phi}{\Delta i}$$

and using Equation 6.7 from the chapter on magnetic circuits modified for mks units

$$\Delta \phi = \frac{4\pi N \Delta i}{\mathscr{R}}$$

Thus,

$$L_{\mathrm{avg}} = \frac{4\pi N^2}{\mathscr{R}} \tag{7.10}$$

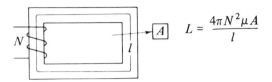

Figure 7-3

where

$$L_{avg} = \text{average inductance in henrys}$$
$$N = \text{total turns}$$
$$\mathcal{R} = \text{the reluctance of the magnetic path}$$

or by using Equation (6.6)

$$L_{avg} = \frac{4\pi N^2 \mu A}{l} \tag{7.11}$$

where

$$L_{avg} = \text{average inductance in henrys}$$
$$N = \text{total turns}$$
$$\mu = \text{permeability of magnetic path in henrys/meter}$$
$$A = \text{cross-sectional area of magnetic circuit in meters}^2$$
$$l = \text{length of flux path in meters}$$

The inductance L is in henrys if the mks system of units is used.

Example (7.2):

What is the inductance of a coil of 500 turns wound on a steel core whose length is 0.2 meter and whose cross section is 4×10^{-2} meter²? The permeability is 5×10^{-4} henry/meter.

Solution:

$$L_{avg} = \frac{4\pi N^2 \mu A}{l}$$

$$= \frac{4\pi(500)^2(5 \times 10^{-4})(4 \times 10^{-4})}{0.2}$$

$$= 25 \text{ henrys}$$

7.4 MUTUAL INDUCTANCE

When two inductors L_1 and L_2 are placed so that magnetic flux from L_1 links the turns of L_2, there is said to be a mutual inductance from L_1 to L_2 and vice versa. (See Figure 7-4.) Mutual inductance is designated by

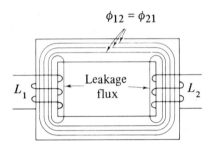

Figure 7-4

M and is also measured in henrys.

$$M_{12} = N_2 k \left(\frac{d\phi_1}{di_1}\right)$$ (7.12)

and

$$M_{21} = N_1 k \left(\frac{d\phi_2}{di_2}\right)$$ (7.13)

where

M_{12} = mutual inductance from coil 1 to coil 2
M_{21} = mutual inductance from coil 2 to coil 1
N_1 = number of turns on coil 1
N_2 = number of turns on coil 2
$k \left(\frac{d\phi_1}{di_1}\right)$ = rate of change of flux from coil 1 linking coil 2 with respect to the current in coil 1
$k \left(\frac{d\phi_2}{di_2}\right)$ = rate of change of flux from coil 2 linking coil 1 with respect to the current in coil 2

With ordinary core materials $M_{12} = M_{21} = M$. If Equations 7.12 and 7.13 are multiplied together

$$M^2 = N_1 N_2 k^2 \left(\frac{d\phi_1}{di_1}\right) \left(\frac{d\phi_2}{di_2}\right)$$ (7.14)

If we use Equations 7.14 and 7.5

$$M^2 = L_1 L_2 k^2$$

or

$$k = \frac{M}{\sqrt{L_1 L_2}}$$ (7.15)

The factor k is called the *coefficient of coupling*. It is a measure of the degree of magnetic coupling between two coils. The maximum value of k is unity, which means all the flux links both coils. A value of k equal to zero implies no magnetic coupling. The coefficient of coupling can be varied by varying the physical position of one coil with respect to the other.

7.5   SERIES AND PARALLEL INDUCTORS

When two coils are connected in series, the total inductance can be shown to be

$$L_t = L_1 + L_2 \pm 2M \qquad (7.16)$$

The plus sign is used if the coils are connected so that their magnetic fields aid and the minus sign is used when their magnetic fields oppose. If there is no magnetic coupling between the coils, the mutual inductance is zero and Equation 7.16 becomes

$$L_t = L_1 + L_2 \qquad (7.17)$$

Example (7.3):
   A 10 henry inductor and an 8.1 henry inductor are connected in series aiding. The mutual inductance between them is 8 henrys. What is the equivalent inductance and the coefficient of coupling?

Solution:

$$L_t = L_1 + L_2 + 2M$$
$$= 10 + 8.1 + 16$$
$$= 34.1 \text{ henrys}$$

$$k = \frac{M}{\sqrt{L_1 L_2}}$$

$$= \frac{8}{\sqrt{(10)(8.1)}}$$

$$= 0.89$$

When there are more than two coils in series and no magnetic coupling, the total inductance is the sum of the individual self-inductances.

$$L_t = L_1 + L_2 + L_3 + \ldots + L_n \qquad (7.18)$$

Two inductors connected in parallel can be shown to have an equivalent inductance

$$L_t = \frac{L_1 L_2 - M^2}{L_1 + L_2 \pm 2M} \qquad (7.19)$$

Here the negative sign is used when the coils are aiding and the plus sign is used when the coils are opposing. If $M = 0$, Equation 7.19 reduces to

$$L_t = \frac{L_1 L_2}{L_1 + L_2} \qquad (7.20)$$

When more than two inductors are in parallel with no mutual inductance between them, their equivalence is found in the same way as resistance in parallel.

$$L_t = \frac{1}{1/L_1 + 1/L_2 + 1/L_3 + \dots + 1/L_n} \qquad (7.21)$$

Example (7.4):
Three inductors are connected in parallel. Two are 10 henrys and the other one is 5 henrys. What is the equivalent inductance if there is no magnetic coupling between the two?

Solution:

$$L_t = \frac{1}{\dfrac{1}{L_1} + \dfrac{1}{L_2} + \dfrac{1}{L_3}}$$

$$= \frac{1}{\dfrac{1}{10} + \dfrac{1}{10} + \dfrac{1}{5}}$$

$$= 4 \text{ henrys}$$

7.6 *RL* CIRCUITS WITH D-C SOURCES

If an inductor, a resistor, and a battery are connected as shown in Figure 7-5 and the switch is thrown to the number 1 position, a current

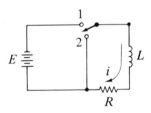

Figure 7-5

will try to build up in the circuit. Without the inductor in the circuit, the current would reach a value of $I = E/R$ at the instant the switch was thrown. However, the fundamental property of an inductor is to oppose any change in current. Therefore, the current does not rise instantly. Instead, it rises as shown in Figure 7-6. The equation for this current is[1]

$$i = \frac{E}{R}(1 - \epsilon^{-(R/L)t}) \qquad (7.22)$$

---

[1] Equation 7.22 is the solution to the differential equation $L\,(di/dt) + iR = E$, which is obtained by writing Kirchhoff's voltage law around the circuit in terms of the instantaneous current.

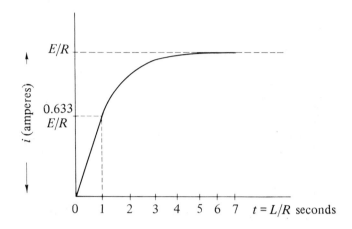

Figure 7-6

where

i = instantaneous current in amperes
E = the applied voltage in volts
R = resistance in ohms
L = inductance in henrys
t = time in seconds
ϵ = 2.71828

The quantity L/R is called the *time constant* for the circuit.

$$T = \frac{L}{R} \tag{7.23}$$

It is the time required for the current to reach 63.3% of its final value of E/R volts. In five time constants the current is nearly equal to its final value of E/R volts.

If the switch is now thrown to position number 2, the current in the circuit will not drop to zero instantly, but will decay as shown in Figure 7-7. Here again the inductor is opposing any change in its current. The equation for this current is

$$i = \frac{E}{R}\epsilon^{-(R L)t} \tag{7.24}$$

In one time constant the current decays to 36.7% of its initial value and in five time constants is almost zero.

The instantaneous voltage across the resistor is obtained from Ohm's law. When the current is building up in the circuit this voltage is

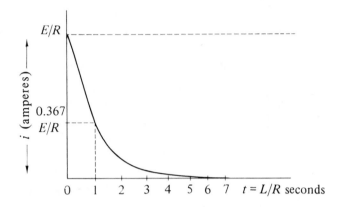

Figure 7-7

$$v_R = E(1 - \epsilon^{-(R/L)t}) \qquad (7.25)$$

While the current is decaying, the voltage across the resistor is

$$v_R = E\epsilon^{-(R/L)t} \qquad (7.26)$$

The instantaneous voltage across the inductor can be found by sub-tracting the voltage across the resistor from the source voltage. Thus, when the current is building up in the circuit

$$v_L = E - E(1 - \epsilon^{-(R/L)t}) \qquad (7.27)$$

$$= E\epsilon^{-(R/L)t}$$

For the case when current in the circuit is decaying

$$v_L = 0 - E\epsilon^{-(R/L)t} \qquad (7.28)$$

$$= -E\epsilon^{-(R/L)t}$$

Example (7.5):
In the circuit in Figure 7-5, let $R = 10$ kΩ, $L = 500$ mh and $E = 100$ volts. What is the current 10 μsec after the switch is placed in position 1? What is the voltage across the resistor and inductor at this time?

Solution:
From Equation 7.22

$$i = \frac{E}{R}(1 - \epsilon^{-(R/L)t})$$

$$= \frac{100}{10 \times 10^3}\left[1 - 2.718^{-\left(\frac{10 \times 10^3}{500 \times 10^{-3}}\right)10 \times 10^{-6}}\right]$$

$$= 10 \times 10^{-3}(1 - 0.819)$$

$$= 0.181 \text{ ma}$$

The voltage across the resistor is merely the product of the current times the resistance.

$$v_R = iR$$

$$= (0.181 \times 10^{-3})(10 \times 10^3)$$

$$= 1.81 \text{ volts}$$

The voltage across the inductor is then given by the source voltage minus the voltage across the resistor

$$v_L = E - v_R$$

$$= 100 - 1.81$$

$$= 98.19 \text{ volts}$$

Example 7.6:

The switch in Figure 7-5 has been in position 1 for a long time (several time constants). It is now switched to position 2. How much time will it take the current to decay to 5 ma after the switch is put into position 2? The values of elements are the same as in the example above.

Solution:

From Equation 7.24

$$i = \frac{E}{R} \epsilon^{-(R/L)t}$$

$$\epsilon^{-(R/L)t} = \frac{iR}{E}$$

$$\ln \epsilon^{-(R/L)t} = \ln \frac{iR}{E}$$

$$-\frac{R}{L}t = \ln \frac{iR}{E}$$

$$t = -\frac{L}{R}\left(\ln \frac{iR}{E}\right)$$

$$t = \frac{500 \times 10^{-3}}{10 \times 10^3}\left[\ln \frac{(5 \times 10^{-3})(10 \times 10^3)}{10^2}\right.$$

$$= -(5 \times 10^{-5})(\ln 0.5)$$

$$= 5 \times 10^{-5} \ln 2$$

$$= 34.7 \ \mu \text{ sec}$$

7.7   ENERGY STORED IN THE MAGNETIC FIELD OF AN INDUCTOR

The energy stored in the magnetic field of an inductor is given by

$$W = \tfrac{1}{2}LI^2 \qquad\qquad (7.29)$$

where

$$W = \text{energy in joules}$$
$$L = \text{inductance in henrys}$$
$$I = \text{current in amperes}$$

In transferring energy from the source to the field of the inductor, it can be shown that half of the energy is lost in the series resistance of the circuit. Thus, the energy from the source is always twice the energy stored in the inductor.

Example (7.7):

A current of 5 amp flows in an inductor of 8 henrys. What is the energy stored? What is the energy lost in the resistor?

Solution:

$$W = \tfrac{1}{2} LI^2$$
$$= \tfrac{1}{2}(8)(25)$$
$$= 100 \text{ joules}$$
$$= \text{energy loss in the resistor}$$

7.8 SUMMARY

The fundamental property of an inductor is to oppose any change in current.

Faraday's law says that the magnitude of induced voltage in a circuit is proportional to the rate of change of flux with respect to time. For a coil of N turns

$$e = N\frac{d\phi}{dt} \tag{7.4}$$

Lenz's law says that the direction of induced emf is always such that it opposes the cause producing it.

Self-inductance is the rate of change of flux with respect to current. For a coil of N turns

$$L = N\frac{d\phi}{di} \tag{7.6}$$

The average inductance is given by

$$L_{avg} = \frac{4\pi N^2}{\mathcal{R}} \tag{7.10}$$

The instantaneous voltage appearing across an inductor is given by the product of the inductance times the rate of change of current with respect to time.

$$e = L\frac{di}{dt} \tag{7.8}$$

When two inductors are placed such that there is a flux linkage between them, there is said to be *mutual inductance M* between them.

Another measure of the coupling between coils is the *coefficient of coupling*.

$$k = \frac{M}{\sqrt{L_1 L_2}} \tag{7.15}$$

When there is no magnetic coupling, inductances combine in the same way as resistors.

In series

$$L_t = L_1 + L_2 + L_3 + \ldots + L_n \tag{7.18}$$

In parallel

$$L_t = \frac{1}{\dfrac{1}{L_1} + \dfrac{1}{L_2} + \dfrac{1}{L_3} + \ldots + \dfrac{1}{L_n}} \tag{7.21}$$

When 2 coils with mutual coupling between them are in series, the equivalent inductance is

$$L_1 + L_2 \pm 2M \tag{7.17}$$

When two coils with magnetic coupling are in parallel, the equivalent inductance is

$$L_t = \frac{L_1 L_2 - M^2}{L_1 + L_2 \pm 2M} \tag{7.20}$$

In a simple series RL circuit, the rising current is given by

$$i = \frac{E}{R}\left(1 - \epsilon^{-(R/L)t}\right) \tag{7.22}$$

while the decaying current is given by

$$i = \frac{E}{R}\epsilon^{-(R/L)t} \tag{7.24}$$

The quantity L/R is called the *time constant* for the circuit. In one time constant the current in an inductor builds up to 63% of its final value. In five time constants it is very near its final value. In one time constant the current decays to 38% of its maximum value and in five time constants is nearly zero.

The energy stored in a magnetic field is

$$W = \tfrac{1}{2}LI^2 \tag{7.29}$$

7.9   QUESTIONS AND PROBLEMS

Questions

1. What is the fundamental property of an inductor?   (Introduction)
2. What is Faraday's law?   (7.1)

3. What is meant by flux linkage? (7.1)
4. What is the difference between instantaneous induced voltage and average induced voltage? Explain. (7.1)
5. What is Lenz's law? (7.2)
6. If voltage is induced by a changing flux, the current resulting will be in such a direction as to oppose _____. (7.2)
7. What is self-inductance? (7.3)
8. What is average inductance? (7.3)
9. Are real inductors pure? (7.3)
10. Inductance is (directly, inversely) proportional to permeability. (7.3)
11. Inductance is directly proportional to the number of turns _____. (7.3)
12. How does inductance depend upon the reluctance of the magnetic circuit? (7.3)
13. Explain the effect of an air gap on inductance. (7.3)
14. What is mutual inductance? (7.4)
15. What is the coefficient of coupling? How is it related to mutual inductance? (7.4)
16. How do inductances combine in series? (7.5)
17. How do inductances combine in parallel? (7.5)
18. Explain the plus or minus sign in Equation 7.16 and Equation 7.19. (7.5)
19. What is a time constant? (7.6)
20. Explain the buildups of current and decay of current in a simple *RL* circuit. (7.6)
21. What is the significance of four time constants? (7.6)
22. How do you determine the energy stored in an inductor? (7.7)
23. In a simple *RL* circuit, compare the energy taken by the resistor with that stored in the inductor. (7.7)

Problems

1. A 100 turn inductor experiences a flux change of 0.1 weber in 1 μ sec. What is the average induced voltage? (7.1)
2. A 250 turn coil experiences a change in flux from 0.3 weber to 0.15 weber in 10 μ sec. What is the average induced voltage? (7.1)
3. What change in flux must an inductor experience in a period of 1 msec if an average voltage of 50 volts is to be induced? (7.1)
4. Over what time interval must a change of 500 milliwebers occur if a 500 turn coil is to produce an average voltage of 10 volts? (7.1)
5. What is the average inductance of a 100 turn coil if a flux change of 0.1 weber produces a current change of 0.01 amp? (7.3)
6. An inductor of 8 henrys experiences a change in its current of 0.01 amh. What is the corresponding change in flux linkage? (7.3)
7. An inductor of 2 henrys experiences a change in current of 20 ma in 5 msec. What is the average induced voltage? (7.3)
8. What is the inductance of a coil if the diameter is 1 cm, the length is 10 cm, the permeability of the core is 10×10^{-4}, and the number of turns is 325? (7.3)
9. Fifty turns are removed from an inductor of 1 henry. What is the new inductance if there were originally 150 turns on the coil? (7.3)
10. An inductor has an inductance of 20 henrys. If the reluctance of the magnetic path is doubled, what is the new inductance? (7.3)
11. An inductor has an inductance of 10 henrys. If the cross-sectional area of the core is reduced to one-half its previous value, what is the new inductance? (7.3)
12. What is the coefficient of coupling between 2 coils if a flux change of 0.5 weber induces

a voltage of 50 volts in the other coil which has 300 turns?   (7.4)

13. The coefficient of coupling between two coils is 0.6. If the inductance of one coil is 30 mh and the inductance of the other is 70 mh, what is the mutual inductance between the two?   (7.4)

14. The coils are magnetically coupled. The inductance of one coil is 100 mh. The mutual inductance is 70 mh and the coefficient of coupling is 0.7. What is the inductance of the second coil?   (7.4)

15. Two coils are connected in series. The inductance of one coil is 300 mh and the total inductance is 350 mh. What is the inductance of the other coil if there is no magnetic coupling between the coils?   (7.5)

16. Two coils are connected in series-opposing and the total inductance is found to be 2 henrys. The coils each have an inductance of 3 henrys. What is the mutual inductance between them?   (7.5)

17. Two coils are connected in series-aiding so that their total inductance is 30 henrys. The same two coils are then connected in series-opposing and the total inductance is 10 henrys. If one coil has an inductance of 15 henrys, what is the inductance of the other coil?   What is the coefficient of coupling?   (7.5)

18. A 20 henry choke and an 8 henry choke are connected in parallel and separated far enough that there is no coupling between them. What is the equivalent inductance? (7.5)

19. Two 200 mh chokes are connected in parallel. The coupling coefficient is 0.8. What is the equivalent inductance?   (7.5)

20. A 100 mh choke and a 200 mh choke are connected in parallel. The mutual inductance between them is 100 mh. What is the equivalent inductance of the combination? (7.5)

21. In Figure 7-5, the resistor has a resistance of 500 ohms and the inductor is 8 henrys. The battery voltage is 20 volts. How soon after the switch is placed in position 1 will the current reach 20 ma?   (7.6)

22. In Figure 7-5, with the switch in position 1, the current has reached 20 ma. If the switch is now moved to position 2, how long will it take for it to reach 5 ma?   (7.6)

23. In a series RL circuit the current is to decay from 40 ma to almost zero in 15 μ sec. What is the time constant?   (7.6)

24. A relay has an inductance of 0.5 henry. The coil resistance is 50 ohms and the relay closes with 5.0 ma. What resistance must be added in series to cause the relay to activate 0.5 sec after 100 volts are applied?   (7.6)

25. The current in a certain RL circuit builds up from zero to 126 ma in 0.5 sec. The final value current is 200 ma. What is the time constant?   (7.6)

26. The current in a series RL circuit decays from 200 ma to 76 ma in 0.5 sec. What is the time constant?   (7.6)

27. In Figure 7-5, $R = 1500$ ohms, $L = 0.2$ henry, $E = 100$ volts. Find all the instantaneous currents and voltages in the circuit.   (7.6)

28. For a certain series RL circuit, $R = 2500$ ohms, $L = 1$ henry and $E = 100$ volts. What is the maximum energy stored in the inductor's magnetic field? In storing this energy, how much is lost in the resistor?   (7.7)

8

Capacitors and Capacitance

Any two conducting surfaces separated from each other by an insulating medium, called the *dielectric*, form a *capacitor*. Such a device, like the inductor, is capable of storing electrical energy. However, the capacitor stores energy in the form of an electric field, whereas the inductor stores energy in the form of a magnetic field. Another important property of the capacitor is that it tends to oppose any change in its voltage as compared with the inductor, which tends to oppose any change in its current. This chapter is concerned with the use of capacitors in simple d-c circuits. The analysis of capacitive a-c circuits will be discussed in Section II.

8.1 CAPACITANCE

The *electrical capacitance* of a capacitor is defined by the equation

$$C = \frac{Q}{V_c} \tag{8.1}$$

where

   C = the capacitance in farads
   Q = the magnitude of charge on either conducting surface of the capacitor in coulombs
   V_c = the voltage between the conductive surfaces in volts

The farad is rather large as a practical unit. Therefore it is more common to use microfarads (10^{-6} farad) or picofarads (10^{-12} farad), abbreviated mfd or μf and pf.[1]

Sometimes it is convenient to speak of the inverse of capacitance, which is called *elastance S*.

$$S = \frac{1}{C} \tag{8.2}$$

where

S = elastance in darafs ("farads" spelled backwards)
C = capacitance in farads

In terms of voltage and charge

$$S = \frac{V_c}{Q} \tag{8.3}$$

The capacitance of a capacitor depends on its dimensions, geometrical shape, and the type of dielectric material used in its construction.

8.2   PARALLEL PLATE CAPACITORS

For simplicity consider a capacitor constructed from two parallel plates separated by a dielectric as shown in Figure 8-1a. If a battery is connected

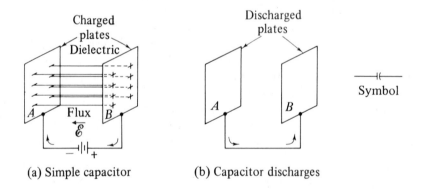

(a) Simple capacitor   (b) Capacitor discharges

Figure 8-1

to the terminals of the capacitor, electrons will flow from the negative terminal of the battery to plate A. The charges on plate A will repel an equal number of negative charges at plate B which will then flow back to the positive terminal of the battery. This process continues until the voltage across the plates of the capacitor equals the source voltage. At this time the capacitor is said to be charged to the battery voltage.

---

[1]   The abbreviation mfd is an exception to the rule that m stand for milli or 10^{-3}. An older abbreviation for pf is $\mu\mu f$ or micro-micro farad. The latter is no longer used.

If, once the capacitor is fully charged, the battery is removed and re-placed by a conductor as shown in Figure 8-1b, electrons will flow from plate A back to plate B until there is no longer a difference in potential across the plates. At this time the capacitor is said to be discharged.

The electrical energy stored in the capacitor is stored in an electric field between the plates. The electric field between parallel plates is given by

$$\mathscr{E} = \frac{V}{d} \tag{8.4}$$

where

$\mathscr{E}$ = electric field intensity between the plates in volts/meter
V = potential in volts between the plates
d = distance between the plates in meters

The concentration of charge on the plates that determines the field is the charge density or *electric flux density* D. It is defined as the total charge on each plate divided by the area of one plate.

$$D = \frac{Q}{A} \tag{8.5}$$

where

D = electric flux density in coulombs/meter^2
Q = total charge on each plate in coulombs
A = area of each plate in meters^2

Electric field intensity and electric flux density are related to each other by the capacitivity or permittivity (ϵ) of the dielectric in much the same way as magnetic flux and magnetic field intensity are related by the perme-ability of the core material.

$$D = \epsilon\mathscr{E} \tag{8.6}$$

where

D = electric flux density in coulombs/meter^2
ϵ = capacitivity in coulombs/volt-meter or farads/meter
   (8.854 $\times$ 10^{-12} farad/meter for free space)
$\mathscr{E}$ = electric field intensity in coulombs/meter

When Equations 8.4, 8.5, and 8.6 are combined to form the ratio of charge to voltage, the capacitance of the parallel plates becomes

$$C = \frac{\epsilon A}{d} \tag{8.7}$$

where

C = capacitance of parallel plates in farads
ϵ = capacitivity of the dielectric in farads/meter
A = area of one plate in meters^2
d = distance between the plates in meters

It should be emphasized here that all capacitors are not of the parallel plate variety and that Equation 8.7 does not apply to other configurations. If there are more than one pair of plates, multiply Equation 8.7 by the number of pairs of plates.

Equation 8.7 shows that the capacitance of a parallel plate capacitor is directly proportional to the surface area of the plates and inversely proportional to their separation. It also indicates that the capacitance is directly proportional to the capacitivity of the dielectric between the plates. Sometimes this capacitivity is expressed as the product of the capacitivity of a vacuum ϵ_v and another quantity called the *relative capacitivity* or *relative dielectric constant* ϵ_r. When the capacitivity is expressed in relative terms, the symbol ϵ in Equation 8.7 is replaced by $\epsilon_v\epsilon_r$. The relative dielectric constant of a material ϵ_r is defined as the ratio of the capacitance of a capacitor using that material as a dielectric, to the capacitance of the same capacitor using a vacuum as its dielectric. The table in Figure 8-2 gives the relative dielectric constants for some common dielectric materials.

Material	(Range of relative constant)		Selected relative constant	Dielectric constant ϵ
Air or vacuum		$\frac{10^{-9}}{36\pi}$ x	1.0006 ≑	8.854×10^{-12}
Glass	(3.7–9)	$\frac{10^{-9}}{36\pi}$ x	4.50 ≑	3.985×10^{-11}
Mica	(3.0–8.69)	$\frac{10^{-9}}{36\pi}$ x	5.45 ≑	4.825×10^{-11}
Paper, oiled	(3.0–5.8)	$\frac{10^{-9}}{36\pi}$ x	3.5 ≑	3.100×10^{-11}
Porcelain	(5.5–7.0)	$\frac{10^{-9}}{36\pi}$ x	6.5 ≑	5.75×10^{-11}
Polystyrene	(2.55)	$\frac{10^{-9}}{36\pi}$ x	2.55 ≑	2.25×10^{-11}
Teflon	(2.1)	$\frac{10^{-9}}{36\pi}$ x	2.1 ≑	1.86×10^{-11}
Distilled water		$\frac{10^{-9}}{36\pi}$ x	78.0 ≑	6.910×10^{-10}

Figure 8-2

Example (8.1):

Determine the capacitance of a parallel plate capacitor using a mica dielectric.

$$\epsilon_r = 3, \ d = 0.001 \text{ meter}$$

$$A = 1 \times 10^{-4} \text{ (meter)}^2$$

Solution:

$$C = \frac{\epsilon_r \epsilon_v A}{d}$$

$$= \frac{(3)(8.854 \times 10^{-12})(1 \times 10^{-4})}{1 \times 10^{-3}}$$

$$= 265.6 \text{ pf}$$

Besides affecting the capacitance of a capacitor, the dielectric determines the *breakdown voltage* of a capacitor. After the voltage across a capacitor reaches a certain value, the dielectric breaks down or punctures. This value of voltage is known as the breakdown voltage of the capacitor. It is dependent on both the type of material used for the dielectric and the thickness of the dielectric. The thicker the dielectric, the higher the voltage rating but the lower the capacitance for a given set of plates.

The type of material used as the dielectric as well as its thickness also determine the *leakage current* for the capacitor. This leakage current is the current that actually flows through the dielectric, for no insulating material is perfect. In the equivalent circuit of a practical capacitor this leakage current can be accounted for by placing an ideal[2] resistor in parallel with an ideal capacitor. The value of the resistor is given by taking the voltage across the capacitor and dividing it by the leakage current.

8.3 TYPES OF CAPACITORS

One common type of capacitor is the paper capacitor, which is constructed of strips of aluminum foil separated by a waxed-paper dielectric. To make the unit compact, the assembly is usually wound into the form of a cylinder. The entire assembly is then sealed in a container of cardboard, plastic, or sometimes even metal. The thicker the paper dielectric, the higher the breakdown voltage and the lower the leakage current.

In order to increase the breakdown voltage of a paper capacitor, the paper dielectric is sometimes saturated in a special oil and then the entire unit is immersed in oil.

Another very common type of capacitor is the electrolytic capacitor. It consists of an aluminum plate coated with a special electrolyte. When a properly polarized voltage is applied between the electrolyte and the foil,

---

[2] Ideal refers to an element that is linear and has only the properties of that element. Thus, an ideal resistor has only the property of resistance, no inductance or capacitance.

a very thin insulating film "forms" and becomes the dielectric. Because the film is very thin, values of capacitance can be obtained in much smaller sizes than with paper capacitors. There are, however, two major objections to electrolytic capacitors. First of all, the leakage current is high compared with that of other types of capacitors. In addition, the fact that ordinary

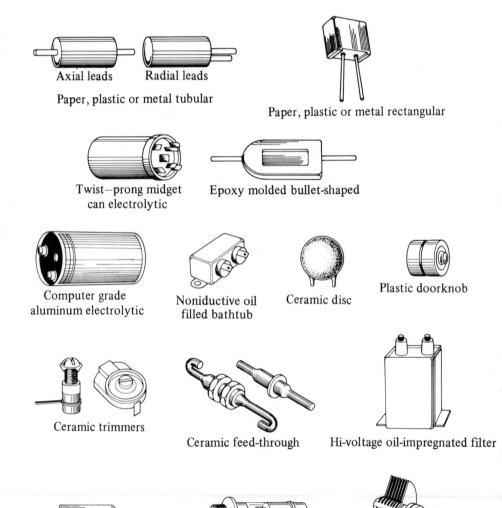

Axial leads   Radial leads

Paper, plastic or metal tubular

Paper, plastic or metal rectangular

Twist—prong midget
can electrolytic

Epoxy molded bullet-shaped

Computer grade
aluminum electrolytic

Noninductive oil
filled bathtub

Ceramic disc

Plastic doorknob

Ceramic trimmers

Ceramic feed-through

Hi-voltage oil-impregnated filter

Molded mica

Piston trimmer

Variable tuning

Figure 8-3

electrolytic capacitors are polarized means that they can be used only in d-c circuits. If a voltage of the wrong polarity is connected to an electrolytic capacitor, the dielectric film does not "form" and the capacitor passes large amounts of current, which may destroy the unit. If a nonpolarized capacitor is required, two electrolytics can be connected "back to back," that is, in series with the two negative terminals or the two positive terminals tied together.

Capacitors using air as a dielectric are mainly of the variable type and have a relatively low capacitance. Such capacitors are often constructed with a set of stationary plates and a set of rotor plates. The plates on the rotor can be moved in and out between the stationary plates to change capacitance.

Mica is often used as a dielectric for low-capacitance, high-voltage capacitors. Mica capacitors are noted for having a very low leakage current.

At the present time both mica capacitors and paper capacitors are being replaced with ceramic disc capacitors which are physically smaller in size.

Figure 8-3 shows some of the various types of capacitors employed today.

8.4 CAPACITORS IN PARALLEL AND IN SERIES

Assume that there are n capacitors connected in parallel as shown in Figure 8-4. The total charge Q_T on all the capacitors together is readily

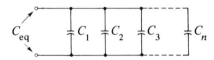

Figure 8-4

seen to be the sum of the charges on the individual capacitors.

$$Q_T = Q_1 + Q_2 + Q_3 + \ldots + Q_n$$
$$= C_1 V + C_2 V + C_3 V + \ldots + C_n V$$
$$= (C_1 + C_2 + C_3 + \ldots + C_n)V$$

Thus, the parallel combination is equivalent to a single capacitor having a capacitance equal to the sum of the individual capacitances.

$$C_{eq} = C_1 + C_2 + C_3 + \ldots + C_n \qquad (8.8)$$

If Equation 8.8 is rewritten in terms of elastance S, we have

$$\frac{1}{S} = \frac{1}{S_1} + \frac{1}{S_2} + \frac{1}{S_3} + \ldots + \frac{1}{S_n}$$

$$S = \frac{1}{\dfrac{1}{S_1} + \dfrac{1}{S_2} + \dfrac{1}{S_3} + \ldots + \dfrac{1}{S_n}} \qquad (8.9)$$

Now assume that the n capacitors are in series as shown in Figure 8-5. The total voltage across the combination is equal to the sum of the individual voltages.

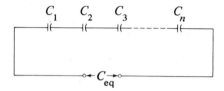

Figure 8-5

$$V_T = V_1 + V_2 + V_3 + \ldots + V_n$$

$$= \frac{Q_1}{C_1} + \frac{Q_2}{C_2} + \frac{Q_3}{C_3} + \ldots + \frac{Q_n}{C_n}$$

$$= Q_1 S_1 + Q_2 S_2 + Q_3 S_3 + \ldots + Q_n S_n$$

The charge on each capacitor, however, is equal, for the charge flowing onto one plate of a capacitor must equal the charge leaving the plate of the other capacitor; thus,

$$q = Q_1 + Q_2 + Q_3 + \ldots + Q_n$$

and

$$V_T = Q(S_1 + S_2 + S_3 + \ldots + S_n)$$

The expression in brackets can be considered the equivalent elastance of the combination, i.e.

$$S_{eq} = S_1 + S_2 + S_3 + \ldots + S_n \qquad (8.10)$$

Substituting $S = 1/C$ yields

$$\frac{1}{C_{eq}} = \frac{1}{C_1} + \frac{1}{C_2} + \frac{1}{C_3} + \ldots + \frac{1}{C_n}$$

$$C_{eq} = \frac{1}{\dfrac{1}{C_1} + \dfrac{1}{C_2} + \dfrac{1}{C_3} + \ldots + \dfrac{1}{C_n}} \qquad (8.11)$$

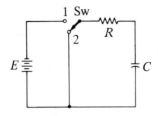

Figure 8-6

Example (8.2):

Two 8 μf capacitors are connected in parallel and then the parallel combination is connected in series with a 10 μf capacitor. What is the total capacitance of the combination?

Solution:

The two 8 μf capacitors in parallel are equivalent to

$$C_t = 8 + 8 = 16 \ \mu\text{f}$$

$$C_t = \frac{(16)(10)}{16 + 10} = \frac{160}{26} = 6.15 \ \mu\text{f}$$

8.5 *RC* CIRCUITS WITH D-C SOURCES

Refer to the circuit in Figure 8-6 and assume the capacitor initially discharged. When the switch is thrown to position 1, the capacitor begins to charge. The initial voltage across the capacitor is equal to zero since there was assumed to be no charge on it. However, as time passes, a charge accumulates on the capacitor plates and the voltage across the capacitor increases in such a direction as to oppose the source voltage. As a result, the source current gradually decreases toward zero while the voltage across the capacitor continues to build up to the value of the source voltage.

In the above process both the charge on the capacitor and the voltage across the terminals of the capacitor are changing with respect to time. Equation 8.1 relates the voltage across the capacitor to its charge at any instant of time, and may be written in terms of instantaneous charge and voltage as

$$C = \frac{q}{v}$$

Since the capacitance C is a constant in this equation, the ratio of the rate of change of charge to the rate of change of voltage must also equal this constant.

$$C = \frac{dq}{dt} \bigg/ \frac{dv}{dt}$$

or

$$\frac{dq}{dt} = C\left(\frac{dv}{dt}\right)$$

The rate of change of charge with respect to time, however, is the instantaneous current. Thus,

$$i = C\left(\frac{dv}{dt}\right) \tag{8.12}$$

where

i = instantaneous current in amperes
C = capacitance in farads
dv/dt = rate of change of voltage with respect to time in volts/second

and average current is given by

$$I_{avg} = C\frac{\Delta V}{\Delta t} \tag{8.13}$$

where

I_{avg} = average current in amperes over the period of time considered
C = capacitance in farads
ΔV = a small change in voltage
Δt = change in time corresponding to the change in voltage

Example (8.3):
The voltage across a certain capacitor changes from 200 volts to 250 volts in 10 seconds. The average current during this time is 100 μa. What is the value of capacitance for the capacitor?

Solution:
Rewriting equation 8.13, we obtain

$$C = \frac{I_{avg}\Delta t}{\Delta V}$$

$$= \frac{100 \times 10^{-6}(10)}{250 - 200}$$

$$= 20 \ \mu f$$

With the switch in Figure 8-6 in position 1, Kirchhoff's voltage law is

$$E = Ri + v_c$$

Substituting Equation 8.12 in the above equation yields

$$E = RC\frac{dv_C}{dt} + v_c$$

This is a differential equation, the solution of which yields the instantaneous voltage v_c across the capacitor.

$$v_c = E(1 - \epsilon^{-t/RC}) \tag{8.14}$$

where

v_c = instantaneous voltage across the capacitor in volts
E = battery voltage

$\epsilon = 2.71828$

t = time in seconds

R = resistance in ohms

C = capacitance in farads

Equation 8.14 is called the capacitance-charge equation. The charge on the capacitor is given by the product of the capacitance and the voltage across the capacitor.

$$q = EC(1 - \epsilon^{-t\ RC}) \qquad (8.15)$$

where q is the instantaneous charge in coulombs.

The instantaneous current in the circuit is found by calculus from Equation 8.12 as

$$i = \frac{E}{R} \epsilon^{-t/RC} \qquad (8.16)$$

The product of R and C is known as the *time constant* for the circuit

$$T = RC \qquad (8.17)$$

When $t = RC$, the current in the circuit will have approximately 36.7% of its initial value. In five time constants the current is nearly equal to zero. Both the charge and voltage of the capacitor reach about 63.3% of their final value in one time constant and are nearly equal to the final value in five constants.

Assuming the capacitor in Figure 8-6 is fully charged, place the switch in position 2. The potential across the plates will now cause a current to flow through the resistive circuit. This discharge current is given by

$$i = \frac{E}{R} \epsilon^{-t/RC} \qquad (8.18)$$

while the charge is given by

$$q = EC \epsilon^{-t/RC} \qquad (8.19)$$

and the voltage is given by

$$v_c = E \epsilon^{-t/RC} \qquad (8.20)$$

The curves in Figure 8-7 show how the charge, current, and voltage vary as a function of time in a simple RC circuit.

Example (8.4):

In Figure 8-6, let $R = 250K$, $E = 100$ volts, and $C = 8$ μf. Determine the voltage across the capacitor, the charge on the capacitor, and the current in the circuit 1 second after the switch is placed in position 1.

Solution:

$$v_c = E(1 - \epsilon^{-t/RC})$$

$$= 100(1 - 2.718^{-1/(25 \times 10^{4})(8 \times 10^{-6})})$$

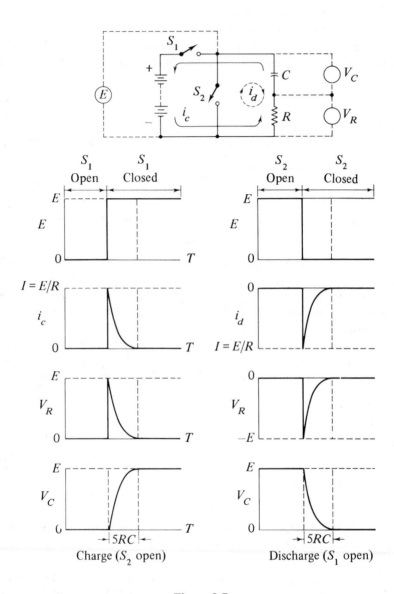

Charge (S_2 open)   Discharge (S_1 open)

Figure 8-7

$$= 100(1 - 2.718^{(0.5)})$$
$$= 39.4 \text{ volts}$$
$$q = Cv$$
$$= (8 \times 10^{-6})(39.4)$$

$$= 3.15 \times 10^{-4} \text{ coulomb}$$

$$i = \frac{E}{R}\epsilon^{-t/RC}$$

$$= \frac{100}{250 \times 10^3}(2.718)^{0.5}$$

$$= 0.242 \text{ ma}$$

8.6 ENERGY STORED IN A CAPACITOR

When a capacitor is being charged, energy is stored in the electrostatic field. The energy stored in the field is given by

$$W = \tfrac{1}{2}CV^2 \tag{8.21}$$

where

$W =$ energy stored in joules
$C =$ the capacitance in farads
$V =$ voltage across the capacitor in volts

By substituting $Q = CV$ in Equation 8.21

$$W = \tfrac{1}{2}QV \tag{8.22}$$

In charging or discharging a capacitor, it can be shown that an amount of energy equal to that which is stored is lost in the resistance of the circuit. Thus, in a simple RC circuit the energy from the source is twice the energy stored in the capacitor.

Example (8.5):
What is the energy stored in the capacitor in the example in Section 8.1?

Solution:

$$W = \tfrac{1}{2}CV^2$$
$$= \tfrac{1}{2}(10 \times 10^{-6})(100)^2$$
$$= 5 \times 10^{-2} \text{ joule}$$

8.7 SUMMARY

A *capacitor* is formed whenever any two conducting surfaces are separated by an insulating material. This insulating material is called the *dielectric*.

The *capacitance* of a capacitor is defined as

$$C = \frac{V}{Q} \tag{8.1}$$

The inverse of capacitance is called *elastance*.

$$S = \frac{1}{C} \tag{8.2}$$

The capacitance of a parallel plate capacitor is directly proportional to the cross-sectional area of the plates and the dielectric constant and inversely proportional to the distance between the plates.

$$C = \frac{\epsilon A}{d} \tag{8.7}$$

The *breakdown voltage* of a capacitor is the voltage at which the dielectric punctures. It depends on the type and thickness of the dielectric material.

Leakage current is the current that actually flows through the dielectric.

There are numerous types of capacitors in use today. The most common types are the paper, mica, ceramic, and electrolytic. Electrolytic capacitors are used when a large capacitance along with a small size is desired. Unlike the other capacitors, the electrolytic capacitor is polarized. It also has a high leakage current.

The equivalent capacitance of capacitors in parallel is given by

$$C_{eq} = C_1 + C_2 + C_3 + \ldots + C_n \tag{8.8}$$

The equivalent capacitance of capacitors in series is given by

$$C_{eq} = \frac{1}{\dfrac{1}{C_1} + \dfrac{1}{C_2} + \dfrac{1}{C_3} + \ldots + \dfrac{1}{C_n}} \tag{8.11}$$

Instantaneous current in a capacitor is related to the instantaneous voltage across a capacitor by

$$i = C \frac{dv}{dt} \tag{8.12}$$

In a simple series *RC* circuit, the charging current is given by

$$i = \frac{E}{R} \epsilon^{-t/RC} \tag{8.16}$$

while the voltage across the capacitor is

$$v_c = E(1 - \epsilon^{-t/RC}) \tag{8.14}$$

and the charge on the capacitor is

$$q = EC(1 - \epsilon^{-t/RC}) \tag{8.15}$$

In a simple *RC* circuit the discharge current is given by

$$i = \frac{E}{R} \epsilon^{-t/RC} \tag{8.18}$$

while the charge on the capacitor is

$$q = EC \epsilon^{-t/RC} \tag{8.19}$$

and the voltage on the capacitor is

$$v_c = E \epsilon^{-t/RC} \tag{8.20}$$

The quantity *RC* is called the *time constant* for the circuit. In one time constant the voltage across a capacitor builds up to 63.3% of its final value, and in five time constants it is very close to its final value. In one time constant the voltage across a capacitor decays to 36.7% of its maximum value and in five time constants it is almost zero.

The energy stored in a capacitor is given by

$$W = \tfrac{1}{2}CV^2 \tag{8.21}$$

or

$$W = \tfrac{1}{2}QV \tag{8.22}$$

8.8   QUESTIONS AND PROBLEMS

Questions

1. What is a capacitor? (Introduction)
2. What is capacitance? What units is it measured in? (8.1)
3. Compare some of the properties of a capacitor with like ones of an inductor. (Introduction)
4. What is elastance? (8.1)
5. What factors influence the capacitance of a capacitor? (8.2)
6. Explain the derivation of Equation 8.7. (8.2)
7. What is electric flux density? Compare it with magnetic flux density. (8.2)
8. What is meant by the capacitivity of a material? (8.2)
9. What is meant by the relative dielectric constant of a material? (8.2)
10. How does the area of the plates affect the capacitance of a capacitor? (8.2)
11. What effect does the separation of the plates of a capacitor have on its capacitance? (8.2)
12. How does the dielectric material affect the capacitance of a capacitor? (8.2)
13. What is meant by "breakdown voltage" of a capacitor? (8.2)
14. What determines the breakdown voltage? (8.2)
15. What is leakage current as referred to in a capacitor? (8.2)
16. How are paper capacitors constructed? (8.3)
17. What is an oil-impregnated capacitor? (8.3)
18. How does the electrolytic capacitor differ from the ordinary paper capacitor? (8.3)
19. What happens when an electrolytic capacitor is connected backwards? (8.3)
20. Why is the capacitance of an electrolytic capacitor so much greater than that of a a paper capacitor of the same physical size? (8.3)
21. What is "forming"? (8.3)
22. How can electrolytic capacitors be used in circuits where the polarity changes? (8.3)
23. How are capacitances combined in parallel? in series? (8.4)
24. Describe the charging and discharging of a capacitor in a simple *RC* circuit. (8.5)
25. What is meant by the time constant of an *RC* circuit? (8.5)
26. In what form is energy stored in a capacitor? (8.6)

Problems

1. The voltage across the plates of a capacitor of 10 μf is 100 volts. Find the charge stored on the plates of the capacitor. (8.1)

2. When 50 volts is applied to a capacitor, it accumulates a charge of 2×10^{-6} coulomb. What is the capacitance of the capacitor in μf? (8.1)

3. A 0.01 μf capacitor has a charge of 1×10^{-8} coulomb on its plates. What is the voltage across the capacitor? (8.1)

4. What is the elastance of a 0.01 μf capacitor? (8.1)

5. What is the elastance of a 20 μf capacitor? (8.1)

6. When 60 volts are applied to a capacitor, it accumulates a charge of 3×10^{-6} coulomb. What is the elastance? (8.1)

7. A capacitor has 100 volts applied to it. The plates are separated a distance of 1×10^{-4} meter. What is the electric field between the plates? (8.2)

8. If the dielectric in Problem 7 is mica, what is the electric flux? (8.2)

9. What is the capacitance of a parallel plate capacitor which has a plate area of 0.1 square meter? The dielectric is 5×10^{-4} meter thick glass. (8.2)

10. A certain parallel plate capacitor has a capacitance of 10 μf. If the thickness of the dielectric is doubled, what is the new value of capacitance? How is the breakdown voltage affected? (8.2)

11. A parallel plate capacitor has a capacitance of 0.005 μf. If the dielectric is changed from mica to glass, what is the new capacitance? (8.2)

12. The area of one of the plates of a parallel plate capacitor is doubled. How is the capacitance affected? (8.2)

13. What plate area in square meters is needed to make a one-farad capacitor if the plates are separated by a 1×10^{-6} meter thick dielectric having a relative capacitivity of 10? (8.2)

14. What is the capacitance of a 0.05 μf capacitor and a 0.005 μf capacitor connected in parallel? (8.4)

15. What is the total capacitance of four 20 μf capacitors connected in series? (8.4)

16. What is the total capacitance of a 0.001 μf capacitor connected in series with a 0.002 μf capacitor? (8.4)

17. Find the equivalent capacitance for the circuit shown in Figure 8-8. (8.4)

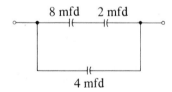

8 mfd   2 mfd

4 mfd

Figure 8-8

18. Find the equivalent capacitance for the circuit shown in Figure 8-9. (8.4)

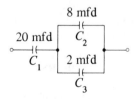

8 mfd

20 mfd C_2

C_1 2 mfd

C_3

Figure 8-9

19. If a voltage of 100 volts is applied to the terminals of a 0.001 μf capacitor and a 0.002 μf capacitor connected in series, what is the voltage across each capacitor and the charge on each capacitor? (8.4)

20. If 100 volts are applied to the terminals of the circuit in Figure 8-8, determine the voltage across each capacitor and the charge on each capacitor. (8.4)

21. Repeat Problem 20 for Figure 8-9. (8.4)

22. A 10 μf capacitor and a 20 μf capacitor are connected in series across a 100 volt battery. After they are both fully charged, the capacitors are connected in parallel. What is the voltage across the combination and the charge on each capacitor? (Two possibilities.) (8.4)

23. A 10 μf capacitor and a 20 μf capacitor are connected in parallel across a 100 volt source. After both are fully charged, they are disconnected from the source and then connected in series with each other. After the terminals of the series combination are shorted together, what is the charge on each capacitor and the voltage across each capacitor? (Two possibilities.) (8.4)

24. In Figure 8-9, the voltage across C_2 is 50 volts. What is the voltage across the terminals of the network? (8.4)

25. The voltage across a 0.1 μf capacitor changes from 30 to 50 volts in one millisecond. What is the average current? (8.5)

26. The voltage across a 10,000 μf capacitor is 1 volt at 10:45 A.M. At 10:47 A.M. the voltage is 10 volts. What is the average current? (8.5)

27. The voltage across a certain capacitor changes from 25 volts to 50 volts in 2 seconds The average current is 10 ma. What is the capacitance? (8.5)

28. The average current in a 10 μf capacitor over a period of 5 milliseconds is found to be 0.05 amp. What is the voltage change across the capacitor? (8.5)

29. In Figure 8-6, the resistance is 50,000 ohms and the capacitance is 0.25 μf What are the current, charge, and voltage for the capacitor 0.125 sec after the switch is thrown into position one? The battery voltage is 10 volts. (8.5)

30. Assume the capacitor in Problem 29 is allowed to become fully charged. At this point the switch is placed in position 2. What is the value of current, charge, and voltage 0.125 sec after the switch is placed in position 2? (8.5)

31. In Problem 29, how long will it take for the voltage across the capacitor to reach 2 volts? (8.5)

32. In Problem 30, how long will it take for the voltage across the capacitor to reach 8 volts? (8.5)

33. In the circuit shown in Figure 8-10, the switch S_1 is placed in the closed position for a long time so the capacitor will become fully charged. What is the charge on the capacitor one time constant after the switch is opened? (8.5)

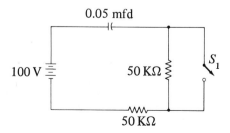

Figure 8-10

34. In the circuit shown in Figure 8-10, the switch S_1 is placed in the open position for a long time. What is the voltage across the capacitor one time constant after the switch is closed? (8.5)

35. A 16 μf capacitor has a voltage of 250 volts across it. What is the energy stored in the capacitor? (8.6)

36. What is the energy stored in the capacitor of Problem 1? (8.6)

37. How large must the voltage across a 0.1 μf capacitor be in order that one joule of energy be stored? (8.6)

Section II

Alternating-Current Fundamentals

Mainly because of the ease with which alternating-current voltages can be transformed from high values to low values and from low values to high values, almost all electrical power distribution systems today use sinusoidal alternating current rather than direct current. This section deals with the basic principles of sinusoidal currents and voltages and the steady state solution of a-c circuit problems.

9

Alternating Currents and Voltages

Direct currents and voltages are completely described by their magnitude and direction. In working with alternating currents and voltages, however, it is necessary to use many new terms and relationships. As an example, one must deal with instantaneous values, maximum values, average values, and effective values of currents and voltages. Frequency and phase relationships must also be considered. It is the purpose of this chapter to define these quantities and to apply these definitions to a basic sine wave of voltage or current.

9.1 SIMPLE A-C GENERATOR

When a loop of wire is rotated in a uniform magnetic field, as shown in Figure 9-1, an emf gradually builds up from zero to a maximum in one direction, falls back to zero, again builds up to a maximum in the opposite direction, and finally returns to zero. This process is repeated with each revolution of the loop. For each revolution we say there is one *cycle* of a-c voltage. The *frequency* of this voltage is the number of cycles per second. Increasing the speed of the rotating loop increases the frequency of the output voltage while decreasing the speed decreases the frequency.

A more rapid rotation also results in the generation of a higher voltage. The reason for this is that the voltage induced in a conductor depends on the speed with which it cuts the magnetic lines of force. The value of the a-c voltage can also be increased by increasing the strength of the magnetic field.

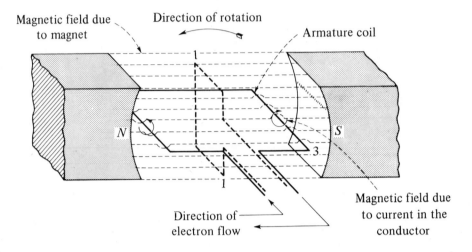

Magnetic field due to magnet

Direction of rotation

Armature coil

N

S

3.

Direction of electron flow

Magnetic field due to current in the conductor

Figure 9-1

In commercial a-c generators, several electromagnetic coils are usually used to supply the strong magnetic field through which the conductors on the armature rotate. These electromagnets are called *field coils*, and the loop is called the *armature winding*. All a-c generators consist fundamentally of the field coils and the armature winding. A higher-output voltage also results if more turns of wire are added to the loop in such an arrangement that the voltage induced in each turn adds to the voltage induced in the others.

The variations in the emf produced in the simple generator throughout one cycle can be represented by a curve called a *sine curve* (Figure 9-2). The study of how this sine curve is generated is essential to provide a background for the further study of alternating current.

In Figure 9-2 the revolving radius of the circle, called the rotating vector **E**, represents one conductor in the armature of a generator rotating counterclockwise in a magnetic field. In *1*, corresponding to 0-degree rotation of the generator armature, no flux is being cut; therefore the voltage amplitude is zero. In *2*, corresponding to the 45-degree rotation, the voltage has reached an amplitude represented by the line *a*, and a 45-degree portion of the sine wave has been generated. At this point the amplitude is 0.707 of the maximum amplitude, because the sine of 45 degrees is 0.707 of the maximum sine value of 1. Since the generator armature must turn 360 degrees to complete one revolution, it now has rotated through 45/360, or one-eighth of a cycle.

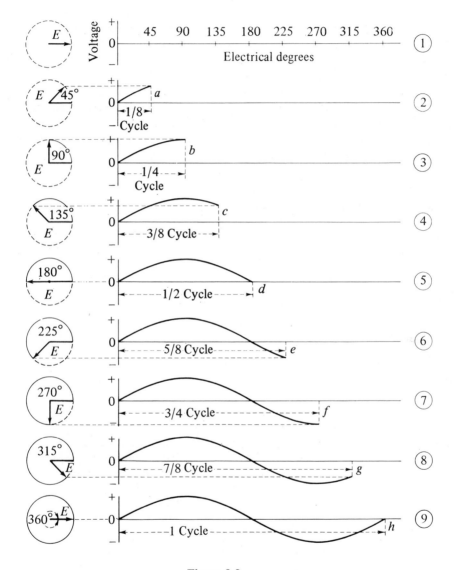

Figure 9-2

In *3*, corresponding to 90 degrees, the voltage represented by the line *b* is at maximum in the positive direction; 90/360, or one-fourth, of a cycle of the sine wave has now been completed. In *4*, corresponding to 135 degrees, the voltage is dropping back to zero (*c* is at 0.707 of the maximum) and three-eighths of a cycle has been generated. In *5*, corresponding to 180 degrees, the voltage amplitude is again zero, since there are no flux lines being cut. One-half of the sine-wave cycle, called *half-wave*, has been made. All of this half-wave is on the positive side of the axis.

In *6*, corresponding to 225 degrees, the voltage represented by line *e* has started to rise, but this time in a negative direction, since it is opposite to the 45-degree line developing a positive voltage. In *7*, corresponding to the 270-degree position, the voltage has reached a maximum in the negative direction. The voltage amplitude at this position, represented by the line *f*, equals the voltage amplitude at position *3* but is opposite in polarity. In *8*, corresponding to 315 degrees, the voltage is again dropping toward zero; seven-eighths of the sine wave has now been completed. In *9*, corresponding to 360 degrees, the voltage amplitude has again reached zero and one cycle has been completed.

9.2 SINE WAVE CHARACTERISTICS

The sine wave shown in Figure 9-3 is expressed mathematically by

$$e = E_m \sin \omega t \qquad (9.1)$$

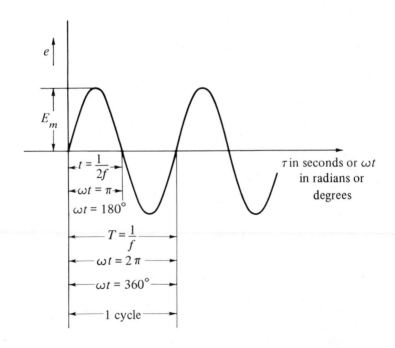

Figure 9-3

where

$e =$ the *instantaneous voltage* in volts
$E_m =$ the *maximum or peak voltage* in volts
$\omega =$ the *angular velocity or frequency* in radians[1]/sec
$t =$ the time in seconds

In terms of current, Equation 9.1 takes the form

$$i = I_m \sin \omega t$$

where

$i =$ the instantaneous current in amperes
$I_m =$ the maximum or peak current in amperes

A look at a sine table will show that as the angle ωt ranges from 0 to 2π radians (0 to 360°) the sine passes through one complete sequence of values before starting to repeat the same sequence. Thus, 2π radians correspond to the completion of one cycle and we can therefore write

$$\omega = 2\pi f \qquad (9.2)$$

where

$\omega =$ angular frequency in radians
$f =$ frequency in cycles/sec, or hertz

The period T is defined as the time it takes to complete one cycle. Therefore, T is found by merely taking the inverse of the frequency f

$$T = \frac{1}{f} \qquad (9.3)$$

where

$T =$ period in seconds
$f =$ frequency in cycles/sec, or hertz

Example (9.1):

If $e = 10 \sin 377t$, what is the frequency f, the frequency ω, the period T, and the maximum amplitude of voltage?

Solution:

Comparing with Equation (9.1), we obtain

$$E_m = 10 \text{ volts}$$

$$\omega = 377 \text{ rad/sec}$$

$$\omega = 2\pi f = 377$$

$$f = \frac{377}{2\pi} = 60 \text{ cycles/sec, or hertz}$$

---

[1]   The radian is a measure of angular displacement where 2π radians $= 360°$ or 1 radian $= 57.2958°$.

$$T = \frac{1}{f} = \frac{1}{60} = 0.0167 \text{ sec}$$

Example (9.2):

A sine wave of current has a maximum value of 15 amp and a frequency of 50 hertz. Write the expression for the instantaneous current. What is the value of the current when $t = 0.01$ sec?

Solution:

$$I_m = 15 \text{ amp}$$

$$f = 50 \text{ hertz}$$

$$\omega = 2\pi f = (6.28)(50) = 314 \text{ rad/sec}$$

$$i = I_m \sin \omega t = 15 \sin 314\, t \text{ at } t = 0.01 \text{ sec}$$

$$i = 15 \sin (3.14)$$

$$3.14 \text{ rad} = 3.14 \text{ rad} \times \frac{360°}{2\pi \text{ rad}} = 180°$$

$$i = 15 \sin (180°) = 0$$

Instantaneous voltages and currents may be plotted with ωt or t as the independent variable. The quantity ωt may also appear in either radians or degrees. All three methods are shown in Figure 9-3.

It is not always convenient to have the sine wave start at zero when $t = 0$. One must, therefore, be able to express mathematically sine waves which start before or after time $t = 0$. Figure 9-4 shows two such waveforms. Wave A starts $\phi_A^°$ before $t = 0$ and wave B starts $\phi_B^°$ after $t = 0$.

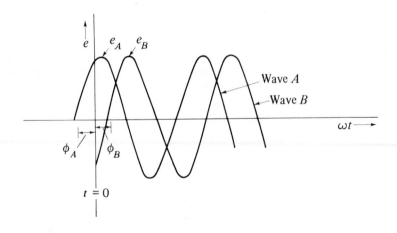

Figure 9-4

The instantaneous value of wave A is expressed as

$$e_A = E_m \sin (\omega t + \phi_A^\circ) \qquad (9.4)$$

and the instantaneous values of B are given by

$$e_B = E_m \sin (\omega t - \phi_B^\circ) \qquad (9.5)$$

Furthermore, the voltage e_A is said to *lead* e_B by an angle of $(|\phi_A| + |\phi_B|)$ or the voltage e_B may be said to *lag* e_A by an angle of $(|\phi_A| + |\phi_B|)$.

Example (9.3):
Express the three currents shown in Figure 9-5 mathematically. What is ω and f?

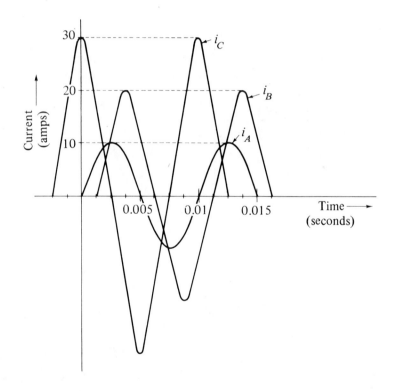

Figure 9-5

Solution:

$$\omega = 2\pi f$$

$$f = \frac{1}{T}$$

$$\omega = \frac{2\pi}{T} = \frac{6.28}{0.01} = 628 \ \text{rad/sec}$$

$$f = \frac{1}{T} = \frac{1}{0.01} = 100 \ \text{hertz}$$

$$i_A = 10 \sin 628t$$

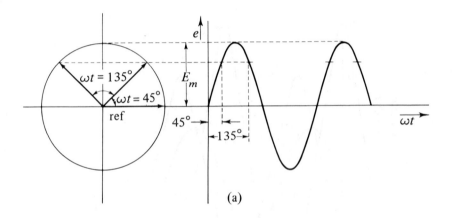

(a)

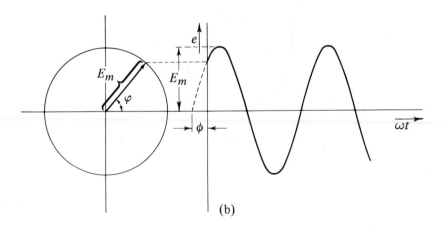

(b)

Figure 9-6

$i_B = 20 \sin (628t - 45°)$

$i_C = 30 \sin (628t + 90°)$

i_A leads i_C by 90° or i_C lags i_A by 90°

i_A lags i_B by 45° or i_B leads i_A by 45°

i_B lags i_C by 135° or i_C leads i_B by 135°

9.3 VECTOR REPRESENTATION OF SINE WAVES

Since the expressions for sine waves are rather cumbersome to handle mathematically, it is convenient to represent them by *rotating vectors or phasors*. Figure 9-2 and Section 9.1 show and explain how the vector rotates to develop a sine wave. Figure 9-6a shows how the vertical projections of a rotating vector whose length is equal to the maximum amplitude of a sine wave, takes on all the instantaneous values of that sine wave. This vector is rotating at the same frequency as the sine wave.

In Figure 9-6a the sine wave started at zero degrees at time $t = 0$, so the phasor was initially at zero degrees. If the reference time $t = 0$ is taken when the sine wave is shifted in phase, the phasor will begin at an angle equal to the phase angle of the sine wave. See Figure 9-6b. Thus, the phasor taken at $t = 0$ not only gives the maximum value of the sine wave, but also the phase angle of the sine wave. Having these two quantities and given the frequency, we may easily write the equation for the sine wave, or given the equation for the sine wave, we may easily plot the phasor at time $t = 0$.

As long as sine waves are of the same frequency, the phasors representing the sine waves at a given time may be added or subtracted to give a vector representation of the sum or difference of the sine waves. The reason for the above statement is obvious if one considers all the vectors rotating at the same frequency or velocity, for this means the angle between the phasors does not change at any time.

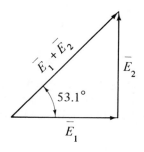

Figure 9-7

Example (9.4):

Two voltages $e_1 = 30 \sin \omega t$ and $e_2 = 40 \sin (\omega t + 90°)$ are to be added together. Represent the two voltages by phasors and add them. Write the equation for the resultant sine wave.

Solution:

Voltage e_1 is represented by a phasor $\mathbf{E}_1$ and e_2 is represented by the phasor $\mathbf{E}_2$, as shown in Figure 9-7. The resultant phasor is found by attaching the tail of $\mathbf{E}_2$ to the head of $\mathbf{E}_1$ and is the vector $\mathbf{E}_3$, which has a magnitude of 50 ($\sqrt{30^2 + 40^2} = 50$) and is at an angle of 53.1° ($\sin 4/5 = \sin 0.8 = 53.1°$). Therefore, $e_3 = 50 \sin (\omega t + 53.1°)$.

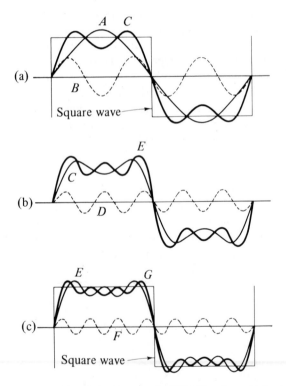

(A) Fundamental; (B) Third harmonic; (C) Fundamental plus third harmonic; (D) Fifth harmonic; (E) Fundamental plus third and fifth harmonics; (F) Seventh harmonic; (G) Fundamental plus third, fifth, and seventh harmonics.

Figure 9-8

9.4 NON-SINUSOIDAL WAVES

It should be pointed out here that not all voltages and currents are sinusoidal. In electronics, one must deal with many different complex wave shapes. Nevertheless, it is always possible to express any periodic waveform as an infinite series of sine waves of different frequencies and amplitudes. This series is known as a *Fourier Series*. Figure 9-8 shows the composition of a square wave, the Fourier Series of which is

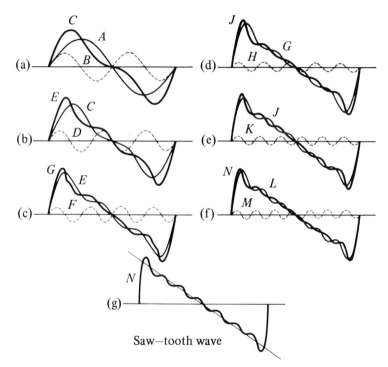

Saw—tooth wave

(A) Fundamental; (B) Second harmonic; (C) Fundamental plus second harmonic; (D) Third harmonic; (E) Fundamental plus second and third harmonics; (F) Fourth harmonic; (G) Fundamental plus second, third, and fourth harmonics; (H) Fifth harmonic; (J) Fundamental plus second, third, fourth, and fifth harmonics; (K) Sixth harmonic; (L) Fundamental plus second, third, fourth, fifth, and sixth harmonics; (M) Seventh harmonic; (N) Fundamental plus second, third, fourth, fifth, sixth, and seventh harmonics.

Figure 9-9

$$e = f(t)$$

$$= \frac{4}{\pi} \left(E_m \sin \omega t + \frac{E_m}{3} \sin 3\omega t + \frac{E_m}{5} \sin 5\omega t \ldots \right).$$

The fundamental frequency of the square wave is the same as the frequency of the lowest frequency sine wave present in the wave shape. Note, however, that the frequencies of the other sine waves are some multiple of the fundamental. These are called the *harmonics* of the fundamental. Thus, one speaks of the 2nd harmonic, 3rd harmonic, etc. In the case of the square wave the harmonics are all odd, i.e., 3rd, 5th, etc. Also note that the magnitude of the harmonics decreases as frequency increases. This enables one to approximate the square wave with only the first few terms of the series. Figures 9-9 and 9-10 show how a sawtooth wave and a peaked wave

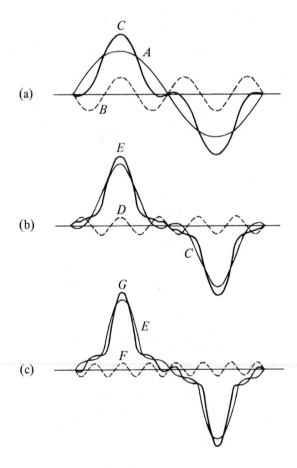

Figure 9-10

are composed of a fundamental and different harmonics. From the above it should be obvious that sine waves are basic in the study of electrical circuits.

9.5   AVERAGE VALUE

The average value of any voltage or current over a given interval of time is found by taking the area under the voltage or current curve and then dividing by the time interval. (See Figure 9-11.)

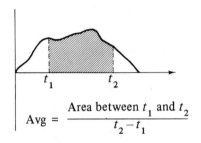

$$\text{Avg} = \frac{\text{Area between } t_1 \text{ and } t_2}{t_2 - t_1}$$

Figure 9-11

$$E_{avg} = \frac{\text{area under curve from } t_2 \text{ to } t_1}{t_2 - t_1} \tag{9.6}$$

It is sometimes convenient to consider an average over a complete period while at other times it is convenient to consider an average over a half-period. For the complete period average

$$E_{avg} = \frac{\text{area under curve for one cycle}}{T} \tag{9.7}$$

For the half-period average

$$E_{avg} = \frac{\text{area under one-half cycle}}{T/2} \tag{9.8}$$

Example (9.5):
Find the average over a full period for the waveform shown in Figure 9-12.

Solution:
Area under 1 cycle $= (10)(T/2) - 2(T/2)$

$$= 5T - T = 4T$$

$$E_{avg} = \frac{\text{area}}{T} = \frac{4T}{T} = 4 \text{ volts}$$

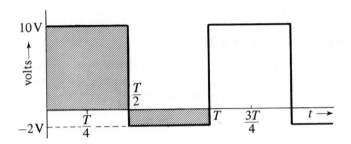

Figure 9-12

Example (9.6):

Find the half-period average for the waveform shown in Figure 9-13.

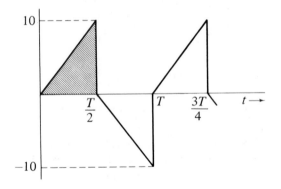

Figure 9-13

Solution:

Area under 1/2 cycle = $(1/2) (10)(T2) = 2.5T$

$$E_{\text{avg}} = \frac{\text{area}}{T/2} = \frac{2.5T}{T/2} = 5 \text{ volts}$$

The average over one period for a sine wave is obviously zero because the area under the positive cycle equals the area under the negative half-cycle.

The half-period average for a sine wave is found by taking the area of the positive or negative half-cycle and dividing by one-half the period. The area under the sine is found from integral calculus to be $(T/\pi) E_m$ so that

$$E_{\text{avg}} = \frac{TE_m}{\pi} / \frac{T}{2} = \frac{2}{\pi} E_m = 0.636E_m \qquad (9.9)$$

Example (9.7):
>   If $i = 10 \sin \omega t$, what is the half-period average current?

Solution:

$$I_m = 10$$
$$I_{avg} = 0.636 I_m = (0.636)(10) = 6.36 \text{ amp}$$

Average values of currents are useful in rectifier circuits in electronics.

9.6 EFFECTIVE VALUES

In the case of d-c, the power dissipated in a resistor is given by the square of the current through the resistor times the resistance $I^2 R$, or the square of voltage across the resistance divided by the resistance V^2/R. If these same equations are to hold for a-c voltages and currents, it is necessary to equate the expressions for average a-c power to the expression for d-c power and solve for an equivalent value of a-c current or voltage. This equivalent is called an effective or root-mean-square (rms) value of current or voltage. It is found by squaring the instantaneous value, taking the area under the squared curve for one cycle, dividing by the period, and then taking the square root.

$$E = \sqrt{\frac{\text{area under } e_2}{T}} \qquad (9.10)$$

For a sine wave

$$E = \frac{E_m}{\sqrt{2}} = 0.707 E_m \qquad (9.11)$$

Example (9.8):
>   Find the rms value for the waveform in Figure 9-12 and the average power dissipated in a resistor of 10 ohms.

Solution:

$$e^2 = 100 \text{ from } 0 - T/2 \text{ and 4 from } T/2 - T$$
$$\text{area} = 100(T/2) + 4(T/2) = 52T$$
$$E = \sqrt{\frac{52T}{T}} = \sqrt{52} \text{ volts} = 7.21 \text{ volts}$$
$$P = \frac{E^2}{R} = (\sqrt{52})^2/(10) = 5.2 \text{ watts}$$

Example (9.9):
>   If $i = 10 \sin (\omega t + 30°)$, find the rms value of current.

Solution:

$$I = 0.707 I_m = (0.707)(10) = 7.07 \text{ volts}$$

9.7 RESISTANCE IN A-C CIRCUITS

When a sinusoidal voltage is applied to a pure resistor, the resulting current is also sinusoidal and in phase. Assume the voltage in Figure 9-14 to be

$$v_R = V_m \sin \omega t$$

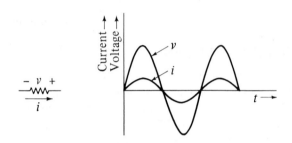

Figure 9-14

The instantaneous current is then given by Ohm's law as

$$i_R = \frac{v_R}{R} = \frac{V_m}{R} \sin \omega t \qquad (9.12)$$

where V_m/R is identified as the maximum current

$$I_m = \frac{V_m}{R} \qquad (9.13)$$

Since $I = I_m/\sqrt{2}$ and $V = V_m/\sqrt{2}$ it also follows that

$$I = \frac{V}{R} \qquad (9.14)$$

The plot of current and voltage for a pure resistance is shown in Figure 9-14.

The product of instantaneous voltage times instantaneous current in an alternating current circuit is called the *instantaneous power.*

$$p = ei \qquad (9.15)$$

For a resistor

$$p = (V_m \sin \omega t)(I_m \sin \omega t)$$
$$= V_m I_m \sin^2 \omega t \qquad (9.16)$$

From the trigonometry identity

$$\sin^2 \omega t = \frac{1 - \cos 2\omega t}{2}$$

Equation 9.16 becomes

$$p = \frac{V_m I_m}{2} (1 - \cos 2\omega t) \qquad (9.17)$$

Note that this is a constant term plus a time-varying term of twice the frequency of the current or voltage. This indicates that the instantaneous power for the resistor is oscillating about an average value of $V_m I_m/2$, as shown in Figure 9-15. Whereas the power delivered to a resistive load

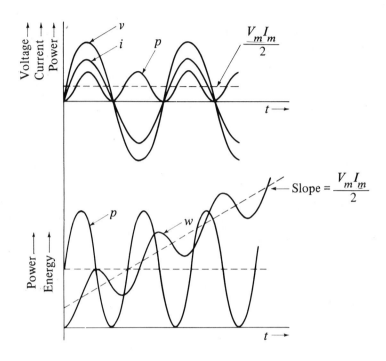

Figure 9-15

in a d-c circuit is constant, in the a-c circuit the power delivered to the load will pulse at a frequency of twice the frequency of the current or voltage.

The average power $V_m I_m/2$ can be found by taking the area under the instantaneous power curve for one cycle and dividing by the period. It is this average power that we are mainly concerned with in a-c circuits.

$$P = \frac{1}{T} \text{ (area under } P \text{ curve for 1 cycle)} \qquad (9.18)$$

$$P = \frac{V_m I_m}{2} \qquad (9.19)$$

$$P = VI \qquad (9.20)$$

In the case of the resistor, the average power is given by the same equation as in the case of d-c.

$$P = VI$$
$$= \frac{V^2}{R}$$
$$= I^2 R$$

Energy is always found by taking the area under the curve of power. For a resistor the energy is always increasing with time since the area under the power curve is always positive. The equation for energy is found from calculus by integrating the expression for instantaneous power.

$$W = VI(t_2 - t_1) - \tfrac{1}{2}(\sin \omega t_2 - \sin \omega t_1) \tag{9.21}$$

For one cycle the energy is

$$W = VI(T - 0) - \tfrac{1}{2}(\sin \omega t - \sin 0)$$
$$= VIT \tag{9.22}$$

Example (9.10):

The current in the resistor shown in Figure 9-14 is given by

$$i = 10 \sin 628t$$

The resistor has a resistance of 5 ohms. What is the expression for instantaneous voltage drop across R and the average power dissipated in R? What is the energy dissipated in 1 complete cycle?

Solution:

$$I = \frac{5}{\sqrt{2}}$$

$$V_{max} = I_{max}R = (10)(5) = 50$$

$$V = \frac{50}{\sqrt{2}}$$

$$v_R = 50 \sin \omega t$$

$$P = \frac{V_{max}I_{max}}{2} = \frac{(50)(10)}{2} = 250 \text{ watts}$$

$$T = \frac{2\pi}{\omega} = \frac{6.28}{628} = 0.01 \text{ sec}$$

$$W = VIT = \left(\frac{50}{\sqrt{2}}\right)\left(\frac{10}{\sqrt{2}}\right)(0.01) = 2.5 \text{ joules}$$

or

$$W = PT$$
$$= (250)(0.01) = 2.5 \text{ joules}$$

9.8 SUMMARY

The sine wave is basic in the study of alternating current and is expressed mathematically as

$$e = E_m \sin \omega t \quad \text{and} \quad i = I_m \sin \omega t \tag{9.1}$$

The voltage e is the *instantaneous value* of voltage at any time t. E_m is the *maximum amplitude* of the voltage. ω is the *angular velocity or frequency* of the voltage and may be expressed as

$$\omega = 2\pi f \tag{9.2}$$

where f is the *frequency* in cycles per second (or hertz). A *cycle* is the sequence of all values taken on by Equation 9.1 before it repeats these values. The *period* of a sine wave is given by

$$T = \frac{1}{f} \tag{9.3}$$

When a sine wave starts $\phi°$ before $t = 0$, it is written as

$$e = E_m \sin (\omega t + \phi°) \tag{9.4}$$

When a sine wave starts $\phi°$ after $t = 0$, it is written as

$$e = E_m \sin (\omega t - \phi) \tag{9.5}$$

If the first maximum of a sine voltage e_A occurs after the first maximum of another sine voltage e_B, then e_A is said to lag e_B or e_B is said to lead e_A.

Sinusoidal voltages and currents are easier to handle if they are treated as *rotating vectors or phasors*. The length of the vector is scaled to the maximum voltage or current and the angle of the vector is given by the angle between the time the sine wave is zero and increasing and the time $t = 0$.

Any periodic waveform can be expressed in a *Fourier Series* of sines. The *average value* of a waveform is given by

$$E_{avg} = \frac{\text{area under curve from } t_2 - t_1}{t_2 - t_1} \tag{9.6}$$

For a sine wave the average over a complete cycle is zero but the *half-period average* is

$$E_{avg} = 0.636 E_m \tag{9.9}$$

The *effective or rms value* of a waveform is

$$E = \sqrt{\frac{\text{area under } e^2}{T}} \tag{9.10}$$

For a sine wave

$$E = 0.707 E_m \tag{9.11}$$

The effective values are useful in determining power in an a-c circuit.

When a sinusoidal voltage is applied to a resistor, the current in the resistor is always in phase with this voltage. The relation between a-c currents and voltages for a resistor is the same as d-c currents and voltages. That is

$$i_R = \frac{v_R}{R} \tag{9.12}$$

$$I_m = \frac{V_m}{R} \tag{9.13}$$

$$I = \frac{V}{R} \qquad (9.14)$$

The instantaneous power is always the product of the instantaneous current and the instantaneous voltage. For a resistance, this power oscillates at a frequency of twice that of the voltage, about an average power given by

$$P = VI \qquad (9.20)$$

Energy is always the area under the power curve. For a resistor, the energy loss in one cycle is

$$W = VIT \qquad (9.22)$$

9.9   QUESTIONS AND PROBLEMS

Questions

1. Explain the operation of a single loop a-c generator. (9.1)
2. What is meant by angular frequency? (9.2)
3. What is meant by a cycle of a-c voltage or current? (9.1)
4. How does the speed of a generator affect the feequency of the voltage output? (9.1)
5. How does the speed of a generator affect the magnitude of the output voltage? (9.1)
6. What are field coils? What is an armature? (9.1)
7. Explain each of the quantities in Equation 9.1. (9.2)
8. What is instantaneous voltage or current? (9.2)
9. What is meant by "peak voltage"? (9.2)
10. What is meant by "phase lead" and "phase lag"? (9.2)
11. How are sine waves represented by phasors? (9.3)
12. Why are phasors used to represent sine waves? (9.3)
13. Why are sine waves basic in the study of electricity? (9.4)
14. How can a square wave or triangular wave be expressed in terms of sine waves? (9.4)
15. What is meant by the term "harmonic"? (9.4)
16. What is meant by the average value of a sine wave? (9.5)
17. What is the difference between "full-period average" and "half-period average"? (9.5)
18. What is meant by the effective value of voltage? (9.6)
19. Why is the effective value of voltage or current important? (9.6)
20. What does "rms" mean? (9.6)
21. What is the phase relation between the voltage and current in a resistor? (9.7)
22. How are rms current and voltage related in a resistor? (9.7)
23. What is instantaneous power? (9.7)
24. What is average power? (9.7)
25. How can you determine the average power dissipated in a resistor? (9.7)
26. Is the instantaneous power delivered to a resistor in an a-c circuit constant? Explain. (9.7)
27. What is the relationship between energy and power? (9.7)
28. How do you determine the energy loss in a resistor? (9.7)

Problems

1. Sketch a 25 hertz and a 60 hertz sine wave on the same plot. Plot using seconds, degrees, and radians. What is the time required in each case for one cycle?   (9.1)

2. If $e = 15 \sin 377t$, what is the maximum amplitude of the sine wave? What is the radian frequency and the frequency in hertz? What is the period?   (9.2)

3. A sine wave of current has a maximum value of 10 amp and a frequency of 25 hertz. Write the eqution for the instantaneous value of current.   (9.2)

4. A sine wave of voltage has a value of 10 volts when $\omega t = 45°$. The frequency is 50 hertz. Write the equation for the instantaneous voltage.   (9.2)

5. A sine wave of voltage has a value of 10 volts at $\omega t = 135°$. The period is 0.01 sec. Write the equation for the instantaneous voltage.   (9.2)

6. If $i = 5\sqrt{2}\sin [2\pi(30)t]$, what is the maximum amplitude of current and the angular frequency? What is the period?   (9.2)

7. If $i = 25 \sin 100t$, what is the value of the current at $t = 0.001$ sec?   (9.2)

8. If $e = 30 \sin 1000t$, what is the value of e at $t = 20$ sec?   (9.2)

9. At time $t = 0$, a sine wave of voltage is at 45°. Its maximum value is 140 volts and the frequency is 400 hertz. Write the equation for the instantaneous value. What is the value of voltage at $t = 0$?   (9.2)

10. A certain voltage is expressed as $e_1 = 300 \sin \omega t$. Another voltage has a maximum value of 50 volts and lags e_1 by 31°. Write the equation for the instantaneous value of the second voltage.   (9.2)

11. A certain current is expressed as $i_1 = 0.1 \sin (\omega t + 30°)$. Another current has a maximum value of 1 amp and leads i_1 by 32°. Write the equation for the instantaneous value of the second current.   (9.2)

12. A certain 60 hertz sinusoidal voltage has a value of 5 volts when $t = 0$ and a maximum value of 10 volts. Another 60 hertz sine wave of voltage has a maximum value of 10 volts and at $t = 0$ is -8.66 volt. What is the phase relation between the two voltages? Plot them.   (9.2)

13. Show $e_1 = 10 \sin (\omega t + 30°)$ and $e_2 = 5 \sin (\omega t + 60°)$ as vectors, and find the sum of $e_1 + e_2$ graphically.   (9.3)

14. In Problem 13, subtract e_1 from e_2 graphically.   (9.3)

15. If $i_1 = 6 \sin (\omega t + 30°)$, $i_2 = 5 \sin (\omega t + 30°)$, and $i_3 = \sin (\omega t - 60°)$, find the sum $i_1 + i_2 + i_3$.   (9.3)

16. What is the half-period average for the waveform shown in Figure 9-16?   (9.5)

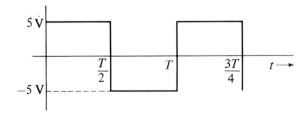

Figure 9-16

17. Repeat Problem 16 for Figure 9-17. (9.5)

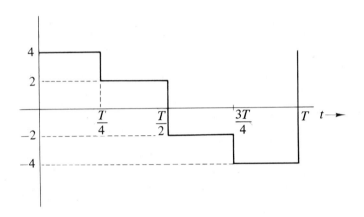

Figure 9-17

18. If $e = 30 \sin 377t$, what is the average value? (9.5)
19. The half-cycle average of a certain 60 hertz sine wave of current is 12.72 volts. What is the expression for the instantaneous current? (9.5)
20. Find the rms value for the waveform in Figure 9-16. (9.6)
21. Find the rms value for the waveform in Figure 9-17. (9.6)
22. If $v = 172 \sin (377t + 20°)$, what is the rms value of v? (9.6)
23. What is the relation between the peak value of a half-wave rectified sine wave and its rms value? (Figure 9-18) (9.6)

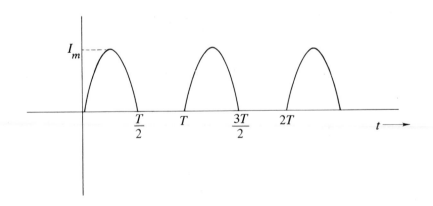

Figure 9-18

24. Find E_{rms} for a full-wave rectified sine wave in terms of E_{max}. (Figure 9-19) (9.6)

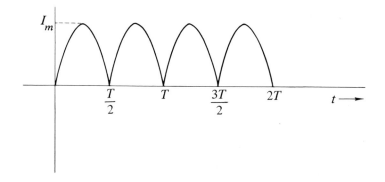

Figure 9-19

25. A current $i = 12 \sin 314t$ is flowing in a resistor of 100 ohms. What is the expression for the instantaneous voltage across the resistor? What is the rms voltage? What is the expressions for instantaneous power? What is the average power? (9.7)

26. A voltage of 20 volts rms is measured across a resistor of 5000 ohms. What are the equations for instantaneous current, voltage, and power? What is the average power dissipated in the resistor? (9.7)

27. An rms current of 0.5 amp is measured in a certain resistor. The instantaneous voltage is $v = 35 \sin t$. What is the resistance? What is the average power? If the energy loss is 2.4 joules in one cycle, what is the angular frequency? (9.7)

28. The rms voltage across a resistor is 30 volts. The rms current through the same resistor is 300 ma. What is the resistance of the resistor? What is the average power dissipated in the resistor? How much energy is lost in the first quarter of the positive cycle? (9.7)

29. The average power dissipated in a 300 ohm resistor is 100 watts. What is the rms current and voltage? (9.7)

30. The energy lost in 600 ohm resistor in one cycle is 3 joules. What is the rms voltage and current? (9.7)

10

Reactance

A fundamental property of the inductor is that it opposes any change in its current. On the other hand, a fundamental property of the capacitor is that it opposes any change in its voltage. From these two statements and the knowledge that alternating current is constantly changing in both magnitude and direction it should not be difficult for one to deduce that both the inductor and capacitor present an opposition to alternating current. The *reactance* of these elements is a measure of this opposition.

10.1 INDUCTIVE REACTANCE

According to the Equation 7.8, the instantaneous voltage across an inductor is given by the product of the inductance times the time rate of change of the instantaneous current in the inductor. In Figure 10-1 assume a sinusoidal current of the form

$$i_L = I_m \sin \omega t \tag{10.1}$$

The mathematics of calculus tells us that the time rate of change of this current is given by

$$\frac{di}{dt} = I_m \cos \omega t \tag{10.2}$$

which may also be expressed as

$$\frac{di}{dt} = I_m \sin (\omega t + 90°) \tag{10.3}$$

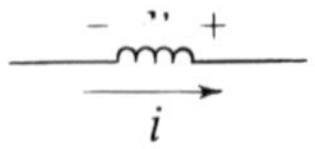

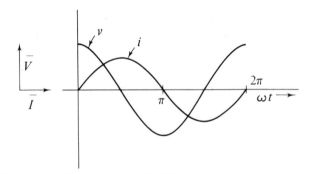

Figure 10-1

since $\cos \omega t$ equals $\sin(\omega t + 90°)$. The voltage across the inductor is then given by

$$v_L = L\frac{di}{dt}$$
$$= LI_m \omega \sin(\omega t + 90°) \qquad (10.4)$$

The quantity $\omega\, LI_m$ is the maximum value of the voltage across the inductor which occurs at $0°$.

$$V_m = (\omega L)\, I_m \qquad (10.5)$$

where $(\omega\, L)$ is called the inductive reactance of the inductor and is a measure of opposition to a-c current. Like resistance, it is measured in ohms. The symbol X_L is used to denote inductive reactance.

$$X_L = \omega L = 2\pi f L \qquad (10.6)$$

Equation 10.4 also tells us that the voltage across the inductor is leading the current by $90°$. This relation between the current and voltage is shown in Figure 10-2.

Figure 10-2

Example (10.1):

Let the voltage across the inductor in Figure 10-1 be given by $e = 10 \sin 100t$. The inductance $L = 1$ henry. What is the expression for the instantaneous current in the inductor?

Solution:

The inductive reactance is given by

$$X_L = \omega L$$
$$= (100)\ 1$$
$$= 100\ \text{ohms}$$

The maximum current is

$$I_m = \frac{E_m}{X_L}$$
$$= \frac{10}{100}$$
$$= 0.1\ \text{amp}$$

and the expression for instantaneous current is

$$i = 0.1\ \sin(100t - 90°)$$

since the current lags the voltage by 90°.

Since $V_m = \sqrt{2}\,V$ and $I_m = \sqrt{2}\,I$, it is sometimes convenient to remember that the rms current and voltage can be related in the same way as the maximum values.

$$I_L = \frac{V_L}{X_L} \qquad (10.7)$$

Example (10.2):
Let the voltage source be 115 volts. An inductor is to be connected across the source such that there are 10 amp of current in the circuit. What is the inductive reactance? What is the inductance if the frequency is 60 hertz?

Solution:
The inductive reactance is found from Equation 10.7.

$$X_L = \frac{E}{I}$$
$$= \frac{115}{10}$$
$$= 11.5\ \text{ohms}$$

The inductance is found from Equation 10.6

$$L = \frac{X_L}{2\pi f}$$
$$= \frac{11.5}{(6.28)60}$$
$$= 0.305\ \text{henry}$$

10.2   POWER IN THE INDUCTOR

In Chapter 7 the instantaneous power was given as the product of the instantaneous voltage times the instantaneous current. For the inductor

$$p(t) = v(t)i(t)$$
$$= (V_m \sin \omega t)(I_m \cos \omega t) \qquad (10.8)$$

With use of the trigonometric identity

$$\sin 2\omega t = 2\sin \omega t \cos \omega t \qquad (10.9)$$

the instantaneous power becomes

$$p(t) = \frac{V_m I_m}{2} \sin 2\omega t \qquad (10.10)$$

Figure 10-3 is a graph of the instantaneous voltage, current, and power. The power is sinusoidal at twice the frequency of the current or voltage.

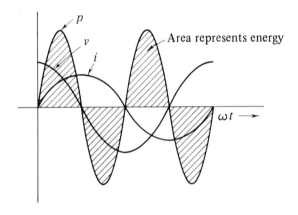

Figure 10-3

The average power dissipated in the inductor must be zero since the instantaneous power makes equal excursions above and below zero. A pure inductor can never dissipate real power. Although the inductor takes no power, it will pass current, and in the circuit shown in Figure 10-4 this

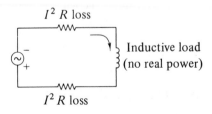

Figure 10-4

current would pass through the series resistance and thus cause a power loss in the resistor.

The product of the rms voltage across the inductor and the rms current through an inductor is called the inductive reactive power.

$$\text{VARS} = I_L V_L \qquad (10.11)$$

Reactive power is not real power and the units are not watts but reactive volt-amperes or simply VARS. Power companies meter and charge for reactive volt-amperes in many industrial plants where inductive loads are large. Although reactive power is not useful to the consumer, it does represent a loss in the power company's distribution lines.

Example (10.3):

The current through an inductor is given by $i_L = 10 \sin 100t$ and the reactance of the inductor is 1 ohm. Determine the instantaneous power, the average power, and the inductive reactive power.

Solution:

The voltage across the inductor is

$$v_L = (10)(1) \sin (100t - 90°)$$
$$= 10 \sin (100t - 90°)$$

The instantaneous power is given by

$$p = v_L i_L$$
$$= 100[\sin (100t)] [\sin (100t - 90°)]$$
$$= 50 \sin 200t$$

The inductive reactive volt-amperes

$$\text{VARS} = V_L I_L$$
$$= \left(\frac{10}{\sqrt{2}}\right)\left(\frac{10}{\sqrt{2}}\right)$$
$$= 50$$

The average power $= 0$.

10.3   ENERGY IN THE INDUCTOR

Energy is defined as the integral of instantaneous power.

$$W = \int_{t_1}^{t_2} \frac{V_m I_m}{2} \sin 2\omega t \, dt \qquad (10.12)$$

and is measured in watt-seconds or joules. That is, energy is found by taking the area under the instantaneous power curve. The curve in Figure 10-3 shows that the energy for the inductor is positive while the current is increasing but negative when current decreases. This means that energy is being stored in the magnetic field with increasing current and energy is returning from the magnetic field when the current is decreasing.

For the first quarter cycle of current or voltage the area under the power curve is

$$W = \tfrac{1}{2} LI_m^2 \qquad (10.13)$$

For the next quarter cycle it is the same value but opposite in sign. The area between any two values of current is given by

$$W = \tfrac{1}{2} L \left(I_2^2 - I_1^2\right) \qquad (10.14)$$

which is the change in energy between these two values of current.

Example (10 4):
What is the energy stored in an inductor of 1 henry from the time the current is zero until the current reaches 1 amp? If 1 amp occurs at 45° what is the maximum energy that is stored in the inductor at any one time?

Solution:

The current rises from $I_1 = 0$ to

$$I_2 = 1 \text{ amp}$$

$$W = \tfrac{1}{2} L(I_2^2 - I_1^2)$$

$$= \tfrac{1}{2} (1)(1 - 0)$$

$$= \tfrac{1}{2} \text{ joule}$$

The maximum energy stored occurs when $i = I_m$, therefore we must first determine I_m as follows:

$$i = I_m \sin \omega t$$

at 45°, with an instantaneous current of 1 amp

$$i = I_m \sin 45°$$

$$I_m = \frac{1}{0.707}$$

$$= 1.41 \text{ amp}$$

$$W_{max} = \tfrac{1}{2} (1)(1.41^2 - 0)$$

$$\approx 1 \text{ joule}$$

10.4   CAPACITIVE REACTANCE

Consider the circuit shown in Figure 10-5 and assume the voltage across the capacitor to be

$$v_c = V_m \sin \omega t \qquad (10.15)$$

The instantaneous current is given by the product of the capacitance times the time rate of change of the voltage.

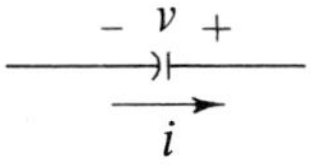

Figure 10-5

$$i = C\frac{dv_c}{dt}$$

$$= \omega C V_m \cos \omega t \qquad (10.16)$$

which can be rewritten as

$$i = \omega C V_m \sin (\omega t + 90°) \qquad (10.17)$$

The quantity $\omega C V_m$ is seen to be the maximum current, so we can write

$$I_m = V_m \omega C$$

$$= \frac{V_m}{1/\omega C} \qquad (10.18)$$

where $1/\omega C$ is called the capacitive reactance of the capacitor and is a measure of opposition to a-c current. Like inductive reactance and resistance, it is measured in ohms. The symbol X_c is used to denote capacitive reactance.

$$X_c = \frac{{}_m 1}{\omega C}$$

$$= \frac{1}{2\pi f C} \qquad (10.19)$$

Equation 10.17 also indicates that the current through the capacitor is sinusoidal and that it leads the voltage across the capacitor by an angle of 90° (opposite that of the inductor). This relation between the current and voltage in the capacitor is shown in Figure 10-6.

Example (10.5):
    The voltage across the capacitor in Figure 10-5 is given by $v_c = 10 \sin (100t + 30°)$ and the capacitance is 1 μf. What is the expression for instantaneous current in the capacitor?

Solution:
    The capacitive reactance is given by

$$X_c = \frac{1}{\omega C}$$

$$= \frac{1}{(100)(1 \times 10^{-6})}$$

$$= 1 \times 10^8 \text{ ohms}$$

and the maximum current

$$I_m = \frac{V_m}{X_c}$$

$$= \frac{10}{1 \times 10^8}$$

$$= 10^{-7} \text{ amp}$$

The instantaneous current is given by

$$i = 10^{-7} \sin (100t + 120°)$$

since the current leads the voltage by 90°.

Since $I_m = \sqrt{2}\, I$ and $V_m = \sqrt{2}\, V$, we may also write

$$V_c = X_c I_c \tag{10.20}$$

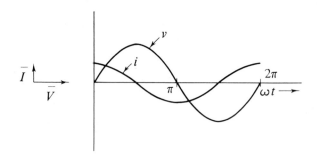

Figure 10-6

10.5   POWER IN THE CAPACITOR

The average real power dissipated in a capacitor, as in the inductor, is zero. The instantaneous power, however, as given by the product of instantaneous voltage and current is

$$p(t) = vi$$

$$= V_m I_m (\sin \omega t \cos \omega t) \tag{10.21}$$

which is identical to the expression for instantaneous power in the inductor and may likewise be rewritten as

$$p(t) = \frac{V_m I_m}{2} \sin 2\omega t \tag{10.22}$$

Figure 10-7 shows the curves of instantaneous voltage, instantaneous current, and instantaneous power for the capacitor. From this curve it should be clear that the average power is zero; for the excursions above and below zero are equal in magnitude. A pure capacitor can never dissipate real power.

The product of the rms voltage across a capacitor and the rms current through a capacitor is called the capacitive reactive power

$$\text{VARS} = E_c I_c \qquad (10.23)$$

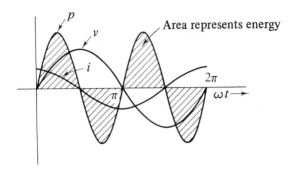

Figure 10-7

and like inductive reactive power is measured in VARS. Although it is not power, it is important in the same sense that inductive reactive power is important. It differs from inductive reactive power in sign, however. Inductive reactive power is usually considered as positive in sign and capacitive volt-amperes negative in sign. Reactive volt-amperes will be discussed in further detail in the following chapter.

10.6 ENERGY IN CAPACITORS

As in the case of the inductor, the energy in a capacitor is found by taking the area under the curve for the power. It is seen from Figure 10-7 that when the voltage across the capacitor is increasing, the energy is positive, and when the voltage is decreasing, the energy is negative. This implies that the capacitor is storing energy in the electric field of the dielectric when the voltage is increasing, and returning this energy when the voltage is decreasing.

For the first quarter cycle of the voltage curve, the area under the curve is given by

$$W = \tfrac{1}{2} C V_m^2 \qquad (10.24)$$

For the next quarter cycle it is the same value, but opposite in sign. By the end of a complete voltage cycle the same amount of energy that was stored is returned.

The area under the power curve between any two voltages and thus the change in energy between any two voltages is given by

$$W = \tfrac{1}{2} C (V_2^2 - V_1^2) \qquad (10.25)$$

Example (10.6):

What is the energy change in a capacitor of 1 farad when the voltage across it changes from 2 volts to 5 volts?

Solution:

From Equation 10.25

$$W = \tfrac{1}{2} C(V_2^2 - V_1^2)$$
$$= \tfrac{1}{2} (1)(2^2 - 5^2)$$
$$= -10.5 \text{ joules}$$

The negative sign indicates the energy was returned to the source.

10.7 SUMMARY

The *reactance* of an inductor or capacitor is a measure of the opposition these elements present to alternating current. The reactance of an inductor is given by

$$X_L = \omega L$$
$$= 2\pi fL \tag{10.6}$$

and

$$V_m = \omega LI_m \tag{10.5}$$

while the reactance of a capacitor is given by

$$X_c = \frac{1}{\omega C}$$
$$= \frac{1}{2\pi fC} \tag{10.19}$$

and

$$I_m = \frac{V_m}{1/\omega C} \tag{10.18}$$

The relationship between the current and voltage in a pure inductor is always such that the current lags the applied voltage by 90°. On the other hand, the current in a capacitor always leads the applied voltage by 90°.

No average power is dissipated in either an inductor or a capacitor. In the inductor, energy is being stored in the magnetic field while the current is increasing and is returned again when the current is decreasing. In the capacitor, energy is being stored in the electric field while its voltage is increasing and energy is returned from the field when the voltage is decreasing. The energy stored in or returned from the magnetic field of an inductor is given by

$$W = \tfrac{1}{2} L (I_2^2 - I_1^2) \tag{10.14}$$

The energy stored in or returned from the electric field of a capacitor is given by

$$W = \tfrac{1}{2} C (V_2^2 - V_1^2) \qquad\qquad (10.25)$$

The product of the effective voltage across a pure reactance and the current in the reactance gives the *reactive volt-amperes or reactive power*. Inductive reactive power is given by

$$\text{VARS} = I_L V_L \qquad\qquad (10.11)$$

and the capacitive reactive power is given by

$$\text{VARS} = I_c V_c \qquad\qquad (10.23)$$

Reactive power associated with an inductor is usually considered to be positive and that associated with a capacitor is usually considered to be negative. Reactive power is not real power. However, it may cause heavy currents in a transmission line resulting in a large voltage drop and $I^2 R$ loss in the transmission line.

10.8   QUESTIONS AND PROBLEMS

Questions

1. What is reactance? (Introduction)
2. What is the difference between inductive reactance and capacitive reactance? (10.1), (10.4)
3. What is the phase relationship between voltage and current in an inductor? (10.1)
4. Does the reactance of an inductor increase or decrease with an increase in frequency? (10.1)
5. Why is there no average power dissipated in an inductor or capacitor? (10.2), (10.5)
6. Is there any instantaneous power associated with a capacitor or inductor? (10.2), (10.5)
7. What is reactive power? Why is it important? (10.2)
8. What is the difference between capacitive reactive power and inductive reactive power? (10.2), (10.5)
9. Sketch the curve of instantaneous power and energy for an inductor. (10.2)
10. When current is increasing in an inductor, is energy being stored or released? (10.3)
11. How does the energy stored in an inductor depend upon the current? (10.3)
12. What is the phase relationship between voltage and current in a capacitor? (10.4)
13. Does the reactance of a capacitor increase or decrease with an increase in frequency? (10.4)
14. Repeat Question 9 for a capacitor. (10.5)
15. When the voltage across a capacitor is increasing, is energy being stored or released? (10.6)
16. How does the energy stored in a capacitor depend upon the voltage? (10.6)

Problems

1. An inductor has a reactance of 300 ohms at 60 hertz. What is the reactance at 30 hertz? What is the reactance at 120 hertz? (10.1)
2. The current in an inductor is given by $i = 0.3 \sin \omega t$. If the inductive reactance is 308 ohms, what is the equation for the instantaneous voltage across the inductor? (10.1)

3. The voltage across an inductor is given by $e = 12 \sin 377t$. The inductance is 8 henrys. What is the inductive reactance? What is the peak current in the inductor? What is the equation for the instantaneous current? (10.1)

4. The voltage across a 16 henry choke is 0.5 volt. The frequency of the voltage is 120 hertz. What is the effective current? (10.1)

5. The instantaneous voltage across an inductor is given by $e = 25 \sin(314t + 30°)$. The effective current is measured as 350 ma. What is the equation for the instantaneous current, and what is the value of the inductance? (10.1)

6. The instantaneous current in an inductor is given by $i = 0.35 \sin (377t - 10°)$. The rms voltage across the inductor is 70.7 volts. What is the inductance and what is the equation for the instantaneous voltage? (10.1)

7. The voltage across an inductor is given as $e = 330 \sin \omega t$. The effective current is 30 ma. Write the expression for the instantaneous power. What is the real power? What is the reactive power? (10.2)

8. The current through an inductor having a reactance of 10 kΩ at 60 hertz is 5 ma. Write the expression for instantaneous power. What is the real power? What is the reactive power? (10.2)

9. The reactive power associated with a certain inductor at 60 hertz is 5 KVARS. The voltage across the inductor is 1000 volts. What is the current? Write the expression for instantaneous power. (10.2)

10. The reactive power associated with a certain inductor at 60 hertz is 1 KVARS. The current in the inductor is 10 amp. What is the voltage across the inductor? Write the expression for the instantaneous power. (10.2)

11. What energy is stored in an inductor of 10 henrys from the time the current is zero until it reaches a value of 1 amp? If 1 amp occurs at 45°, what is the maximum energy that is stored in the inductor at any one time? (10.3)

12. The current in a 250 mh inductor is $i = 10 \sin 720t$. How much energy is stored in the magnetic field after $\frac{1}{4}$ cycle, $\frac{1}{2}$ cycle, $\frac{3}{4}$ cycle, and 1 complete cycle? (10.3)

13. The current in a 500 mh inductor is $i = 0.05 \sin 314t$. What is the energy stored in the magnetic field between $t = 0.01$ seconds and $t = 0.05$ seconds? (10.3)

14. A 16 μf capacitor has a reactance of 500 ohms. What is the frequency? (10.4)

15. A certain capacitor has a reactance of 250 ohms at 60 hertz. What is the reactance at 400 hertz? (10.4)

16. The voltage across a certain capacitor is given by $e = 120 \sin \omega t$. The effective current is 0.25 amp. What is the reactance of the capacitor? Write the equation for instantaneous current. (10.4)

17. If the frequency in Problem 16 is 628 radians/second, what is the value of the capacitor? (10.4)

18. The current in a capacitor is given by $i = 0.03 \sin \omega t$. The voltage across the capacitor is measured as 3 volts. What is the expression for the instantaneous voltage and what is the reactance of the capacitor? (10.4)

19. The instantaneous voltage across a capacitor is given as $v_c = 171 \sin (620t + 33°)$. The capacitance of the capacitor is 0.01 μf. What is the expression for the instantaneous current? (10.4)

20. The voltage across a capacitor is 320 volts. The capacitance is 30 μf. What is the reactive power at 60 hertz? (10.5)

21. The current through a capacitor having a reactance of 5 kΩ at 60 hertz is 5 ma. Write the expression for instantaneous power. What is the real power and the reactive power? (10.5)

22. The reactive power associated with a certain capacitor at 120 hertz is 1 KVARS. The voltage across the capacitor is 1000 volts. What is the current through the capacitor? Write an expression for the instantaneous power. (10.5)

23. The reactive power associated with a certain capacitor at 50 hertz is 50 KVARS. The

current is 50 amp. What is the voltage across the capacitor? Write the expression for instantaneous power. (10.5)

24. The instantaneous voltage across a capacitor of 10 μf is $e = 707 \sin (1000t + 30°)$. What is the reactive power? Write the expression for the instantaneous power. (10.6)

25. What energy is stored in an 8 μf capacitor from the time the current is zero until it reaches a value of -1 amp? If -1 amp occurs at 135°, what is the maximum energy stored in the capacitor? (10.6)

26. The voltage across a 220 μf capacitor is 300 volts. The frequency is 1 mc. How much energy is stored after $\frac{1}{4}$ cycle, $\frac{1}{2}$ cycle, $\frac{3}{4}$ cycle, and 1 complete cycle? (10.6)

27. The voltage across a 4 μf capacitor is $v = 300 \sin 377t$. What is the energy stored in the capacitor between $t = 0.01$ sec and $t = 0.05$ sec? (10.6)

11

Alternating Current Circuits

Up to this point the individual elements of resistance, capacitance, and inductance have been treated in circuits. It is the purpose of this chapter to consider circuits containing various combinations of these elements. In doing so, the introduction of the concept of impedance and the use of complex numbers are helpful in simplifying a-c circuit analysis.

11.1 *R* AND *L* CIRCUITS

Consider the series *RL* circuit in Figure 11-1a. To determine the currents and voltages it is convenient to plot a phasor diagram as shown in

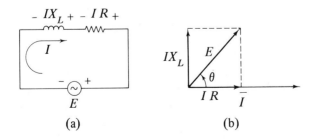

(a)   (b)

Figure 11-1

203

Figure 11-1b. It is also convenient to take the current as reference in a series circuit. Thus, the phasor representing the current is drawn horizontal and to the right. The voltage across the resistor is in phase with the current and is given as the product IR. Therefore, the vector $\mathbf{V}_R$ is also horizontal and to the right. The magnitude of voltage across the inductor is given by the product IX_L and is leading the current by 90° as shown in the figure. The applied voltage $\mathbf{E}$ is the resultant of the voltage across the resistor and the voltage across the inductor. This voltage is seen to be leading the current. In fact, the voltage across a series RL circuit will always lead the current by some angle that lies between 0 and 90°. If the circuit is a pure resistance, the phase angle is 0°. On the other hand, for a pure inductor it is 90°. The phase angle is given by

$$\theta = \text{arc tan}\ \frac{X_L}{R} \tag{11.1}$$

Since the voltage across the inductor leads the voltage across the resistor by 90°, the applied voltage is the hypotenuse of a right triangle. Its magnitude is therefore given by the square root of the sum of the squares of V_R and V_L.

$$E = \sqrt{V_R^2 + V_L^2} \tag{11.2}$$

Equation 11.2 may also be written in terms of current, resistance, and reactance as

$$E = \sqrt{(IR)^2 + (IX_L)^2} \tag{11.3}$$

Factoring out I gives

$$E = I\sqrt{R^2 + X_L^2} \tag{11.4}$$

Example (11.1):
In the circuit in Figure 11-1, the resistor has a value of 3 ohms and the inductive reactance is 4 ohms. If the aplied voltage is 100 volts, what is the current I and the voltage across each element? Draw a phasor diagram.

Solution:
The current is given by rearranging Equation 11.4 as

$$I = \frac{E}{\sqrt{R^2 + X_L^2}}$$

$$= \frac{100}{\sqrt{3^2 + 4^2}}$$

$$= 20 \text{ amp}$$

The magnitude of the voltage across the resistor is

$$V_R = IR$$

$$= (20)\,(3)$$

$$= 60 \text{ volts}$$

The magnitude of the voltage across the inductor is given by

$$V_L = IX_L$$

$$= (20)(4)$$

$$= 80 \text{ volts}$$

If the current is taken as reference, the voltage across the resistor is in phase with this current, while the voltage across the inductor leads this current by 90°. (See Figure 11-2.) The phase angle between E and I is given by Equation 11.1 as

$$\theta = \text{arc tan} \frac{X_L}{R}$$

$$= \text{arc tan} \frac{4}{3}$$

$$= 53.1°$$

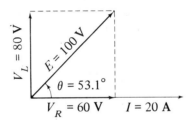

Figure 11-2

When R and L are in parallel as shown in Figure 11-3a, it is convenient to take the voltage across the combination as reference. The voltage phasor

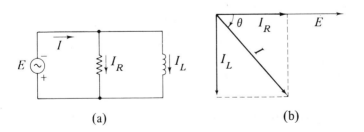

(a)   (b)

Figure 11-3

is then plotted horizontally and to the right as shown in Figure 11-3b. Current through the resistor is given by Ohm's law as

$$I_R = \frac{E}{R}$$

and is in phase with the applied voltage. The current through the inductance is given by

$$I_L = \frac{E}{X_L}$$

and lags the applied voltage by 90°. Total current is the resultant of the current through the resistor and the inductor.

$$I = \sqrt{I_R^2 + I_L^2} \tag{11.5}$$

or

$$I = \sqrt{\frac{E^2}{R^2} + \frac{E^2}{X_L^2}}$$

Factoring out E gives

$$I = E\sqrt{\frac{1}{R^2} + \frac{1}{X^2}} \tag{11.6}$$

The magnitude of the angle θ between the total current and the applied voltage is given by

$$\theta = \text{arc tan } \frac{I_L}{I_R} \tag{11.7}$$

or

$$\theta = \text{arc tan } \frac{R}{X_L} \tag{11.8}$$

Example (11.2):

In Figure 11-3a let $E = 120$ volts and $R = 3$ ohms and $X_L = 4$ ohms. Find all the currents and draw a phasor diagram.

Solution:

The current through the resistor is in phase with the applied voltage and is given by

$$I_R = \frac{E}{R}$$

$$= \frac{120}{3}$$

$$= 40 \text{ amp}$$

Likewise, the magnitude of the current through the inductor is given by

$$I_L = \frac{E}{X_L}$$

$$= \frac{120}{4}$$

$$= 30 \text{ amp}$$

and it is lagging the voltage across it by 90°, as shown in Figure 11-4. Total current from the source is the resultant of these two currents.

$$I = \sqrt{I_R^2 + I_L^2}$$

$$= \sqrt{(40)^2 + (30)^2}$$

$$= 50 \text{ amp}$$

The phase angle θ between the applied voltage and the total current is given by Equations 11.7 or 11.8. With Equation 11.7

$$\theta = \text{arc tan} \frac{I_L}{I_R}$$

$$= \text{arc tan} \frac{30}{40}$$

$$= 36.9°$$

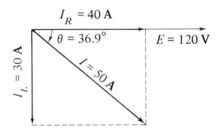

Figure 11-4

11.2 R AND C CIRCUITS

The series RC circuit is very much like the series RL except that the current is always leading the applied voltage at some angle between 0°

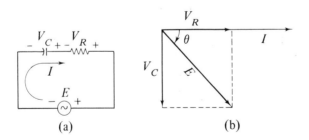

Figure 11-5

and 90°. Figure 11-5 shows the series RC circuit along with the phasor diagram. The following analysis applies to Figure 11-5:

$$V_R = IR \text{ (in phase with } I)$$

$$V_c = IX_c \text{ (lags } I \text{ by } 90°)$$

$$E = \sqrt{V_c^2 + V_R^2} \tag{11.9}$$

$$= \sqrt{(IX_c)^2 + (IR)^2}$$

or

$$E = I\sqrt{(X_c^2 + R^2)} \tag{11.10}$$

$$\tan \theta = \frac{V_c}{V_R} \tag{11.11}$$

or

$$\tan \theta = \frac{X_c}{R} \tag{11.12}$$

Likewise, the parallel RC circuit is like the parallel RL circuit except for the direction of the phase angle. Figure 11-6 shows the parallel circuit

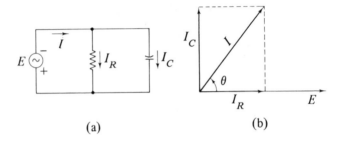

(a)   (b)

Figure 11-6

along with its phasor diagram. The applied voltage is taken as the reference. The following mathematical analysis applies to Figure 11-6:

$$I_R = \frac{E}{R} \text{ (in phase with } E)$$

$$I_c = \frac{E}{X_c} \text{ (leads } E \text{ by } 90°)$$

$$I = \sqrt{I_R^2 + I_c^2} \tag{11.13}$$

$$= \sqrt{\frac{E^2}{R^2} + \frac{E^2}{X_c^2}}$$

or

$$I = E\sqrt{\frac{1}{R^2} + \frac{1}{X_c^2}} \tag{11.14}$$

$$\tan \theta = \frac{I_c}{I_R} \tag{11.15}$$

or

$$\tan \theta = \frac{R}{X_c} \qquad (11.16)$$

11.3 SERIES *RLC* CIRCUITS

Consider the series *RLC* circuit shown in Figure 11-7a. Again, it is convenient to take the current as reference since it is the same in all ele-

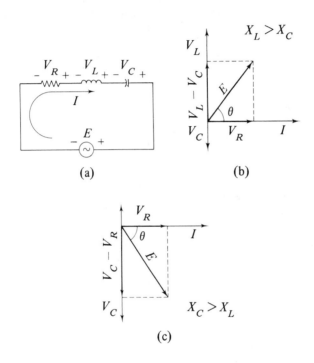

(a)

(b)

(c)

Figure 11-7

ments of the series circuit. The voltage across the resistance is given by the *IR* product and is in phase with the current. The voltage across the capacitor is given by the product of current and capacitive reactance and lags the current by 90°. On the other hand, the voltage across the inductor, which is given by the product of current and inductive reactance, leads the current by 90°. This means that the voltages across the inductor and capacitor are 180° out of phase with each other and therefore subtract. If the voltage across the inductor is greater, the circuit is said to be inductive and looks to the source as if it were a single resistor in series with an inductor. If the voltage across the capacitor is greater, the circuit is said to be capacitive and looks to the source as a series capacitor and resistor. Since the current is the same through the capacitor and inductor, it follows that the circuit is inductive if $X_L > X_c$, or capacitive if $X_c > X_L$. The phasor diagrams for both the inductive and capacitive case are shown in Figures 11-7b and 11-7c.

Example (11.3):

In the circuit in Figure 11-7a, $R = 5$ ohms, $X_c = 10$ ohms, and $X_L = 5$ ohms. Find the current and voltage across each element if the applied voltage is 70.7 volts.

Solution:

The circuit is capacitive because the capacitive reactance is greater than the inductive reactance. The magnitude of current is thus given by

$$I = \frac{E}{\sqrt{R^2 + (X_c - X_L)^2}}$$

$$= \frac{70.7}{\sqrt{(5)^2 + (5)^2}}$$

$$= 10 \text{ amp}$$

The voltage across the resistor is

$$V_R = IR$$

$$= 10(5)$$

$$= 50 \text{ volts}$$

and is in phase with the current. (See Figure 11-8.) The voltage across the inductor is

$$V_L = IX_L$$

$$= 10(5)$$

$$= 50 \text{ volts}$$

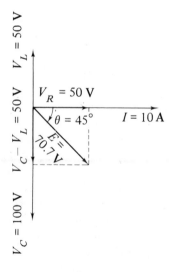

Figure 11-8

and leads the current by 90°. The voltage across the capacitor is

$$V_c = IX_c$$
$$= 10(10)$$
$$= 100 \text{ volts}$$

and lags the current by 90°. The phase angle between the applied voltage and current is

$$\theta = \text{arc tan} \frac{X_c - X_L}{R}$$

$$= \text{arc tan} \frac{5}{5}$$

$$= 45°$$

Note that the sum of magnitudes of voltages does not give the source voltage. This means that in applying Kirchhoff's laws in a-c circuits one must be careful to use phasors only. It is quite possible that the magnitude voltage across one element in the circuit could be greater than the source voltage.

11.4 PARALLEL *RLC* CIRCUIT

A circuit having a resistor, capacitor, and inductor connected in parallel is shown in Figure 11-9a. Since the elements are parallel, the voltage

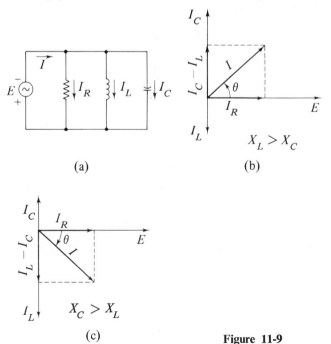

(a)

(b)

(c)

Figure 11-9

across them is the same. It is, therefore, convenient to take this voltage as reference. The current through the resistor is given by the applied voltage E divided by the resistance and is in phase with this voltage. The current through the inductor is found by dividing the voltage E by the inductive reactance. This current lags the applied voltage by 90°. Likewise, the current I_c through the capacitor is obtained by dividing the voltage E by the capacitive reactance. In this case the current leads the applied voltage by 90°. Since the current in the inductor is lagging the voltage by 90° and the current in the capacitor is leading the voltage by 90°, the two currents subtract. Thus, if the current in the capacitor is larger than in the inductor, it will lead the applied voltage and the circuit will act like a resistor and capacitor in parallel with an equivalent capacitive reactance of $1 \left/ \left[\dfrac{1}{X_c} - \dfrac{1}{X_L} \right] \right.$. On the other hand, if the current through the inductor is greater than through the capacitor, the circuit will act like a resistor and inductor in parallel with an equivalent reactance of $1 \left/ \left[\dfrac{1}{X_L} - \dfrac{1}{X_c} \right] \right.$.

Example (11.4):

    Referring to Figure 11-9a, let $R = 200$ ohms, $X_L = 100$ ohms, and $X_c = 200$ ohms. Find the current in each element and the total current delivered by the source if the source voltage is 100 volts. Draw a phasor diagram.

Solution:

    The current in the resistor is

$$I_R = \frac{E}{R}$$

$$= \frac{100}{200}$$

$$= 0.5 \text{ amp}$$

and is in phase with E (Figure 11-10). The current in the inductor is

$$I_L = \frac{E}{X_L}$$

$$= \frac{100}{100}$$

$$= 1 \text{ amp}$$

and is lagging the voltage by 90°. The current in the capacitor is

$$I_c = \frac{E}{X_c}$$

$$= \frac{100}{200}$$

$$= 0.5 \text{ amp}$$

and is leading the voltage by 90° The current I_L is greater than I_c and

$$I_L - I_c = 1 - 0.5$$

$$= 0.5 \text{ amp}$$

This 0.5 amp is lagging the voltage by 90° as though there were only a resistor and inductor in parallel. The total current is then given by

$$I = \sqrt{(I_L - I_c)^2 + I_R{}^2}$$

$$= \sqrt{(0.5)^2 + (0.5)^2}$$

$$= \sqrt{(25 \times 10^{-2}) + (25 \times 10^{-2})}$$

$$= 7.07 \times 10^{-1} \text{ amp}$$

The phase angle is given by

$$\theta = \text{arc tan} \frac{I_L - I_c}{R}$$

$$= \text{arc tan} \frac{(1 - 0.5)}{0.5}$$

$$= 45°$$

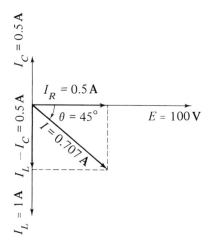

Figure 11-10

11.5 IMPEDANCE

As shown in Section 9.3, sinusoidal voltages and currents can always be expressed as rotating vectors or phasors. Furthermore, it is possible to express these phasors in the form of complex numbers.[1] For example, the voltage $e = \sqrt{2} E \sin (\omega t + \theta_A)$ could be expressed in phasor form as

[1]   An explanation of the use of complex numbers is given in the appendix.

$E\underline{/\,\theta_A}°$ where $\sqrt{2}\,E$ is the maximum voltage and θ_A is the phase angle of the voltage.[2] Likewise, the current $i = \sqrt{2}\,I \sin(\omega t + \theta_B)$ could be expressed in phasor form as $I\underline{/\,\theta_B}°$.

The ratio of voltage to current when both are expressed in terms of complex numbers is called *impedance*. It is measured in ohms and is represented by the symbol **Z**. Since impedance is the ratio of two complex numbers, it will also be a complex number having magnitude and direction. The magnitude of the impedance is the ratio of the voltage magnitude to the current magnitude. The impedance angle is the difference between the phase angle of the voltage and that of the current, and its magnitude represents the phase angle between the voltage and the current in the circuit.

If impedance is converted from polar form to rectangular form it will have a real part and an imaginary part. For example, if $\mathbf{Z} = 5\underline{/\,36.9°}$ its rectangular form is $\mathbf{Z} = 3 + j4$. The real part 3 is the resistive part of the impedance and the imaginary part 4 is the reactive part of the impedance.

Ohm's law for a-c circuits is given in terms of impedance as

$$\mathbf{I} = \frac{\mathbf{E}}{\mathbf{Z}} \qquad (11.17)$$

The inverse of impedance is called *admittance*. It is measured in mhos and represented by the symbol **Y**.

$$\mathbf{Y} = \frac{1}{\mathbf{Z}} \qquad (11.18)$$

Since **Z** is a complex number, **Y** is also a complex number. If **Y** is expressed in rectangular form, the real part is a conductance G while the imaginary part is the inverse of reactance, which is termed the *susceptance B*.

Impedances and admittances for single elements and simple combinations are shown in the table in Figure 11-11 .

Impedances can be combined in the same manner as resistances were combined as long as they are expressed as complex quantities. In series

$$\mathbf{Z}_T = \mathbf{Z}_1 + \mathbf{Z}_2 \qquad (11.19)$$

and in parallel

$$\mathbf{Z}_T = \cfrac{1}{\cfrac{1}{\mathbf{Z}_1} + \cfrac{1}{\mathbf{Z}_2} + \cfrac{1}{\mathbf{Z}_3} + \cdots + \cfrac{1}{\mathbf{Z}_n}} \qquad (11.20)$$

or

$$\mathbf{Y}_T = \mathbf{Y}_1 + \mathbf{Y}_2 + \mathbf{Y}_3 + \cdots + \mathbf{Y}_n \qquad (11.21)$$

Using complex quantities to express currents, voltages, and impedances,

---

[2]   Voltage and current phasors can be expressed either in terms of maximum quantities or rms quantities since $I_{max} = \sqrt{2}\,I$ and $E_{max} = \sqrt{2}\,E$. Because rms values are more useful quantities, we will express all voltage and current phasors in terms of rms values.

 ⎯WW⎯	$\mathbf{Z} = R$	$\mathbf{Y} = \dfrac{1}{R}$
 ⎯mm⎯	$\mathbf{Z} = j\,X_L$	$\mathbf{Y} = -j\,\dfrac{1}{X_L}$
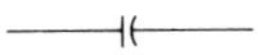 ⎯)(⎯	$\mathbf{Z} = -j\,X_C$	$\mathbf{Y} = j\,\dfrac{1}{X_C}$
 ⎯WW⎯mm⎯	$\mathbf{Z} = R + j\,X_L$	$\mathbf{Y} = \dfrac{R}{R^2 + X_L^{\,2}} - j\,\dfrac{X_L}{R^2 + X_L^{\,2}}$
 ⎯WW⎯)(⎯	$\mathbf{Z} = R - j\,X_C$	$\mathbf{Y} = \dfrac{R}{R^2 + X_C^{\,2}} + j\,\dfrac{X_C}{R^2 + X_C^{\,2}}$
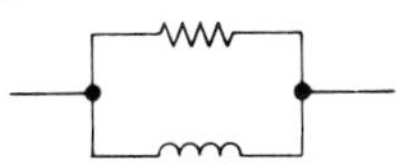 (R ‖ L)	$\mathbf{Z} = \dfrac{R X_L^{\,2}}{R^2 + X_L^{\,2}} + j\,\dfrac{R^2 X_L}{R^2 + X_L^{\,2}}$	$\mathbf{Y} = \dfrac{1}{R} - j\,\dfrac{1}{X_L}$
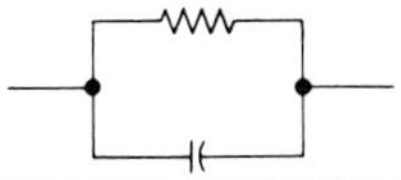 (R ‖ C)	$\mathbf{Z} = \dfrac{R X_C^{\,2}}{R^2 + X_C^{\,2}} - j\,\dfrac{R^2 X_C}{R^2 + X_C^{\,2}}$	$\mathbf{Y} = \dfrac{1}{R} + j\,\dfrac{1}{X_C}$

Figure 11-11

it is possible to apply the same techniques to solving a-c circuit problems as were used in solving d-c circuit problems. This includes the use of Ohm's law, Kirchhoff's law, and the network theorems given in Chapter 5.

Example (11.5):

In the circuit in Figure 11-12, find the total impedance and the current[3] if $E = 100 \; \underline{/\theta°}$.[3]

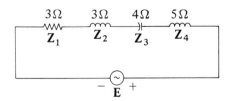

Figure 11-12

[3] An explanation of the use of polar representation is given in the appendix.

Solution:

$$\mathbf{Z} = \mathbf{Z}_1 + \mathbf{Z}_2 + \mathbf{Z}_3 + \mathbf{Z}_4$$
$$= (3) + (j3) + (-j4) + (j5)$$
$$3 + j4 = 5 \underline{/36.9°}$$

$$\mathbf{I} = \frac{\mathbf{E}}{\mathbf{Z}} \qquad \theta_Z = \text{arc tan } \frac{3}{4} = 36.9°$$

$$= \frac{100 \underline{/\theta°}}{5 \underline{/36.9°}}$$

$$= 20 \underline{/-36.9°}$$

Example (11.6):

For the circuit shown in Figure 11-13, find the total impedance.

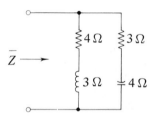

Figure 11-13

Solution:

The impedance of the branch with the capacitor is

$$\mathbf{Z}_1 = 3 - j4 \quad \theta = \text{arc tan } \frac{3}{4} = -36.9°$$

$$= 5 \underline{/36.9°}$$

The impedance of the inductive branch is

$$\mathbf{Z}_2 = 4 + j3 \quad \theta = \text{arc tan } \frac{4}{3} = 53.1°$$

$$= 5 \underline{/53.1°}$$

$$\mathbf{Z}_T = \frac{\mathbf{Z}_1 \mathbf{Z}_2}{\mathbf{Z}_1 + \mathbf{Z}_2}$$

$$= \frac{(5 \underline{/-36.9°})(5 \underline{/53.1°})}{3 - j4 + 4 + j3}$$

$$= \frac{25 \underline{/16.2°}}{7 - j1}$$

$$= \frac{25 \underline{/16.2°}}{7.1 \underline{/8.1°}} \quad \theta = \text{arc tan } \frac{7}{1} = 8.1°$$

$$= 3.52 \underline{/8.1°}$$

Example (11.7):
Find Thévenin's equivalent circuit for the circuit shown in Figure 11-14a.

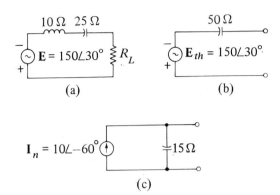

(a)

(b)

(c)

Figure 11-14

Solution :
If we remove the load R_L, the open circuit voltage is the generator voltage $E = 150 \underline{/30°}$. Looking back into the terminals where the load was connected, and replacing the generator by its ideal resistance of zero, we find

$$\mathbf{Z}_{th} = j10 - j25$$
$$= -j15$$
$$= 15 \underline{/-90°}$$

Thévenin's equivalent circuit is shown in Figure 11-14b.

Example (11.8):
Find Norton's equivalent circuit for the circuit shown in Figure 11-14a.

Solution:
The parallel impedance is the same as in the example above. The short-circuit current found by shorting the load terminals is

$$\mathbf{I}_{sc} = \frac{\mathbf{E}}{\mathbf{Z}_{th}}$$
$$= \frac{150 \underline{/30°}}{15 \underline{/-90°}}$$
$$= 10 \underline{/-60°}$$

Example (11.9):
In Figure 11-15, use superposition to determine the current through the capacitor.

Solution:
Let $E_A = 0$. The impedance seen by E_B is then

$$\mathbf{Z}_B = j5 + \frac{(-j4)(j2)}{j2 - j4}$$
$$= +j1$$

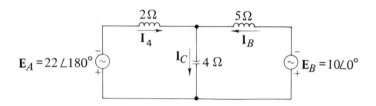

Figure 11-15

The current from E_B is

$$\mathbf{I}_B = \frac{\mathbf{E}_B}{\mathbf{Z}_B}$$

$$= \frac{10}{+j1} = \frac{10\ \underline{/0°}}{1\ \underline{/90°}}$$

$$= 10\ \underline{/-90°}$$

Current through the capacitor due to E_A is

$$\mathbf{I}'_c = (10\ \underline{/-90°})\left(\frac{2\ \underline{/90°}}{2\ \underline{/-90°}}\right)$$

$$10\ \underline{/90°}$$

Next, let $E_B = 0$. The impedance seen by E_A is then

$$\mathbf{Z}_A = j2 + \frac{(-j4)(j5)}{j5 - j4}$$

$$= -j18$$

and

$$\mathbf{I}_A = \frac{\mathbf{E}_A}{\mathbf{Z}_A}$$

$$= \frac{22\ \underline{/180°}}{18\ \underline{/-90°}}$$

$$= 1.22\ \underline{/270°}$$

Current through the capacitor due to E_A is

$$\mathbf{I}''_c = (1.22\ \underline{/270°})\left(\frac{5\ \underline{/90°}}{j5 - j4}\right)$$

$$= \frac{(1.22\ \underline{/270°})(5\ \underline{/90°})}{1\ \underline{/90°}}$$

$$= 6.10\ \underline{/270°}$$

The total current is then

$$\mathbf{I}_c = \mathbf{I}'_c + \mathbf{I}''_c$$

$$= 10 \; \underline{/90°} + 6.10 \; \underline{/270°}$$

$$= +j10 - j6.10$$

$$= +j3.9 = 3.9 \; \underline{/90°}$$

Example (11.10):

Two unknown elements are connected in series and a d-c voltage of 100 volts applied to the combination. A current of 1 amp flows in the circuits. When a source of 100 volts at 60 hertz a-c is applied to the same two terminals, the current is 0.707 amp and lags the applied voltage. What is the impedance?

Solution:

The circuit cannot have a capacitor in it because it passes d-c current. One of the elements is obviously an inductor since the current lags the applied voltage. The other element must be a resistor, since the d-c current would be infinite if there were 2 inductors in series. The value of the resistance is found by

$$R = \frac{E_{dc}}{I_{dc}}$$

$$= \frac{100}{1}$$

$$= 100 \text{ ohms}$$

The magnitude of impedance is

$$Z = \frac{E}{I}$$

$$= \frac{100}{0.707}$$

$$= 141.4 \text{ ohms}$$

but

$$Z = \sqrt{R^2 + X_L^2}$$

or

$$X_L = \sqrt{Z^2 - R^2}$$

$$= \sqrt{(141.4)^2 - (100)^2}$$

$$= 100 \text{ ohms}$$

and

$$\mathbf{Z} = R + jX_L$$

$$= 100 + j100$$

11.6   POWER IN A-C CIRCUITS

Consider any two-terminal network to which a voltage source is connected, as shown in Figure 11-16. For the sake of generality, assume the

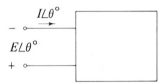

Figure 11-16

voltage applied to be $E \underline{/0°}$ and the resulting current to be $I \underline{/0°}$. The equations for instantaneous current and voltage are then given as

$$e = \sqrt{2} \, E \sin (\omega t)$$

and

$$i = \sqrt{2} \, I \sin (\omega t + \theta)$$

From these two quantities it is desirable to be able to determine the power delivered to the network.

In any circuit the instantaneous power is always given by the product of the instantaneous voltage and the instantaneous current. Thus, for Figure 11-1

$$p = ei$$
$$= [\sqrt{2} \, E \sin (\omega t)] \, [\sqrt{2} \, I \sin (\omega t + \theta)]$$
$$= 2 \, EI \, [\sin (\omega t)] \, [\sin (\omega t + \theta)]$$

By use of trigonometric identity

$$2 \sin \alpha \sin \beta = \cos (\alpha - \beta) - \cos (\alpha + \beta)$$

The above equation becomes

$$p = EI \cos \theta - EI \cos (2 \, \omega t + \theta) \qquad (11.22)$$

A look at the plot of this equation (Figure 11-17) shows the instantaneous power to be oscillating at twice the frequency of the current or voltage about an average value of $EI \cos \theta$. Thus, the average power in the network is given by

$$P = EI \cos \theta \qquad (11.23)$$

where

P = average power
E = effective voltage
I = effective current
θ = angle between the current and voltage

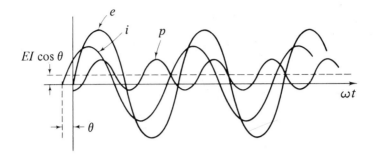

Figure 11-17

The angle θ is sometimes referred to as the *power factor angle* and cos θ is called the *power factor* of the circuit. Since all values of cos θ lie between 0 and 1, the power factor can never be greater than one. If current lags voltage in a circuit, the power factor is said to be a lagging power factor. On the other hand, if the current is leading the voltage, the power factor is referred to as a leading power factor.

In a d-c circuit, power was found by multiplying the current by the voltage. Considering a-c, only in the purely resistive circuit does the product of effective voltage times effective current yield true average power. Under those circumstances the current and voltage are in phase and the power factor is cos $\theta°$ which equals one. With a pure inductor or capacitor, the power factor angle is 90° and cos (90°) equals zero. Therefore, as was pointed out in the last chapter, no average real power is dissipated in an inductor or capacitor. The product of effective voltage times effective current in a-c circuits is referred to as apparent power and is measured in volt-amperes.

$$U = EI \qquad (11.24)$$

where

U = apparent power in volt-amperes
E = effective voltage in volts
I = effective current in amperes

In terms of apparent power, real power becomes

$$P = U \cos \theta \qquad (11.25)$$

where

P = real power in watts
U = apparent power in volt-amperes
cos θ = power factor

Since $\cos \theta$ is always less than or equal to one, the real average power is always less than or equal to the apparent power.

$$P \leq U$$

Further investigation of the inequality above led to the formulation of a discrepancy factor, measured in reactive power or VARS. Reactive volt-amperes are given by the product of the apparent power times the sine of the power factor angle.

$$\text{VARS} = U \sin \theta \qquad (11.26)$$

or

$$\text{VARS} = EI \sin \theta \qquad (11.27)$$

where

$$\text{VARS} = \text{reactive volt-amperes}$$
$$U = \text{apparent power}$$
$$\theta = \text{power factor angle}$$

The quantity $\sin \theta$ is referred to as the reactive factor (rf). Reactive power is usually considered positive for a lagging power factor and negative for a leading power factor.

A convenient way of showing the relation between real power, reactive power, and apparent power is shown in Figure 11-18.

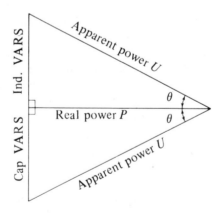

Figure 11-18

Example (11.11):

Assume the voltage applied to a certain network to be given as $100\underline{/0°}$ volts and the current in the network to be $50 \underline{/36.9°}$. Determine the real power, reactive volt-amperes, and the apparent power.

Solution:

The apparent power is the product of effective voltage times effective current.

$$U = EI$$
$$= (100)(50)$$
$$= 5000 \text{ volt-amperes}$$

The real power is given by

$$P = EI \cos \theta$$
$$= (100)\ (50) \cos (36.9°)$$
$$= 4000 \text{ watts}$$

The reactive volt-amperes are given by

$$EI \sin \theta = (100)\ (50) \sin (36.9°)$$
$$= 3000 \text{ volt-amperes reactive}$$

Example (11.12):

A wattmeter is used to measure the power in a certain network. This power is found to be 10 kilowatts. The current and voltage are also measured with an ammeter and voltmeter. The ammeter reads 20 amperes and the voltmeter reads 1000 volts. What are the apparent power, the power factor, and the reactive volt-amperes?

Solution:

The apparent power is given by

$$U = EI$$
$$= (1000)(20)$$
$$= 20,000 \text{ volt-amperes}$$

Since the true power is that measured by the wattmeter,

$$P = U \cos \theta$$

becomes

$$10,000 = 20,000 \cos \theta$$

so that

$$\cos \theta = \frac{10,000}{20,000}$$
$$= 0.5$$

The reactive volt-amperes can now be found from

$$U = \sqrt{P^2 + (\text{VARS})^2}$$

Rewriting gives

$$\text{VARS} = \sqrt{U^2 - P^2}$$
$$\text{VARS} = \sqrt{(20 \times 10^3)^2 - (10 \times 10^3)^2}$$
$$= 17.32 \times 10^3 \text{ volt-amperes reactive}$$

or the reactive volt-amperes may be found by first obtaining the angle

θ from a trigonometry table as 60° and then using

$$\text{VARS} = U \sin \theta$$
$$= (20 \times 10^3)(\sin 60°)$$
$$= (20 \times 10^3)(0.866)$$
$$= 17.32 \times 10^3 \text{ volt-amperes reactive}$$

Power is measured by a device called a *wattmeter*. This instrument has both a voltage coil and a current coil and is connected as shown in Figure 11-19. With the $\pm$ signs connected as shown, the meter will read up-scale

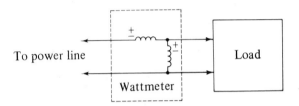

Figure 11-19

when power is being delivered to the load. If one of the coils is reversed, the meter reads up-scale when power is being delivered back toward the generator. Beside wattmeters, there are meters designed to measure reactive volt-amperes and apparent power.

11.7 POWER FACTOR CORRECTION

Because of the large number of inductive devices in use today, particularly in industry, electrical loads frequently have a lagging power factor. Under such conditions the current in the system will be greater than that required to deliver the same amount of energy at unity power factor. This can be clearly seen with the aid of Figure 11-20, which is a phasor plot of the voltage and current at the terminals of a load having a lagging power factor. The figure suggests that the currents can be broken up into two components, one in phase with the load voltage ($I_L \cos \theta$) and the other lagging the load voltage by 90° ($I_L \sin \theta$). Real power will be produced only by the in-phase component of current. The quadrature component of current is only effective in producing reactive volt-amperes. If the same power were delivered at unity power factor, the line current would only need to be $I_L \cos \theta$ rather than I_L.

The larger currents required at power factors less than unity result in a greater power loss in the resistive transmission lines. Furthermore, this requirement causes a greater voltage drop along the transmission line, thus reducing the voltage available at the load terminals.

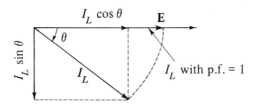

Figure 11-20

In order to keep such loss down, power companies often require that certain industrial consumers keep the power factor above a certain value. In addition, they make a charge for the reactive volt-amperes.

Power-factor correction is usually done by connecting a synchronous machine[4] as a capacitor or a bank of capacitors across the line somewhere near the load. Such capacitor action will draw a current that leads the terminal voltage by 90°, which is opposite to the inductive component of current. (See Figure 11-21.) If the capacity is large enough, the leading

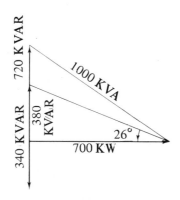

Figure 11-21

current drawn by it can be made equal to the lagging component of current drawn by the load, thus correcting the power factor to unity. However, it is not always economical to correct the power factor to unity. In some cases it may be cheaper to correct the power factor only partially and

[4]   A synchronous motor has an a-c stator and a d-c energized rotor (see Figure 18-3d). It can be made to act like a capacitive load or an inductive load by adjusting the dc excitation.

pay for a certain amount of reactive volt-amperes. It is necessary for the engineer to determine which is more economical.

When there are varying loads and a constant voltage is desired, a synchronous motor (sometimes called a synchronous capacitor when used in this manner) is connected across the line. Such a device has the property of being readily adjustable to operate at almost any leading or lagging power factor.

Example (11.13):

A 1000 KVA induction motor operates at a lagging power factor of 0.7. For the sake of economy it is desired to correct the power factor to 0.9 lag. What is the KVAR of the parallel capacitance required?

Solution:

The real power delivered to the motor is

$$P = U \cos \theta$$

$$= 1000K \ (0.7)$$

$$= 700K \text{ watts}$$

The reactive power is

$$(KVARS) = \sqrt{U^2 - P^2}$$

$$= \sqrt{(1000)^2 - (700)^2}$$

$$= 720$$

which is also the KVARS of parallel capacitance required for correction to unity power factor.

Since a capacitor can only change the reactive volt-amperes, the real power must still be 700K watts. The $\cos-\theta$ is to be 0.9 and from a trigonometric table this is seen to correspond to an angle of 26 degrees. The reactive power can then be found from

$$KVARS = P \tan \theta$$

$$= 700 \ (0.486)$$

$$= 340$$

This must then be subtracted from the reactive volt-amperes in the system to give the reactive power of the capacitor. (See Figure 11-21.)

$$\text{Capacitive } KVARS = KVARS \text{ in system} - KVARS \text{ remaining}$$

$$= 720 - 340$$

$$= 380$$

11.8 SUMMARY

In a series RL circuit the current will always lag the applied voltage by an angle which lies between $0°$ and $90°$. This angle is

$$\theta = \text{arc tan} \frac{X_L}{R} \qquad (11.1)$$

The applied voltage is

$$E = \sqrt{V_R^2 + V_L^2} \tag{11.2}$$

or

$$E = I\sqrt{R^2 + X_L^2} \tag{11.4}$$

In a series RC circuit the current will always lead the applied voltage by an angle which lies between $0°$ and $90°$. This angle is

$$\theta = \text{arc tan} \frac{X_c}{R} \tag{11.12}$$

The applied voltage is

$$E = \sqrt{V_R^2 + V_c^2} \tag{11.9}$$

or

$$E = I\sqrt{R^2 + X_c^2} \tag{11.10}$$

In a parallel RL circuit the total current will lag the applied voltage by an angle which lies between $0°$ and $90°$. This angle is

$$\theta = \text{arc tan} \frac{R}{X_L} \tag{11.8}$$

The total current is

$$I = \sqrt{I_R^2 + I_L^2} \tag{11.5}$$

or

$$I = E\sqrt{\frac{1}{R^2} + \frac{1}{X_L^2}} \tag{11.6}$$

In a parallel RC circuit the total current will lead the applied voltage by an angle between $0°$ and $90°$. This angle is

$$\theta = \text{arc tan} \frac{R}{X_c} \tag{11.16}$$

The total current is

$$I = \sqrt{I_R^2 + I_c^2} \tag{11.13}$$

A series RLC circuit acts like a series RL circuit if $X_L > X_c$ or as a series RC circuit if $X_c > X_L$.

A parallel RLC circuit acts like a parallel RL circuit if $X_c > X_L$ or as a parallel RC circuit if $X_L > X_c$.

It is convenient to express the phasors for voltages and currents as complex numbers. When this is done the ratio of voltage to current is also a complex number which is called the *impedance*. Impedances in series are combined like resistors.

$$\mathbf{Z}_T = \mathbf{Z}_1 + \mathbf{Z}_2 + \mathbf{Z}_3 + \cdots + \mathbf{Z}_n \tag{11.19}$$

Impedances in parallel are combined like resistors in parallel.

$$Z_T = \cfrac{1}{\cfrac{1}{Z_1} + \cfrac{1}{Z_2} + \cfrac{1}{Z_3} + \cdots + \cfrac{1}{Z_n}} \qquad (11.20)$$

The inverse of impedance is called *admittance*.

$$Y = \frac{1}{Z} \qquad (11.18)$$

Ohm's law for a-c circuits is

$$I = \frac{E}{Z} \qquad (11.17)$$

Using the concept of impedance it is possible to apply the same techniques to solving a-c circuits as were used for d-c circuits.

Instantaneous power is always given by the product of the instantaneous current and voltage. The *average real power* is given by

$$P = EI \cos \theta \qquad (11.23)$$

where cos θ is called the *power factor*. *Apparent power* is

$$U = EI \qquad (11.24)$$

and *reactive power* is given by

$$VARS = EI \sin \theta \qquad (11.27)$$

Reactive power causes energy loss and voltage drops in transmission lines. It is often possible to remedy this situation by connecting capacitors in parallel with loads that are normally inductive to make the power factor nearer unity.

11.9   QUESTIONS AND PROBLEMS

Questions

1. How will changing the resistance in a series *RL* circuit affect the phase angle between the current and the applied voltage?   (11.1)
2. How will changing the inductance in a series *RL* circuit affect the phase angle between the current and the applied voltage?   (11.1)
3. What is the maximum and minimum phase angle possible in a series *RL* circuit? (11.1)
4. Can the magnitude of the effective voltage across the resistor be added to the magnitude of the effective voltage accoss the inductor in a series *RL* circuit?   (11.1)
5. What is the phase relation between the current in each element of a series *RL* circuit and a parallel *RL* circuit?   (11.1)
6. What is the phase relationship between the elements of a parallel *RL* circuit?   (11.1)
7. How is the total current related to the current in each element of a parallel *RL* circuit?   (11.1)
8. How does changing the value of inductance or resistance affect the phase angle between the applied voltage and the total current?   (11.1)
9. How does a series *RC* circuit differ from a series *RL* circuit?   (11.2)

10. Does the current in a series RC circuit always lead or lag the applied voltage?   (11.2)

11. How do the voltages across the elements of the series RC circuit add to give the applied voltages?   (11.2)

12. Sketch a phasor diagram showing all the voltages and currents in a simple series RC circuit.   (11.2)

13. What is the effect of frequency on the phase angle of a series RC circuit?   (11.2)

14. Does a series RLC circuit act as an RL circuit at one frequency and as an RC circuit at another frequency? Explain.   (11.3)

15. In a series RLC circuit, is it ever possible that the voltage across the inductor could have a greater magnitude than the source voltage? Explain.   (11.3)

16. Is it ever possible to add only the magnitudes of voltages in a series RLC circuit? Explain.   (11.3)

17. Draw a complete phasor diagram showing all currents and voltages in a series RLC circuit.   (11.3)

18. How does a parallel RLC circuit differ from a series RLC circuit?   (11.4)

19. How do the currents in each element of a parallel RLC circuit add to give the total current?   (11.4)

20. Is it possible to have a higher current in the inductor or capacitor of a parallel RLC circuit than the source current? Explain.   (11.4)

21. If $X_L < X_C$ in a parallel RLC circuit, is the circuit considered capacitive or inductive?   (11.4)

22. How will a parallel RLC circuit change its characteristics as the frequency is varied from 0 to ∞?   (11.4)

23. How do complex numbers simplify a-c circuit analysis?   (11.5)

24. What does the real part of the impedance represent? What does the imaginary part represent?   (11.5)

25. How do you express sinusoidal voltages and currents as complex numbers?   (11.5)

26. How do you combine impedances in parallel?   (11.5)

27. How do you combine impedances in series?   (11.5)

28. What is Ohm's law for a-c circuits?   (11.5)

29. Do Kirchhoff's laws hold when using complex numbers to express impedance, voltage, and current?   (11.5)

30. How would you write mesh equations using the concept of impedance?   (11.5)

31. How would you write node voltage equations using impedance?   (11.5)

32. What is the general equation for average power?   (11.6)

33. How do you find the reactive power in a two-terminal network?   (11.6)

34. What is meant by the term "power factor"? What is the power factor angle?   (11.6)

35. What is the reactive power factor? How is it related to the power factor?   (11.6)

36. Draw a triangle showing the relationship between real power, reactive power, and apparent power.   (11.6)

37. What is apparent power?   (11.7)

38. What is unity power factor?   (11.6), (11.7)

39. Why is reactive power important?   (11.7)

40. Why do we often want to correct a power factor?   (11.7)

41. How do you go about correcting a power factor?   (11.7)

42. Do you always strive to get unity power factor? Why?   (11.7)

43. How does reactive power affect transmission line losses?   (11.7)

44. What is a synchronous capacitor?   (11.7)

Problems

1. A voltage of $e = 100 \sin \omega t$ is applied to a resistor and inductor in series. The resistance of the resistor is 400 ohms and the reactance of the inductor is 300 ohms. Find the current in the circuit and the voltage across each element. Draw a complete phasor diagram. (11.1)

2. The current in a series RL circuit is given by $i = 0.03 \sin \omega t$. The resistance is 800 ohms and the reactance is 600 ohms. Find all the voltages in the circuit and draw a complete phasor diagram. (11.1)

3. The voltage across the resistor in a series RL circuit is given by $v_R = 30 \sin \omega t$. The resistor has a resistance of 5000 ohms and the inductor has a reactance of 5000 ohms. Determine the current and the applied voltage. Draw a complete phasor diagram. (11.1)

4. The voltage across the inductor in a series RL circuit is given by $v_L = 25 \sin \omega t$. If $R = 1200$ ohms and $X_L = 900$ ohms, what is the current in the circuit and the applied voltage? Draw a complete phasor diagram. (11.1)

5. In a certain series RL circuit the voltage across the resistor is 15 volts and the voltage across the inductor is 20 volts. What is the applied voltage? (11.1)

6. In a certain series RL circuit the voltage applied is 150 volts. The voltage across the resistor is 90 volts. What is the voltage across the inductor? (11.1)

7. In a certain series RL circuit the voltage applied is 35 volts. If the voltage across the inductor is 28 volts, what is the voltage across the resistor? (11.1)

8. In a certain series RL circuit the phase angle between the current and applied voltage is 30°. What is the ratio of resistance to reactance in the circuit? (11.1)

9. In a certain series RL circuit the ratio of reactance to resistance is 0.707. What is the phase angle between the applied voltage and the current? (11.1)

10. The phase angle for a certain series RL circuit is 60°. If the resistance is 22,000 ohms, what is the inductive reactance? (11.1)

11. Express the phase angle for a series RL circuit in terms of an arc sine. (11.1)

12. Express the phase angle for a series RL circuit in terms of an arc cosine. (11.1)

13. The current in a series RL circuit is measured as 30 ma. The resistance is 10 kΩ. If the phase angle is 45°, what is the reactance and the voltage across the reactance? (11.1)

14. In a series RL circuit the voltage across the inductor is 30 volts and the voltage across the resistor is 100 volts. What is the phase angle between the applied voltage and the current? (11.1)

15. The current in the resistor of a parallel RL circuit is 15 ma. The current in the inductor is 20 ma. What is the source current? (11.2)

16. The source current to a parallel RL circuit is 100 amp. The current in the resistor is 30 amp. What is the current in the inductor? (11.2)

17. A voltage of 100 volts is applied to a parallel RL circuit. The resistance is 10K and the inductive reactance is 10K. What are the currents in each element and the total source current? (11.2)

18. A voltage of $e = 300 \sin(\omega t + 20°)$ is applied to a parallel RL circuit with 600 ohms resistance and 800 ohms reactance. What is the total current and the current in each element? Draw a complete phasor diagram. (11.2)

19. A current of $i = 5 \sin \omega t$ flows in the resistor of a parallel RL circuit. If the resistance is 5000 ohms and the reactance is 10K, what is the current in the inductance and the source current? (11.2)

20. A current of 866 ma flows through the resistive branch of a parallel RL circuit. A current of 0.5 amp flows in the other branch. What is the phase angle between the voltage and the source current? (11.1)

21. The ratio of reactance to resistance in a certain parallel RL circuit is 1.6. What is the phase angle between the source voltage and source current? (11.1)

22. The phase angle for a certain parallel *RL* circuit is 30°. If the resistance is 5 kΩ, what is the inductive reactance? (11.1)

23. Express the phase angle of a parallel *RL* circuit in terms of an arc sine. (11.1)

24. Express the phase angle of a parallel *RL* circuit in terms of an arc cosine. (11.1)

25. The voltage applied to a series *RC* circuit is 150 volts. The voltage across the capacitor is 90 volts. What is the voltage across the resistor? (11.2)

26. The voltage across a capacitor in a series *RC* circuit is 20 volts. The voltage across the resistor is 30 volts. What is the applied voltage? (11.2)

27. The voltage applied to a series *RC* circuit is $e = 100 \sin \omega t$. The resistance is 30 ohms and the reactance 40 ohms. What is the current and the voltage across each element? Draw a complete phasor diagram. (11.2)

28. The voltage across a capacitor in a series *RC* circuit is $v_c = 15 \sin(\omega t + 30°)$. If the capacitive reactance is 50 ohms and the resistance is 20 ohms, what is the applied voltage? Draw a complete phasor diagram. (11.2)

29. In a certain series *RC* circuit the current leads the voltage by 30°. The resistance is 220 kΩ. What is the capacitive reactance? (11.2)

30. In a certain series *RC* circuit the current leads the applied voltage by 60°. The voltage across the resistor is 20 volts. What is the voltage across the capacitor and the applied voltage? (11.2)

31. The current in the resistive branch of a parallel *RC* circuit is 10 amp. The current in the capacitor is 5 amp. What is the source current? (11.2)

32. The source current to a parallel *RC* circuit is 100 ma. The current in the resistive branch is 25 ma. What is the current in the capacitor? (11.2)

33. The source current to a parallel *RC* circuit is $i = 0.005 \sin(\omega t + 70°)$. The resistance is 1500 ohms and the capacitive reactance is 1500 ohms. What is the applied voltage? Draw a complete phasor diagram. (11.2)

34. The voltage applied to a parallel *RC* circuit is $e = 100 \sin \omega t$. The source current is $i = 0.02 \sin(\omega t + 60°)$. What is the resistance and the capacitive reactance? (11.2)

35. The voltage applied to a parallel *RC* circuit is 1000 volts. The source current is 500 ma. If the current leads the voltage by 45°, what is the resistance and the capacitive reactance? (11.2)

36. A series *RLC* circuit is composed of a 600 ohm resistor, a 1000 ohm capacitive reactance, and an 1800 ohm inductive reactance. If the applied voltage is $e = 141 \sin \omega t$, what is the current in the circuit and the voltage across each element? Draw a complete phasor diagram. (11.3)

37. The current in a series *RLC* circuit is $i = 282 \sin \omega t$. The resistance is 1800 ohms, the capacitive reactance 5400 ohms, and the inductive reactance 3000 ohms. What are the voltages across each element and the applied voltage? Draw a complete phasor diagram. (11.3)

38. A certain series *RLC* circuit has the capacitive reactance equal to the inductive reactance. The applied voltage is one volt and the resistor is one ohm. What is the current? If the inductive reactance is 10^6 ohms, what is the voltage across the inductor? What is the voltage across the capacitor? Does Kirchhoff's voltage law apply here? Explain. (11.3)

39. The voltage across the inductor in a series *RLC* circuit measures 12 volts. The voltage across the capacitor measures 8 volts, and the voltage across the resistor measures 3 volts. What is the applied voltage? (11.3)

40. The voltage across the capacitor in a series *RLC* circuit is 50 volts. The reactance of the capacitor is 5000 ohms. The resistance is 1600 ohms, and the inductive reactance is 3800 ohms. What is the current and the voltage across the resistor and the capacitor together? What is the phase angle? (11.3)

41. The phase angle between the source current and source voltage is 45° for a series *RLC* circuit. If the resistance is 50 kΩ and the inductive reactance is 400kΩ, what is the capacitive reactance? Will the current lead the source voltage or lag the source voltage? (11.3)

42. The current in the resistive branch of a parallel *RLC* circuit is 5 amp. The current in the capacitive branch is 10 amp and in the inductive branch 5 amp. What is the total source current?   (11.4)

43. The voltage across a parallel *RLC* circuit is $e = 282 \sin \omega t$. The resistance is 500 ohms, the capacitive reactance 900 ohms, and the inductive reactance 400 ohms. What are the currents in each element and the total current? Draw a complete phasor diagram. (11.4)

44. In a certain parallel *RLC* circuit the capacitive reactance is equal to the inductive reactance. What is the phase angle between the current and the voltage? Explain. (11.4)

45. If the applied voltage in Problem 44 is 100 volts, the resistance is 10^4 ohms, and the reactances are each one ohm, what is the current in each element and the total current? (11.4)

46. A resistor of 3 ohms and a capacitor having a reactance of 4 ohms are connected in series. Express the impedance in polar form.   (11.5)

47. What is the admittance in Problem 46?   (11.5)

48. A 10 ohm resistor is connected in parallel with an inductive reactance of 10 ohms. What is the equivalent impedance of the combination?   (11.5)

49. An inductor of 10 ohms reactance and a capacitor of 10 ohms reactance are connected in series. What is the equivalent reactance? What is the equivalent reactance of the combination in parallel?   (11.5)

50. Determine the equivalent impedance of the circuit in Figure 11-22.   (11.5)

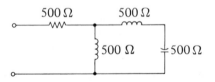

Figure 11-22

51. Repeat Problem 50 for Figure 11-23.   (11.5)

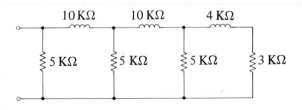

Figure 11-23

52. Repeat Problem 50 for Figure 11-24. (11.5)

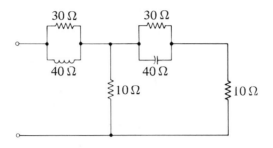

Figure 11-24

53. Repeat Problem 50 for Figure 11-25. (11.5)

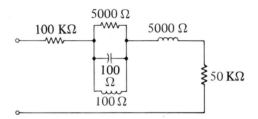

Figure 11-25

54. Determine the equivalent admittance for the circuit in Figure 11-26. (11.5)

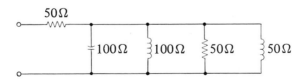

Figure 11-26

55. If a voltage of $e = 141 \sin \omega t$ is applied to the terminals of Figure 11-22, what is the current? (11.5)
56. If the current in an impedance of $3 + j6$ ohms is $15 \underline{/0°}$, what is the voltage across the impedance? (11.5)
57. An impedance is given as $250 \underline{/-30°}$. What are the resistance and reactance? (11.5)

58. In the circuit shown in Figure 11-27, calculate the applied voltage.   (11.5)

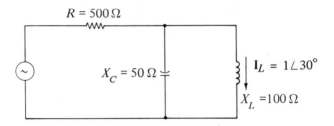

$R = 500 \, \Omega$

$X_C = 50 \, \Omega$

$I_L = 1 \angle 30°$

$X_L = 100 \, \Omega$

Figure 11-27

59. In the circuit shown in Figure 11-28, calculate the voltage across the capacitor C_1.   (11.5)

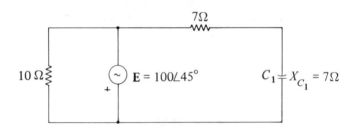

$7 \, \Omega$

$10 \, \Omega$

$E = 100 \angle 45°$

$C_1 \quad X_{C_1} = 7 \, \Omega$

Figure 11-28

60. In the circuit shown in Figure 11-29, calculate the voltage across the inductor L_1.

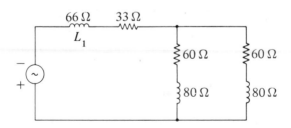

$66 \, \Omega$ $33 \, \Omega$

L_1

$60 \, \Omega$ $60 \, \Omega$

$80 \, \Omega$ $80 \, \Omega$

Figure 11-29

61. In the circuit shown in Figure 11-30, calculate the current in R_L.   (11.5)

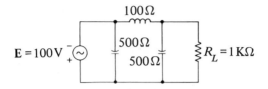

Figure 11-30

62. Find Thévenin's equivalent circuit for Figure 11-30.   (11.5)
63. Find Norton's equivalent circuit for Figure 11-30.   (11.5)
64. Use superposition to find the current in R_3 of Figure 11-31.   (11.5)

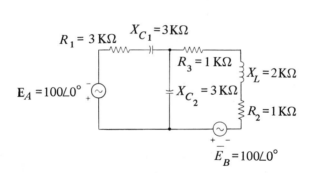

Figure 11-31

65. Write a complete set of mesh equations to solve the circuit in Figure 11-32.   (11.5)

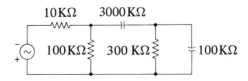

Figure 11-32

66. Repeat Problem 65 for Figure 11-33. (11.5)

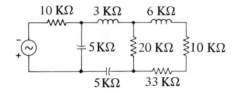

Figure 11-33

67. Solve for the mesh currents I_1 and I_2 of Figure 11-34. (11.5)

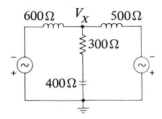

Figure 11-34

68. Write a complete set of node voltage equations for the circuit in Figure 11-32. (11.5)
69. Repeat Problem 68 for Figure 11-33. (11.5)
70. Solve for the voltage V_x in Figure 11-34 using the methods of mesh currents. (11.5)
71. Calculate the real power, reactive power, and apparent power for Figure 11-35. (11.6)

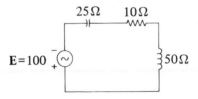

Figure 11-35

72. When a voltage of 220 volts is applied to a two-terminal network, the current is measured as 10 amp. What is the apparent power? If the real power is measured as 1000 watts, what are the power factor and the reactive power? (11.6)
73. The apparent power delivered by a source is 1000 VA. If the real power is 600 watts, what is the reactive power? (11.6)

74. The reactive power delivered to a circuit is 10 KVARS. The source voltage is 3300 volts and the current is 10 amp. What is the power factor and what is the real power? (11.6)

75. The voltage applied to a certain network is $e = 150 \sin \omega t$, and the current is given by $i = 10 \sin(\omega t = 45°)$. What are the apparent power, real power, and reactive power? (11.6)

76. In Problem 75, what is the instantaneous power? (11.6)

77. The impedance of a load is $5 - j6$. If the power factor is to be unity, what is the capacitive reactance that must be placed in parallel with the load? (11.7)

78. A 500 KVA load operates at 0.6 lagging power factor. For the sake of economy it is desired to correct the power factor to unity. What KVAR of parallel capacitance is necessary? (11.7)

79. In Problem 78, what KVAR of parallel capacitance is necessary if the power factor is only corrected to 0.9 lagging? (11.7)

80. A 500 watt load is connected in parallel with a 1 KVA induction motor that has a lagging power factor of 0.7. What is the power factor of the combined load and what KVA capacitance must be placed in parallel to correct the power factor to unity? (1.7)

12

Frequency-Selective Circuits

The reactance of a capacitor or inductor was found to depend on the frequency of the applied voltage or current. This implies that *every circuit containing an inductor or capacitor is frequency-selective*. That is, its response depends upon frequency. Such networks are sometimes referred to as *filters* and find important application in all areas of electricity and electronics. Every time we tune in a radio station or television station we are using a frequency-selective network. The ability to crowd more than one conversation onto the same pair of telephone wires is possible only because of filters. In some industrial manufacturing plants machine switches are controlled via a system of filter networks. Frequency-selective networks are one of the most important classes of electrical networks. In this chapter we will be concerned with some of the more basic *LC*, *RC*, and *RL* filter networks.

12.1 SERIES RESONANCE

One of the most basic filters is the series resonant circuit. By definition the series *RLC* circuit in Figure 12-1 is said to be resonant when the capacitive reactance is equal to the inductive reactance.

$$\frac{1}{2\pi fC} = 2\pi fL \qquad (12.1)$$

From Equation 12.1 the frequency at which resonance occurs is given by

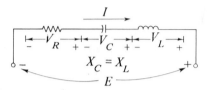

Figure 12-1

$$f_r = \frac{1}{2\pi\sqrt{LC}} \tag{12.2}$$

Since the resonant frequency is inversely proportional to the square root of the LC product, there are an infinite number of combinations of L and C that will yield the same resonant frequency.

The magnitude of the current in the series circuit in Figure 12-1 is given by

$$I = \frac{E}{\sqrt{R^2 + \left(2\pi fL - \frac{1}{2\pi fC}\right)^2}} \tag{12.3}$$

At resonance this reduces to

$$I_r = \frac{E}{R} \tag{12.4}$$

That is, at resonance the source sees only the series resistance in the circuit and thus the current and voltage at the source are in phase.

The voltage across the capacitor at resonance is given by

$$\mathbf{V}_C = \mathbf{I}_r X_C \underline{/-90°} \tag{12.5}$$

and the voltage across the inductor is given by

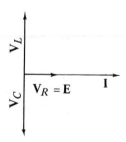

Figure 12-2

$$\mathbf{V}_L = \mathbf{I}_r X_L \underline{/90°} \qquad\qquad (12.6)$$

Equations 12.5 and 12.6 show that the voltages across both the capacitor and the inductor are equal in magnitude but opposite in direction. A vector diagram for the circuit at resonance is shown in Figure 12-2.

Note that it is possible to have a voltage across the inductor and the capacitor which is greater than the source voltage. This shown in the example below,

Example (12.1):

> In Figure 12-1, $R = 1$ ohm, $X_c = 10,000$ ohms, and $X_L = 10,000$ ohms. The source voltage is 1 volt. Determine the current and voltage for each element in the circuit.

Solution:

> The current at resonance is

$$I_r = \frac{E_s}{R}$$

$$= \frac{1}{1}$$

$$= 1 \text{ amp}$$

The voltage across the resistor is

$$V_R = I_r R$$

$$= 1 \text{ volt}$$

The voltage across the capacitor is

$$V_C = I_r X_C$$

$$= (1)\,(10,000)$$

$$= 10,000 \text{ volts}$$

and lags the current by 90°.
The voltage across the inductor is

$$V_L = I_r X_L$$

$$= (1)\,(10,000)$$

$$= 10,000 \text{ volts}$$

and leads the current by 90°.

The sum of the voltages around the loop is still zero since the voltages across the inductor and the capacitor are of opposite polarity.

12.2 SERIES RESONANCE CURVES

At frequencies below resonance, the series *RLC* circuit becomes capacitive, for the capacitive reactance becomes greater than the inductive reactance. On the other hand, at frequencies above resonance, the inductive reactance is greater than the capacitive reactance and the circuit is inductive.

It is of interest here to plot the magnitude of the current in the resonant circuit as a function of frequency. This plot is shown in Figure 12-3 with

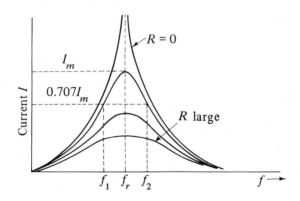

Figure 12-3

several values of series resistance R. It is referred to as a selectivity curve. At zero frequency, the current is zero because of the capacitor. At an infinite frequency it is again zero because of the inductor. The maximum value of current is at resonance and is given by Equation 12.4.

The series resonant circuit is essentially a band-pass filter, that is, it passes a certain group of frequencies while rejecting all others. The ideal band-pass filter would have characteristics as shown in Figure 12-4.

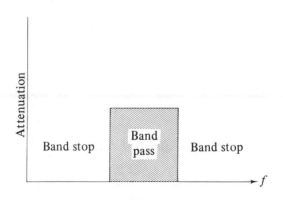

Figure 12-4

However, like most real things in life, there is no such thing as a perfect band-pass filter.

The band-pass or band-width of the series resonant circuit is considered to be the band of frequencies which lie between the two points where the current drops to 0.707 the maximum value at resonance. (See Figure 12-3.) Those frequencies outside the band-pass comprise the band-stop region.

Figure 12-3 shows the effect of resistance in the circuit. With no resistance in the circuit it is a single frequency-selective circuit with infinite current at resonance. If more resistance is added, the band-width becomes larger but the maximum current at resonance decreases. Thus, the series resistance is important in determining the maximum current in the circuit and the band-width of the circuit.

It is of interest to determine how the voltage across the three elements in the series circuit varies with frequency. The voltage across the resistance varies in exactly the same manner as the current in the circuit reaching its maximum at resonance, since it is the current multiplied by a constant value R. A plot of V_C versus frequency is shown in Figure 12-5. This figure

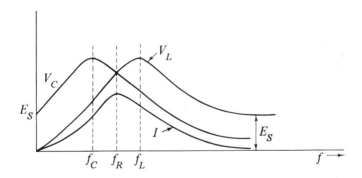

Figure 12-5

shows that V_C begins with the source voltage E_S at zero frequency and increases to its maximum at a frequency f_C below the resonant frequency. The voltage across the capacitor then decreases to zero at infinite frequency. The frequency f_C at which V_C is maximum can be determined by methods of calculus and is found to be

$$f_C = \frac{1}{2\pi} \sqrt{\frac{1}{LC} - \frac{R^2}{2L^2}} \qquad (12.7)$$

Note that when $R = 0$, Equation 12.7 becomes the equation for the resonant frequency. In other words, the smaller the resistance in the circuit, the closer f_C is to f_r.

Figure 12-5 also shows the plot of the voltage across the inductor as a function of frequency. At zero frequency the voltage is zero and then increases to the frequency f_L where it reaches a maximum value. It then decreases to the value of the source voltage E_S. The frequency at which maximum voltage occurs is given by

$$f_L = \frac{1}{2\pi \sqrt{LC - \dfrac{R^2C^2}{2}}} \tag{12.8}$$

which again reduces to the equation for f_r when $R = 0$.

Example (12.2):
> Calculate the resonant frequency, the frequencies f_L and f_C for a series circuit with $R = 100$ kΩ, $C = 5$ pf and $L = 50$ mh.

Solution:
> From Equation (12.2)

$$f_r = \frac{1}{2\pi\sqrt{LC}}$$

$$= \frac{1}{2\pi\sqrt{(5 \times 10^{-2})(5 \times 10^{-12})}}$$

$$= \frac{0.159}{5 \times 10^{-7}}$$

$$= 3.2 \times 10^{-5} \text{ cps or 320 Khz}$$

From Equation 12.7

$$f_C = \frac{1}{2\pi}\sqrt{\frac{1}{LC} - \frac{R^2}{2L^2}}$$

$$= \frac{1}{2\pi}\sqrt{\frac{1}{25 \times 10^{-14}} - \frac{10^{10}}{2 \times 25 \times 10^{-4}}}$$

$$= 0.159(2 \times 10^{12})$$

$$= 224 \text{ Khz}$$

From Equation 12.8

$$f_L = \frac{1}{2\pi\sqrt{LC - \dfrac{R^2C^2}{2}}}$$

$$= \frac{1}{2\pi\sqrt{25 \times 10^{-14} - \dfrac{(10^{10})(25 \times 10^{-24})}{2}}}$$

$$= \frac{0.159}{\sqrt{12.5 \times 10^{-14}}}$$

$$= 449 \text{ Khz}$$

12.3   FIGURE OF MERIT

The figure of merit or quality factor Q of an electrical circuit is defined as

$$Q = 2\pi \left(\frac{\text{max energy stored}}{\text{energy dissipated/cycle}}\right) \qquad (12.9)$$

and is a measure of the efficiency of energy storage in a circuit. If Equation 12.9 is multiplied by f in both the numerator and denominator it becomes

$$Q = \frac{\text{max energy stored}}{\text{avg power dissipated}} \qquad (12.10)$$

Any real inductor has resistance due to the wire used in forming the inductor. Therefore, we can represent the real inductor by an equivalent circuit consisting of the ideal inductor and the ideal resistor in series as shown in Figure 12-6.

R_S $\qquad$ L

Figure 12-6

The maximum energy stored in the inductor's magnetic field is given by 1/2 the maximum current through the inductor times the inductance L_1 (Equation 7.29), while the average power dissipated in the resistor R is given by 1/2 the square of the maximum current times the resistance. Thus, we have for the quality factor of the circuit in Figure 12-6

$$Q = \frac{\omega\left(\frac{1}{2}LI^2_{\text{max}}\right)}{\frac{1}{2}I_{\text{max}}^2 R}$$

$$= \frac{\omega L}{R} \qquad (12.11)$$

That is, the Q is the ratio of the inductive reactance to the resistance in the circuit. If the resistor were connected in parallel to the inductor, the Q would be

$$Q = \frac{R}{\omega L} \qquad (12.12)$$

This is left for the student to verify. (Problem 12.12.)

For a capacitor and resistor in series

$$Q = \frac{1}{\omega CR} \qquad (12.13)$$

while for a capacitor and resistor in parallel

$$Q = \omega CR \qquad (12.14)$$

The inverse of Equation 12.14 is often called the *dissipation factor* for a capacitor.

The quality factor of the inductor is important in determining the selectivity of a resonant circuit, for the higher the Q, the better the selectivity. A look at Figure 12-3 shows this to be true for the series circuit, since L is constant and R is varied to obtain the different curves. Lower R in this case means higher Q. It will be shown in the next section that Q affects the selectivity of the parallel circuit in the same way.

The value of the current in the series circuit is given by Equation 12.3. At the frequencies f_1 and f_2 this current is by definition 0.707 times the current at resonance. This means that the denominator divided by R must equal $\sqrt{2}$ in magnitude at both f_1 and f_2.

$$\sqrt{R^2 + \left(2\pi f_1 L - \frac{1}{2\pi f_1 C}\right)^2} \Big/ R = \sqrt{2}$$

$$\sqrt{R^2 + \left(2\pi f_2 L - \frac{1}{2\pi f_2 C}\right)^2} \Big/ R = \sqrt{2}$$

or

$$\sqrt{1 + \frac{(X_L - X_C)^2}{R^2}} = \sqrt{2}$$

The only way this can be true is when

$$\frac{|X_L - X_C|}{R} = 1$$

or, stated in another way

$$|X_L - X_C| = R \tag{12.15}$$

Above resonance, we may write Equation 12.15 as

$$2\pi f_2 L - \frac{1}{2\pi f_2 C} = R \tag{12.16}$$

and below resonance it becomes

$$\frac{1}{2\pi f_1 C} - 2\pi f_1 L = R \tag{12.17}$$

Solving Equation 12.17 for $\frac{1}{2\pi C}$, we have

$$\frac{1}{2\pi C} = (R + 2\pi f_1 L) f_1 \tag{12.18}$$

Substituting Equation 12.18 into 12.16 and solving for $f_2 - f_1$, we obtain

$$f_2 - f_1 = \frac{R}{2\pi L} \tag{12.19}$$

Q at resonance is defined as

$$Q = \frac{2\pi f_r L}{R}$$

so Equation 12.19 can be written in terms of Q as

$$f_2 - f_1 = \frac{f_r}{Q} \tag{12.20}$$

Thus, the band-width is inversely proportional to the Q and directly proportional to the resonant frequency of the series circuit.

12.4 PARALLEL RESONANCE

A parallel circuit containing capacitance, inductance, and resistance, as shown in Figure 12-7, is said to be resonant when the susceptance

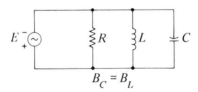

$$B_C = B_L$$

Figure 12-7

part of the admittance is equal to zero.

$$B_C - B_L = 0 \tag{12.21}$$

Applying Equation 12.21 to Figure 12-7

$$2\pi fC - \frac{1}{2\pi fL} = 0$$

and then solving for the resonant frequency f_r, we obtain

$$f_r = \frac{1}{2\pi\sqrt{LC}}$$

just in the series resonant case.

Since the susceptance of the capacitor and inductor are equal, the current in the capacitor branch of the parallel circuit and in the inductor branch are of equal magnitude. However, the two currents are $180°$ out of phase as shown in Figure 12-8 and therefore cancel each other. The source current at resonance is only the current taken by the resistor.

$$I_r = \frac{E}{R}$$

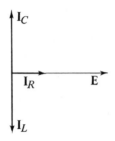

Figure 12-8

A more realistic parallel resonant circuit is shown in Figure 12-9. Here the resistance is considered to be the series resistance of the coil.

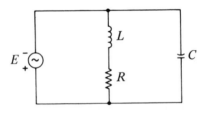

Figure 12-9

In this case the capacitive susceptance is given by

$$B_C = 2\pi fC$$

and the susceptance of the inductive branch is given by

$$B_L = \frac{2\pi fL}{R^2 + (2\pi fL)^2}$$

At resonance, from Equation 12.21

$$2\pi fC = \frac{2\pi fL}{R^2 + (2\pi fL)^2}$$

Solving this equation for the resonant frequency, we have

$$f_r = \frac{1}{2\pi\sqrt{LC}}\sqrt{1 - \frac{CR^2}{L}} \qquad (12.22)$$

Note that the resonant frequency is dependent on R. However, for many cases R is small enough that it may be neglected in the calculation for the resonant frequency. Equation 12.22 then becomes the same as Equation 12.2.

In the parallel resonant circuit the maximum current in the capacitor occurs at infinite frequency since the reactance is zero at an infinite frequency.

Curves of the source current versus frequency for a parallel resonant circuit are shown in Figure 12-10. Note again how the resistance affects

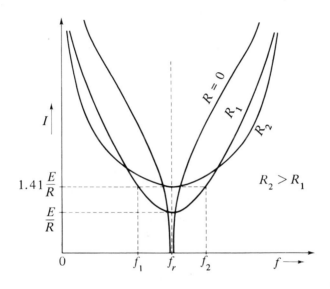

Figure 12-10

the band-width in a manner similar to that of the series resonant circuit. (See Problem 23.)

A parallel resonant circuit is essentially a band rejection filter. The ideal characteristics of a band rejection filter are shown in Figure 12-11.

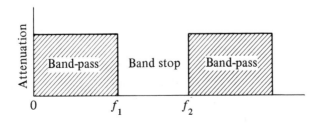

Figure 12-11

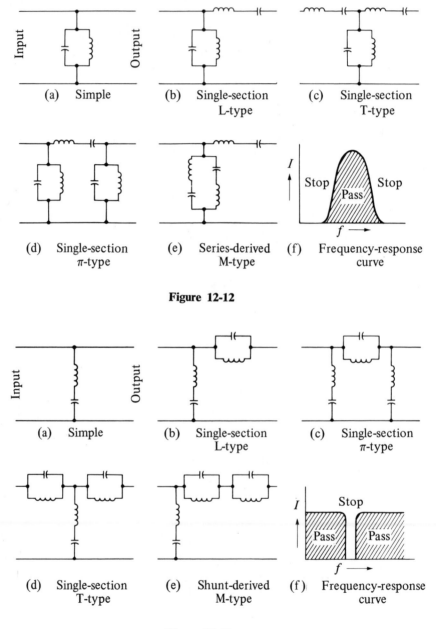

(a)   Simple

(b)   Single-section
L-type

(c)   Single-section
T-type

(d)   Single-section
π-type

(e)   Series-derived
M-type

(f)   Frequency-response
curve

Figure 12-12

(a)   Simple

(b)   Single-section
L-type

(c)   Single-section
π-type

(d)   Single-section
T-type

(e)   Shunt-derived
M-type

(f)   Frequency-response
curve

Figure 12-13

12.5 *LC* FILTERS

Combinations of series resonant circuits and parallel resonant circuits can be used to get better selection or rejection characteristics and obtain proper impedance matching between source and load. Some possibilities are shown in Figures 12-12 and 12-13.

Combinations of *L* and *C* may also be used to make two other types of filters, namely the low-pass and high-pass filter. The characteristics of the low-pass filter are given in Figure 12-14 and those of the high-pass

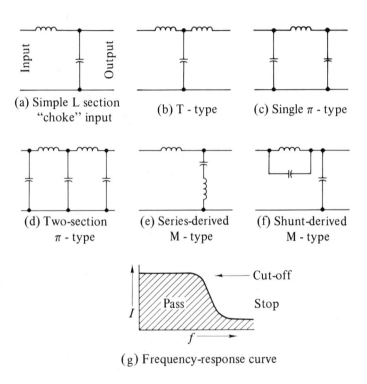

(a) Simple L section "choke" input

(b) T - type

(c) Single π - type

(d) Two-section π - type

(e) Series-derived M - type

(f) Shunt-derived M - type

(g) Frequency-response curve

Figure 12-14

filter in Figure 12-15. Some simple high- and low-pass filters are also shown in Figures 12-14 and 12-15.

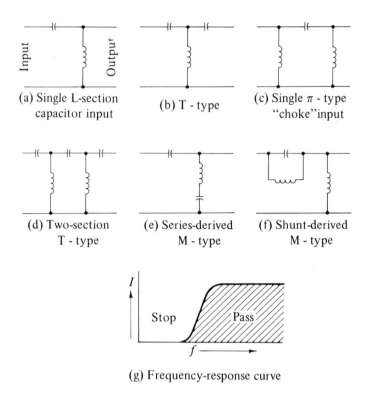

(a) Single L-section
capacitor input

(b) T - type

(c) Single π - type
"choke" input

(d) Two-section
T - type

(e) Series-derived
M - type

(f) Shunt-derived
M - type

Stop   Pass

(g) Frequency-response curve

Figure 12-15

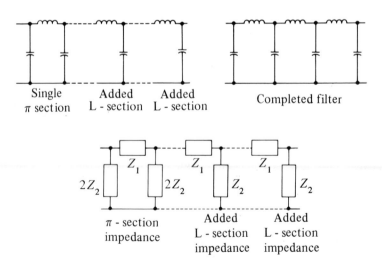

Single
π section

Added
L - section

Added
L - section

Completed filter

$2Z_2$ Z_1 $2Z_2$ Z_1 Z_2 Z_1 Z_2

π - section
impedance

Added
L - section
impedance

Added
L - section
impedance

Figure 12-16

(a) Band-pass sections

Circuit	Formulas	Notes
L_1, C_1 series; L_2, C_2 shunt (parallel)	$L_1 = \dfrac{R}{\pi(f_2-f_1)} \qquad L_2 = \left(\dfrac{f_2-f_1}{4\pi f_1 f_2}\right)R$ $C_1 = \dfrac{f_2-f_1}{4\pi f_2 f_1 R} \qquad C_2 = \dfrac{1}{\pi(f_2-f_1)R}$	f_1 = Lower cut-off freq. f_2 = Upper cut-off freq.
L_1, C_1 series; C_2 shunt	$L_1 = \dfrac{R}{\pi(f_2-f_1)} \qquad C_2 = \dfrac{1}{\pi(f_1+f_2)R}$ $C_1 = \dfrac{f_2-f_1}{4\pi f_2 f_1 R}$	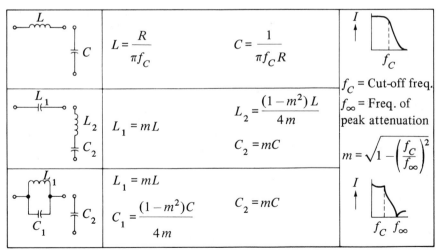 I vs f, $f_1\ f_2$
C_1 series; L_2, C_2 shunt	$C_1 = \dfrac{f_1+f_2}{4\pi f_1 f_2 R} \qquad L_2 = \dfrac{f_2-f_1}{4\pi f_1 f_2}$ $C_2 = \dfrac{f_1}{\pi f_2(f_2-f_1)R}$	R = Nominal terminating resistance

(a) Band-pass sections

(b) Band stop sections

Circuit	Formulas	Notes
L_1, C_1 parallel series; L_2, C_2 shunt	$L_1 = \dfrac{(f_2-f_1)R}{\pi f_1 f_2} \qquad L_2 = \dfrac{R}{4\pi(f_2-f_1)}$ $C_1 = \dfrac{1}{4\pi(f_2-f_1)R} \qquad C_2 = \dfrac{f_2-f_1}{\pi f_1 f_2 R}$	I vs f, $f_1\ f_2$

(b) Band stop sections

(c) Low-pass sections

Circuit	Formulas	Notes
L series; C shunt	$L = \dfrac{R}{\pi f_C} \qquad\qquad C = \dfrac{1}{\pi f_C R}$	I vs f, f_C
L_1, C_1 series; L_2, C_2 shunt	$L_1 = mL \qquad L_2 = \dfrac{(1-m^2)L}{4m}$ $\qquad\qquad\quad C_2 = mC$	f_C = Cut-off freq. f_∞ = Freq. of peak attenuation $m = \sqrt{1-\left(\dfrac{f_C}{f_\infty}\right)^2}$
L_1 series; C_1, C_2 shunt	$L_1 = mL \qquad\qquad C_2 = mC$ $C_1 = \dfrac{(1-m^2)C}{4m}$	I vs f, $f_C\ f_\infty$

(c) Low-pass sections

Figure 12-17

253

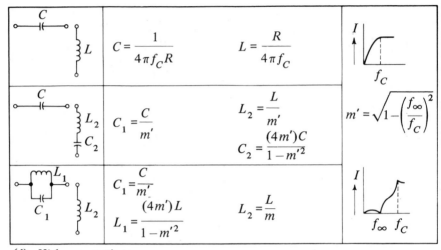

(d) High-pass sections

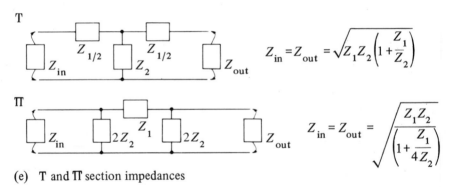

(e) T and π section impedances

Figure 12-17 (Cont'd)

Filters can be designed by sectioning as shown in Figure 12-16. Each section is then designed using the formulas given in Figure 12-17. During the design a compromise often has to be made between the desired impedance values and the necessary frequency response. If the specifications call for a band-width or cut-off frequencies which cannot be met by one section, additional sections can be added. Computer techniques have simplified the mechanics of filter design and made possible better quality filters.

12.6 *RC* AND *RL* FILTERS

Figure 12-18 shows two simple *RC* filter networks. The circuit in Figure 12-18a is a low-pass filter. At the low frequencies, the reactance

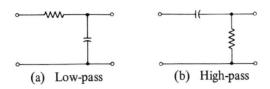

(a) Low-pass   (b) High-pass

Figure 12-18

of the shunt capacitor is large, while at the high frequencies it becomes small, thereby reducing the output voltage.

The circuit shown in Figure 12-18b is a high-pass filter. Here the capacitor is connected between the input and output terminals so that it offers a small opposition to high frequencies, but blocks out the lower frequencies.

Figure 12-19b shows a simple RL high-pass filter and Figure 12-19a

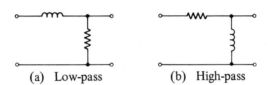

(a) Low-pass   (b) High-pass

Figure 12-19

illustrates an RL low-pass filter. The principle of operation is the same as in the RC cases. The half-power frequencies for these networks are obtained by writing an equation for the ratio of output to input voltage and then determining at what frequency this ratio is equal to 0.707 times its maximum value. (See Problem 26.) For the RC networks above, the half-power frequencies are given by

$$f_0 = \frac{1}{2\,\pi\,RC} \tag{12.23}$$

For the RL networks above, the half-power frequencies are

$$f_0 = \frac{1}{2\,\pi\,R/L} \tag{12.24}$$

RL and RC networks like those just discussed are frequently used in coupling networks and tone control circuits in electronic amplifiers.

An *RC* filter which is frequently used in electronics is the bridged T circuit shown in Figure 12-20. It is frequently called a notch filter because of its selective frequency response characteristics.

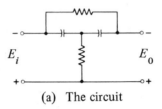

(a) The circuit

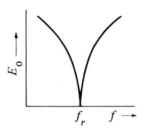

(b) The frequency response

Figure 12-20

12.7 SUMMARY

All circuits containing inductance or capacitance are frequency-selective. Frequency-selective networks are called *filters*.

A *series resonant* circuit is basically a band-pass filter. Resonance of a series *RLC* circuit occurs when the reactive portion of its impedance is equal to zero. Its resonant frequency is

$$f_r = \frac{1}{2\pi\sqrt{LC}} \tag{12.2}$$

At resonance, the current is maximum and is given by

$$I_r = \frac{E}{R} \tag{12.4}$$

The voltage across the capacitor, however, reaches its maximum below the resonant frequency, while the voltage across the inductor reaches its maximum above resonance.

The quality factor or figure of merit Q is defined as

$$Q = 2\pi\left(\frac{\text{max. energy stored}}{\text{energy dissipated/cycle}}\right) \qquad (12.9)$$

For an inductor with a series resistance, the Q is given by

$$Q = \frac{\omega L}{R} \qquad (12.11)$$

The band-width of a resonant circuit is given by

$$f_2 - f_1 = \frac{f_r}{Q} \qquad (12.20)$$

where Q is the quality factor of the inductor.

Parallel resonance occurs when the susceptance part of the admittance is equal to zero. If the resistance in the inductive branch is small, the resonant frequency is given by the same equation as for series resonance. If the resistance is not negligible

$$f_r = \frac{1}{2\pi\sqrt{LC}}\sqrt{1 - \frac{CR^2}{L}} \qquad (12.22)$$

The band-width of a parallel resonant circuit is affected by Q in the same way as a series resonant circuit.

Various combinations of series resonant circuits and parallel resonant circuits can be used to get better filter characteristics and provide better impedance matches.

Simple combinations of resistance and capacitance or resistance and inductance can be used as low-pass and high-pass filters. Such networks are frequently used in the coupling between stages in electronic amplifiers and in tone control circuitry.

The bridged T network is an RC notch filter often used in electronic circuits. It is useful in rejecting a single frequency.

12.8 QUESTIONS AND PROBLEMS

Questions

1. What is a filter? (Introduction)
2. What is series resonance? (12.1)
3. What is the impedance of a series resonant circuit?   (12.1)
4. What effect does resistance have on a series resonant circuit? (12.1)
5. In a series resonant cirucit, are the voltages across the inductor and capacitor maximum at the same time the current is maximum? Explain. (12.2)
6. In a series resonant circuit, is it ever possible to have the voltage across the capacitor or inductor greater than the applied voltage? Explain. (12.2)
7. What type of filter is a series resonant circuit? What are the ideal characteristics of this type of filter? (12.2)
8. What is Q? (12.3)

9. Why is Q important? (12.3)
10. What is $1/Q$ called? (12.3)
11. What is meant by "band-width"? (12.3)
12. How is band-width affected by Q? (12.3)
13. What is parallel resonance? How does it differ from series resonance? (12.4)
14. What is the impedance of a parallel resonant circuit? (12.4)
15. Does resistance affect the resonant frequency of a parallel RLC circuit? If so, how? (12.4)
16. In a parallel resonant circuit, is it ever possible that the current in the inductor or capacitor could be greater than the source current? Explain. (12.4)
17. How can the band-width of a parallel resonant circuit be increased? (12.4)
18. What type of filter is the parallel resonant circuit? What are the ideal characteristics of this type of filter? (12.4)
19. What is a low-pass filter? (12.5)
20. What is a high-pass filter? (12.5)
21. Why is there often more than one resonant circuit in a filter network? (12.5)
22. How can RC or RL networks act as filters? (12.5)
23. What are some common uses for RC filters? (12.5)

Problems

1. In a certain series RLC circuit, $C = 0.001$ μf, $L = 0.1$ mh, and $R = 10$ ohms. What is the resonant frequency? (12.1)
2. If the applied voltage in Problem 1 is 1 $\underline{/0°}$ volts, what is the current at resonance? What is the voltage across each element? (12.1)
3. Repeat Problem 1 for $C = 0.05$ μf, $L = 1$ mh, and $R = 90$ ohms. (12.1)
4. If the applied voltage in Problem 3 is 1 $\underline{/0°}$ volts, what is the current at resonance? What is the voltage across the capacitor and inductor? (12.1)
5. A series RLC circuit is to resonate at 500 Khz. What is the LC product? (12.1)
6. Repeat Problem 5 for a frequency of 5 mhz. (12.1)
7. At what frequency does the voltage across the capacitor in Problem 1 reach its maximum? (12.2)
8. At what frequency does the voltage across the inductor in Problem 1 reach its maximum? (12.2)
9. At what frequency does the voltage across the inductor in Problem 3 reach its maximum? (12.2)
10. At what frequency does the voltage across the capacitor in Problem 3 reach its maximum? (12.2)
11. What is the Q of a 500 mh inductor with a series resistance of 10,000 ohms at 50 Khz? (12.3)
12. Derive Equation 12.12. (12.3)
13. What is the Q of a 250 μf capacitor with a parallel resistance of 10,000 ohms? (12.3)
14. What is the Q in Problem 13, if the resistance is in series? (12.3)
15. What is the dissipation factor in Problem 13? (12.3)
16. What is the band-width of the circuit in Problem 1? What are the frequencies f_1 and f_2? (12.3)
17. What is the band-width of the circuit in Problem 3? What are the frequencies f_1 and f_2? (12.3)
18. If the resistance in a given series RLC circuit is reduced to half its previous value, how would the band-width be affected? (12.3)

19. If the capacitance in Problem 16 is doubled, what will happen to the band-width? (12.3)
20. An inductor of 0.8 mh and a capacitor of 365 μf are connected in parallel. What is the resonant frequency?   (12.4)
21. Calculate the parallel resonant frequency for a 0.002 μf capacitor paralleled with an inductor and resistor in series. The inductor is 0.2 mh and the resistor is 600 ohms. What is the frequency if the resistor is changed to 60,000 ohms?   (12.4)
22. In Problem 21, what is the current at resonance?   (12.4)
23. Show that for a parallel resonant circuit the relation between the Q of the inductive branch and the band-width is the same as for a series resonant circuit.   (12.4)
24. What is the band-width in each case in Problem 21?   (12.4)
25. Show how a resistor connected in parallel with a parallel resonant circuit will affect the band-width.   (12.4)
26. Derive Equation 12.23 for the circuit in Figure 12-18a.   (12.6)
27. What is the half-power frequency of the network shown in Figure 12-21?   (12.6)

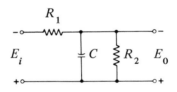

Figure 12-21

28. Repeat Problem 27 for Figure 12-22.   (12.6)

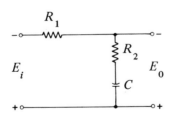

Figure 12-22

13

Transformer Theory

One of the main reasons alternating current is used in the transmission of electrical power is that it is easily transformed from a high voltage to a low voltage or from a low voltage to a higher voltage. In general, the generator voltage is stepped up for low loss transmission and then stepped down again at the point where the energy is to be used. The *transformer* is the device that makes it possible to step up or step down voltages. Voltage transformation is not the only use for the transformer, however, for it can also be used to provide high current at low voltage or to match impedances. In some cases it is also used to isolate a load so that it has no direct physical connection with the source. Such a transformer is termed an isolation transformer. In this chapter we will explore the operation of transformers.

13.1 THE IDEAL TRANSFORMER

The ideal transformer may be thought of as a lossless four-terminal device like that shown in Figure 13-1, having a voltage transformation ratio which is given by

$$a = \frac{V_1}{V_2} \qquad (13.1)$$

where

$$a = \text{transformation ratio}$$

$$V_1 = \text{the source voltage or primary voltage}$$
$$V_2 = \text{the load voltage or secondary voltage}$$

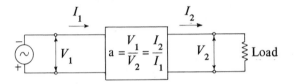

Figure 13-1

The terminals connected to the source are called the primary terminals, while those connecting the load are referred to as the secondary terminals. The terminals are indicated as H and X with the H used to designated the high voltage side.

Since there is to be no loss in the device, the volt-amperes at the primary terminals must equal the volt-amperes at the secondary terminals.

$$V_1 I_1 = V_2 I_2$$

or

$$\frac{I_1}{I_2} = \frac{V_2}{V_1} \tag{13.2}$$

The ratio of I_1/I_2 is called the current transformation ratio and is equal to the inverse of the voltage transformation ratio.

If Equation 13.1 is rewritten as

$$V_1 = aV_2 \tag{13.3}$$

and Equation 13.2 is rewritten as

$$I_1 = \left(\frac{1}{a}\right) I_2 \tag{13.4}$$

then

$$\frac{V_1}{I_1} = a^2 \left(\frac{V_2}{I_2}\right)$$

The ratio $\frac{V_2}{I_2}$ is the load impedance and the ratio $\frac{V_1}{I_1}$ is the input impedance at the primary side. Thus,

$$Z_1 = a^2(Z_2) \tag{13.5}$$

The impedance of the load Z_1 has been transformed to look like $a^2 Z_2$ at the primary terminals.

Example (13.1):

A certain ideal transformer is used to match a 50 ohm transistor load to a 2000 ohm audio generator for maximum power transfer. What is the voltage transformation ratio for the ideal transformer? What is the current transformation ratio?

Solution:

$$\frac{Z_1}{Z_2} = \frac{2000}{50} = 400$$

$$a^2 = \frac{Z_1}{Z_2} = 400$$

$$\frac{V_1}{V_2} = \sqrt{a} = \sqrt{400} = 20$$

$$\frac{I_1}{I_2} = \frac{1}{a} = \frac{1}{20}$$

13.2 TRANSFORMER ACTION

A practical transformer consists of two coils of wire (inductors) magnetically coupled to one another as shown in Figure 13-2. The medium through which the magnetic coupling takes place may be either air or some form

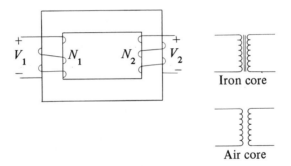

Iron core

Air core

Figure 13-2

of iron. In the first case we have what is called an *air core transformer* and in the latter what is called an *iron core transformer*. Air core transformers are used in high frequency circuits and iron core transformers are used at power distribution frequencies. Powdered iron cores or ferrite cores are also used at intermediate frequencies. High losses in ordinary iron cores at high frequencies prevent their use in circuits employing frequencies above the audio range.

The mutual coupling in the transformer takes place through the magnetic field in the core. When sinusoidal voltage V_1 is impressed on the primary, a back emf appears as

$$E_1 = N_1 \frac{\Delta \phi}{\Delta t} \tag{13.6}$$

where

$$E_1 = \text{back emf}$$
$$N_1 = \text{number of turns on the primary}$$
$$\frac{\Delta\phi}{\Delta t} = \text{average rate of change of flux with respect to time}$$

At the same time, if all of the flux from coil 1 couples all of the turns of coil 2

$$E_2 = N_2 \frac{\Delta\phi}{\Delta t} \tag{13.7}$$

where

$$E_2 = \text{average emf induced in the secondary}$$
$$N_2 = \text{number of turns on the secondary}$$
$$\frac{\Delta\phi}{\Delta t} = \text{average rate of change of flux with respect to time}$$

The ratio of E_1 to E_2 can be given

$$\frac{E_1}{E_2} = \frac{N_1}{N_2} \tag{13.8}$$

If the resistance of the coils is small, then

$$E_1 = V_1$$

and

$$E_2 = V_2$$

thus

$$\frac{V_1}{V_2} = \frac{N_1}{N_2} \tag{13.9}$$

That is, the voltage transformation ratio is equal to the turns ratio.
The average of V_1 can be written as

$$V_1 = \frac{N_1 \, \phi_{max}}{t} \tag{13.10}$$

where

$$V_1 = \text{the average voltage at the primary in volts}$$
$$N_1 = \text{number of turns on the primary}$$
$$\phi_{max} = \text{maximum flux in the core in webers}$$
$$t = \text{time for flux to change from zero to maximum}$$

For a sine wave the flux changes from zero to its maximum value in

$\frac{1}{4}$ cycle. Therefore,

$$V_1 = \frac{N\phi_{max}}{\frac{1}{4}f} = 4Nf\phi_{max} \qquad (13.11)$$

Furthermore,

$$V_{rms} = 1.11 V_{avg} \qquad (13.12)$$

Therefore,

$$V_1 = 4.44 N_1 f_{max} \qquad (13.13)$$

Equation 13.13 is commonly called the transformer equation.

In designing a transformer, ϕ_{max} is obtained from the magnetizing characteristics of the core material. It is chosen near the point where the core begins to saturate. Then the transformer equation is used to determine the number of turns on the primary. The number of turns on the secondary is then determined from Equation 13.9.

Example (13.2):
The maximum flux in a certain core is to be 0.0025 weber. How many turns should be used on each winding if the transformer is to step down 120 volts to 12 volts? $f = 60$ hertz.

Solution:

$$V_1 = 4.44 N_1 f \phi_{max}$$

or, the number of turns per volt is

$$\frac{N_1}{V_1} = \frac{1}{4.44 f \phi_{max}}$$

$$= \frac{1}{(4.44)(60)(2.5 \times 10^{-3})}$$

$$= 1.5$$

Thus,

$$N_1 = (120)(1.5)$$

$$= 180 \text{ turns}$$

and

$$N_2 = (12)(1.5)$$

$$= 18 \text{ turns}$$

13.3   LOSSES IN TRANSFORMERS

There are essentially two types of losses associated with a transformer, copper loss and core losses. The copper loss is the loss due to the current flowing in the resistance of the transformer windings. This loss is directly proportional to the resistance in each winding and the square of the current in each winding.

Losses that occur in the core material arise from two causes: (1) the tendency of ferromagnetic cores to oppose changes in magnetism and (2) the heating of the core material as a result of circulating currents in the core material caused by the changing flux. The first type of loss is called *hysteresis loss* and the latter *eddy current loss*. The sum of hysteresis loss and eddy current loss is called *core loss*.

Hysteresis loss is proportional to the area of the hysteresis loop. The empirical equation for this loss is

$$P_h = \eta f \beta^n_{max} \tag{13.14}$$

where

$$P_h = \text{hysteresis loss}$$
$$\eta \text{ and } n = \text{constants depending upon the material}$$
$$\beta_{max} = \text{maximum flux density in the core}$$

The value of the exponent n depends on the hysteresis-loop shape and varies with the type of material.

For a given transformer and a sinusoidal voltage

$$\beta_{max} \propto \frac{E}{f}$$

Therefore, Equation 13.14 can be written as

$$P_h = K_h \frac{E_n}{f^{n-1}} \tag{13.15}$$

where

$$P_h = \text{hysteresis loss}$$
$$K_h \text{ and } n = \text{constants depending on the core}$$
$$E = \text{the induced voltage}$$
$$f = \text{frequency}$$

Example (13.3):

The hysteresis loss for a certain transformer is 300 watts. If the voltage is kept constant but the frequency is doubled, what is the new hysteresis loss? Assume $n = 2$.

Solution:

For the first case

$$300 = K_h \frac{E^2}{f}$$

For the latter

$$P_h = K_h \frac{E^2}{2f}$$

Taking the ratio of each side of the equations above gives

$$\frac{P_h}{300} = \frac{1}{2}$$

$$P_h = 150 \text{ watts}$$

The eddy current losses in a given core are given by

$$P_e = \frac{\pi^2 f^2 \beta^2_{max} \gamma^2 v}{6 \rho}$$ (13.16)

where

P_e = eddy current loss
π = 3.1416
f = frequency
γ = thickness of laminations
β_{max} = maximum flux density in the core
ρ = the resistivity of the core material
v = volume of core

This equation explains why transformers are constructed of laminated cores as shown in Figure 13-3, for the eddy current losses are directly

Lamination shape

Figure 13-3

proportional to the square of the thickness of these laminations. Equation 13.16 also shows that the eddy current loss is directly proportional to the frequency squared and the flux density squared. It is inversely proportional to the resistivity of the core material.

For a given transformer, Equation 13.16 can be rewritten as

$$P_e = K_h E^2$$ (13.17)

where

P_e = eddy current loss
K_h = a constant for the transformer
E = the induced voltage

Example (13.4):
A certain transformer has an eddy current loss of 160 watts at 120 volts. What is the eddy current loss at 60 volts?

Solution:
The eddy current loss is directly proportional to the square of the voltage. Therefore, the loss at 60 volts is

$$P_{e_2} = \left(\frac{E_2^2}{E_1}\right)(P_{e_1})$$

$$= \left(\frac{60}{120}\right)^2 (160)$$

$$= 40 \text{ watts}$$

13.4   TRANSFORMER EQUIVALENT CIRCUITS

The equivalent circuit of an iron core transformer is shown in Figure 13.4. The transformer T_1 is an ideal transformer with a transformation ratio

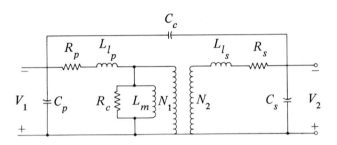

Figure 13-4

of $\frac{N_1}{N_2}$. The resistances R_P and R_S represent the resistances in the primary winding and the secondary winding.

The core losses are represented by the parallel resistance R_c. The inductances L_P and L_S represent what is called the *leakage reactance* of the transformer. The leakage reactance exists because all of the flux from one winding does not link the other winding, as shown in Figure 13-5. The

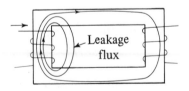

Figure 13-5

reluctance of the path of this leakage flux is mostly due to air, therefore it can be represented in the equivalent circuit by a linear inductor. The inductance L_m is to account for the magnetizing current.

There is also a distributed capacitance between the turns of the windings, which is represented by C_P and C_S. In addition, there is a capacitive coupling between the primary and secondary, which is represented by C_C. At low frequencies these capacitances may often be neglected.

In the case of an air core transformer the equivalent circuit in Figure 13-4 reduces to that shown in Figure 13-6. There are numerous other equivalent circuits for transformers; however, the ones given are the most frequently used.

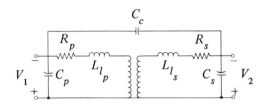

Figure 13-6

13.5 TYPES OF TRANSFORMERS

Besides the conventional power transformers there are many other types including instrument transformers, constant-current transformers, audio transformers, motor-starting transformers, auto-transformers, and radio frequency transformers.

When it is necessary to measure high voltages, a *potential transformer* is sometimes used. It is essentially a step-down transformer with the high-voltage terminals connected to the voltage to be measured and the low-voltage terminals connected to a low-range voltmeter. The low-voltage winding should be grounded for safety.

When it is necessary to measure large currents, a *current transformer* is sometimes used. The primary of a current transformer may consist of only a few turns or even a single turn which is connected in series with the circuit in which the current is to be measured. The secondary, which has a greater number of turns, is connected to a low-range ammeter. As in the case of a voltage transformer, the secondary should be grounded for safety. In addition, the secondary should never be left open as the voltage across the secondary may rise to a high value and break down the transformer insulation. (See Section 16.5.)

Constant-current transformers are used where the current must remain constant even though the load impedance changes. Such transformers are used in some street lighting systems which are connected in series. A sketch of a constant-current transformer is shown in Figure 13-7. With reference to this figure, if the load current tends to increase, the force between the coils

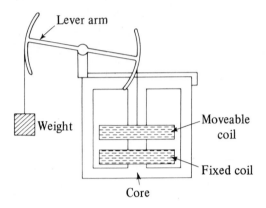

Figure 13-7

causes the coils to separate and increase the leakage reactance, hence reducing the current. If the current tends to decrease, just the opposite occurs.

Transformers used for motor starting are often auto-transformers.
An auto-transformer is shown in Figure 13-8. Coil N_1 is referred to as

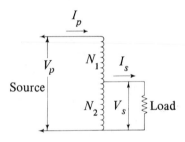

Figure 13-8

the common winding. The voltage transformation ratio is

$$\frac{V_S}{V_P} = \frac{N_2}{N_1 + N_2} \qquad (13.18)$$

and the current transformation ratio is

$$\frac{I_S}{I_P} = \frac{N_1 + N_2}{N_2} \qquad (13.19)$$

The impedance transformation ratio then becomes

$$\frac{Z_P}{Z_S} = \left(\frac{N_1 + N_2}{N_2}\right)^2 \qquad\qquad (13.20)$$

In an ordinary transformer all the power delivered to the load is by transformer action. In the auto-transformer only a portion of the power to the load is via transformer action. The remainder is via direct connection to the load through the series coil. As a result, if an ordinary transformer is connected as an auto-transformer, its KVA capacity will be greater.

Example (13.5):

A certain two-circuit transformer is rated at 100 volts on the primary and 50 volts on the secondary. It is rated at 1 KVA. What is the rating when used as an auto-transformer transforming 150 volts to 50 volts?

Solution:

The current rating on the primary coil is given by the VA rating divided by the primary voltage.

$$I_P = \frac{1000}{100} = 10 \text{ amp}$$

Since this will be the series coil when connected as an auto-transformer, the new VA rating will be

$$VA = (150)\,(10)$$

$$= 1500 \text{ volt-amperes}$$

Audio transformers are iron core transformers that are designed to operate over a wide frequency in the range of 20 to 20,000 hertz. They fall into three classes. Power output transformers are used to match the output circuit of an audio amplifier to a load such as a loudspeaker. Interstage transformers are used as coupling devices between stages in audio amplifiers. Input transformers are used to match the impedance of a source such as a microphone to the input of an amplifier.

Radio frequency transformers are usually air core transformers or have some sort of powdered iron for the core. In many cases they are tuned by placing a capacitor across the winding of either the primary or secondary or both as shown in Figure 13-9. The band-width of such transformers is

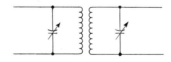

Figure 13-9

not only a function of the Q of the primary and secondary circuits, but also of the coupling between the coils. The further apart the coils are separated, the sharper the selectivity curve. By very close coupling, the selectivity curve becomes broad and may have two humps in it as shown in Figure 13-10.

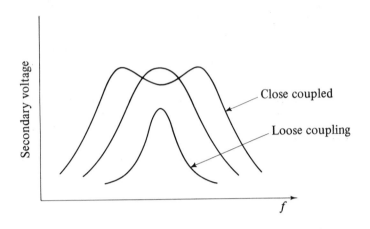

Figure 13-10

13.6 SUMMARY

Transformers are used for voltage transformation, current transformation, impedance transformation, and often only for the purpose of isolating two circuits. The winding of the transformer which is connected to the source is called the *primary*. The load is connected to the *secondary* winding.

The *voltage transformation ratio* "a" of a transformer is given by

$$\frac{V_1}{V_2} = \frac{N_1}{N_2} \qquad (13.9)$$

The *current transformation ratio* is

$$\frac{I_1}{I_2} = \frac{V_2}{V_1} \qquad (13.2)$$

The impedance seen at the primary terminals is

$$Z_1 = a^2 Z_2 \qquad (13.5)$$

The *transformer equation* relates the winding voltages to the number of turns and the maximum flux in the core.

$$V_1 = 4.44 N f \phi_{max} \qquad (13.13)$$

There are two types of losses in a transformer. *Copper losses* occur because of the resistance of the windings. *Core losses* are composed of *hysteresis losses* and *eddy current losses*. Hysteresis losses are given by

$$P_h = \eta f \beta^n_{max} \qquad (13.14)$$

and eddy current losses are given by

$$P_e = K_h E^2 \tag{13.17}$$

Transformer cores are laminated to reduce eddy current losses.

Leakage inductance is present in a transformer because all the flux from one winding does not cut the turns of the other winding.

Winding capacitance and capacitance between windings is important in transformers used at high frequencies.

Potential transformers are used to measure high voltages with a low-range voltmeter.

Current transformers are used to measure large currents with a low-range ammeter.

Constant-current transformers are used to maintain the same output current regardless of the load.

Auto-transformers are often used for motor starting. When an ordinary transformer is connected as an auto-transformer, it can deliver a greater KVA.

Audio transformers are designed to operate over a wide band of frequencies in the range of 20 to 20,000 hertz. There are essentially three types of audio transformers, namely, output, interstage, and input transformers.

Radio frequency transformers usually have air cores or powdered iron cores. They may be tuned or untuned. The selectivity of such transformers is affected by the degree of coupling between the primary and secondary. The closer the coupling, the broader the selectivity curve.

13.7   QUESTIONS AND PROBLEMS

Questions

1. What are some uses of transformers? Explain each one. (Introduction)
2. What is an ideal transformer? (13.1)
3. How is the voltage transformation ratio related to the current transformation ratio in a transformer? How is it related to the turns ratio? (13.1)
4. How is the impedance ratio related to the voltage transformation ratio? (13.1)
5. What is meant by "transformer action"? (13.2)
6. How is the voltage on the primary of a transformer related to the number of turns and the flux density? (13.2)
7. What does the core material have to do with the number of turns/volt? (13.2)
8. What is the transformer equation? (13.2)
9. What are core losses? (13.3)
10. What is meant by "hysteresis loss"? How does it depend on frequency? (13.3)
11. What is eddy current loss? (13.3)
12. Why are cores laminated? (13.3)
13. How does the applied voltage affect eddy current losses? (13.3)
14. Sketch an equivalent circuit for an iron core transformer and indicate the purpose of each element. (13.4)
15. What is leakage reactance? (13.4)

16. Sketch the equivalent circuit for an air core transformer and indicate the purpose of each element. (13.4)

17. What is a potential transformer? (13.5)

18. What is a current transformer? (13.5)

19. What is a constant-current transformer? How does it operate? (13.5)

20. What is an auto-transformer? What are the advantages of an auto-transformer over the conventional two-circuit transformer? (13.5)

21. What is an audio power output transformer used for? What is an interstage transformer? What is an input transformer? (13.5)

22. What types of cores are used in *RF* transformers? (13.5)

23. How does coupling affect the response of a tuned transformer? (13.5)

Problems

1. The voltage transformation ratio for a certain transformer is 10:1. If the current on the secondary side is 1 amp, what is the current on the primary side? (13.1)

2. An impedance of 10 ohms is connected to the 12 volt winding of a 120 volt to 12 volt transformer. What is the impedance seen at the 120 volt terminals? (13.1)

3. The ratio of input impedance to output impedance for a certain transformer is 400. What is the voltage transformation ratio V_1/V_2? (13.1)

4. The current in the primary of a certain transformer is 5 amp. The current in the secondary is 1 amp. What is the ratio of primary voltage to secondary voltage? (13.1)

5. What are the turns ratios in Problems 1, 2, 3, and 4? (13.2)

6. The maximum flux in a certain transformer core is 0.001 weber. How many turns per volt are needed on the windings at 60 hertz? (13.2)

7. A certain transformer must step down 220 volts to 110 volts. The maximum allowable flux in the core is 0.002 weber. How many turns should be used on each winding of the transformer? (13.2)

8. The primary of a certain transformer is rated at 110 volts 60 hertz. What is the voltage rating at 50 hertz, and at 25 hertz, assuming the maximum flux can stay the same in each case? (13.2)

9. The hysteresis loss in a certain transformer is 100 watts. If the voltage is kept constant but the frequency is reduced to half its previous value, what is the new hysteresis loss? Assume $n = 2$. (13.3)

10. The hysteresis loss in a certain transformer is 250 watts. If the frequency remains the same but the voltage is raised 10%, what is the new hysteresis loss? Assume $n = 2$. (13.3)

11. The hysteresis loss in a certain transformer is 500 watts. If the frequency is doubled and the voltage reduced to half its previous value, what is the new hysteresis loss? Assume $n = 3$. (13.3)

12. The eddy current loss for a given transformer is 35 watts. If the thickness of the laminations are doubled, what is the new eddy current loss? (13.3)

13. The eddy current loss for a given transformer is 60 watts. If the core material is changed to one having $\frac{1}{2}$ the resistivity, what is the new eddy current loss? (13.3)

14. If the flux density in the core of a given transformer doubles, what will happen to the eddy current losses? (13.3)

15. The eddy current loss for a given transformer is 300 watts. If the applied voltage is increased 10%, what is the new eddy current loss? (13.3)

16. At 60 hertz, the total core loss is 1200 watts. At 30 hertz and the same voltage, the core loss is 1800 watts. What is the eddy current loss and hysteresis loss at 60 hertz? Let $n = 2$. (13.3)

17. Using the equivalent circuit for a power transformer shown in Figure 13-11, determine the load voltage. (13.4)

0.1Ω
1Ω
5Ω
0.5Ω
220∠0°
N1
N2
1Ω
N1/N2 = 1/5

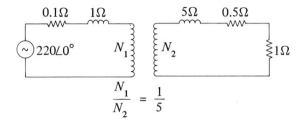

Figure 13-11

18. Sketch an equivalent circuit for the transformer in Figure 13-12. Show all the component values. (13.4)

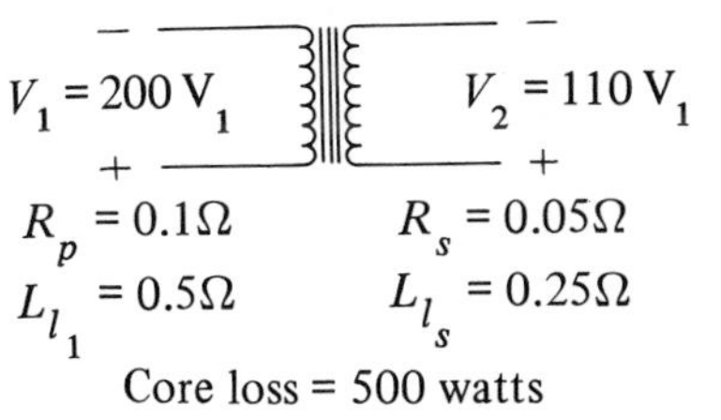

V1 = 200 V1
V2 = 110 V1
Rp = 0.1Ω
Rs = 0.05Ω
Ll1 = 0.5Ω
Lls = 0.25Ω
Core loss = 500 watts

Figure 13-12

19. An ordinary two-circuit transformer rated at 220-110 volts and 10 KVA is to be connected as an auto-transformer to transform 330 volts to 110 volts. What is the KVA rating as an autotransformer? (13.5)
20. In Problem 19, how much power goes to the load by induction and how much by conduction? (13.5)
21. An ordinary two-circuit transformer is rated at 120-10 volts and 1 KVA. Can the transformer be connected so that it will step down 110 volts to 10 volts? Explain. Can it be connected so that it will step down 120 volts to 110 volts? (13.5)
22. An auto-transformer is used to reduce the starting current of a motor. If the starting current is 200 amp at full voltage and the autotransformer reduces this current to $\frac{1}{2}$ this value, what is the new line current? (13.5)

14

Polyphase Systems

The earliest form of alternating current power distribution was by using a single generator and a two-wire system connecting the load to the generator as shown in Figure 14-1a. Such a system is termed a single-phase system. A little later, the Edison three-wire system or split-phase system,

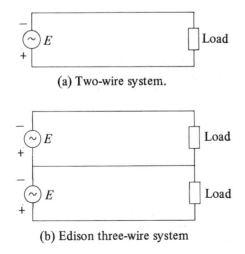

(a) Two-wire system.

(b) Edison three-wire system

Figure 14-1

(c) Three-phase system

Figure 14-1 (Cont'd)

as shown in Figure 14-1b, was introduced. This is also a single-phase system as both generators are in phase.

By merely shifting the phase of one of the generators by 90° with respect to the other in the three-wire single-phase system we have the earliest type of polyphase system, the two-phase system. Although two-phase is not found in power distribution systems, it is used a great deal in servomechanisms.

The two-phase system for power distribution was discarded in favor of the three-phase system, as shown in Figure 14-1c. Each of the three generator voltages in the three-phase system is 120° out of phase with the others.

In general, one may speak of n-phase systems, where n is any integer. Six-phase and twelve-phase systems are sometimes used in industrial applications.

14.1 ADVANTAGES OF POLYPHASE SYSTEMS

In a single-phase circuit it has been shown that the instantaneous power delivered to the load is pulsating at twice the line frequency. Thus, even though its rotor has a large amount of inertia, a single-phase motor operating at 60 hertz will vibrate somewhat at 120 hertz. With a polyphase system the above is not true, for the instantaneous power delivered to the load is constant if the load is balanced (i.e., equal in each phase). Therefore, one important advantage of a polyphase system is that it delivers a constant power to a balanced load.

Another advantage of polyphase systems is that special starting mechanisms are not necessary for starting induction motors. All single-phase induction motors require some device—switch, capacitor, coil, or shaded pole—to assist with starting the motor. These mechanisms are usually connected in the circuit only during the time necessary to start the motor. This further complicates the system.

In electronics it is often necessary to rectify alternating current and filter the rectified current to produce a smooth d-c. The task of filtering is accomplished more easily in polyphase systems than in single-phase systems, and the more phases, the easier the filtering.

Still another advantage of polyphase systems is that, for a system of given voltage, efficiency, and power capacity, the weight of the copper required is less than the weight of the copper for a single-phase system.

14.2 GENERATION OF POLYPHASE VOLTAGES

Although separate generators are shown in schematics of polyphase circuits, in practice only one generator is used for all the phases. The phase shift is accomplished by geometrically displacing identical windings, as shown in Figure 14-2. If two identical windings are displaced 90° as

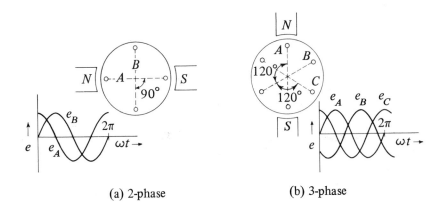

(a) 2-phase   (b) 3-phase

Figure 14-2

shown in Figure 14-2a, the voltage in coil *A* reaches its maximum 90° behind the maximum in coil *B*. Likewise, if three identical windings are distributed 120° apart as shown in Figure 14-2b, the voltage in coil *B* reaches its maximum 120° behind the voltage in coil *A*, and the voltage in coil *C* reaches its maximum 120° behind the maximum in coil *B*.

14.3 WYE OR STAR CONNECTIONS

If the windings of a three-phase generator are connected as shown in Figure 14-3, they are said to be Y-connected. If a *neutral* is connected in the center as shown in Figure 14-3b, it is called a four-wire Y-connected system. The voltages E_{AN}, E_{BN}, and E_{CN} are called the phase voltages, while E_{AB}, E_{BC}, and E_{CA} are called the line-to-line or simply line voltages. When the windings are connected such that E_{AN} reaches its maximum

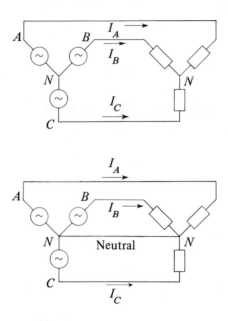

Figure 14-3

first, followed by $\mathbf{E}_{BN}$ and then $\mathbf{E}_{CN}$, it is called a positive sequence or ABC sequence. (See Figure 14-4a.) If the windings are connected such that

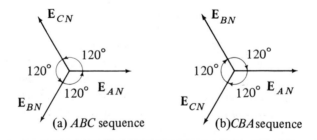

Figure 14-4

$\mathbf{E}_{AN}$ reaches its maximum followed by $\mathbf{E}_{CN}$ and then $\mathbf{E}_{BN}$, we have a negative sequence or CBA sequence as shown in Figure 14-4b.

The relationship between line voltages and phase voltages is shown in Figure 14-5. Phase voltages are used as reference and the line voltages obtained from Kirchhoff's voltage law.

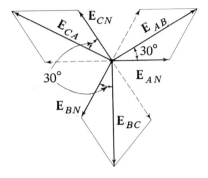

Figure 14-5

$$\mathbf{E}_{AB} = \mathbf{E}_{AN} + \mathbf{E}_{NB} = \mathbf{E}_{NB} - \mathbf{E}_{NA}$$

$$\mathbf{E}_{BC} = \mathbf{E}_{BN} + \mathbf{E}_{NC} = \mathbf{E}_{NC} - \mathbf{E}_{NB}$$

$$\mathbf{E}_{CA} = \mathbf{E}_{CN} + \mathbf{E}_{NA} = \mathbf{E}_{NA} - \mathbf{E}_{NC}$$

The results show that the magnitude of the line voltages for a wye system is always given by

$$E_{\text{line}} = \sqrt{3}\, E_{\text{phase}} \tag{14.1}$$

and the line-to-line voltage always leads the phase voltage by 30° for a positive sequence. With a negative sequence the line voltages always lag the phase voltages by 30°.

The current in the generator of each phase is the same as the line current.

Loads may also be connected in Y, in which case the same relation as to magnitude and phase exists between line voltages and phase voltages.

Example (14.1):

A certain 3-phase source is connected to a Y load. The line voltages are 208 volts. What are the phase voltages and currents if the load is composed of 10 ohms of resistance in each phase? Assume a positive sequence.

Solution:

The phase voltages are

$$E_P = \frac{208}{\sqrt{3}} = 120 \text{ volts}$$

and thus the phase currents are

$$I_P = \frac{120}{10} = 12 \text{ amp}$$

The phase voltages are lagging the corresponding line voltages by 30° and the currents are in phase with the phase voltages.

14.4   DELTA-CONNECTED SYSTEMS

Another method of connecting 3-phase generators or loads is the delta system, shown in Figure 14-6. In this case the phase voltages and line

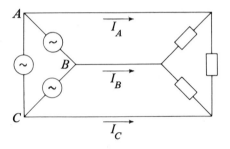

Figure 14-6

voltages are the same. However, the line currents and phase currents are different.

Assume the phase currents to be of positive sequence in the load of

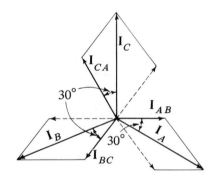

Figure 14-7

Figure 14-6. Figure 14-7 shows the phasor diagram of the currents in the resistive load. From Kirchhoff's law

$$\mathbf{I}_A = \mathbf{I}_{AB} + \mathbf{I}_{AC}$$

$$\mathbf{I}_B = \mathbf{I}_{BC} + \mathbf{I}_{BA}$$

$$\mathbf{I}_C = \mathbf{I}_{CA} + \mathbf{I}_{CB}$$

The results are that the line currents for a delta system are

$$I_{\text{line}} = \sqrt{3}\, I_{\text{phase}} \tag{14.2}$$

and the line currents lag the phase currents by $30°$. If the sequence is changed to a negative one, the line currents will lead the phase currents by $30°$.

Example (14.2):

A certain load is connected in Δ. The line-to-line voltages are 220 volts and each load element is 10 ohms. What are the magnitudes of the line currents and phase currents?

Solution:

The phase currents are given by

$$I\phi = \frac{220}{10} = 22 \text{ amp}$$

The line currents are

$$I_L = \sqrt{3}\, I\phi = \sqrt{3(22)} = 38.2 \text{ amp}$$

14.5   Δ-Y AND Y-Δ CONNECTIONS

It is possible to have a Δ-connected source and a Y-connected load or vice versa, in which case the source and the load must be analyzed individually as in the preceding sections. The load, either Δ or Y, sees only the 3-phase line voltages regardless of how the source is connected.

The Y system of distribution is used most frequently in the United States for the simple reason that from such a system two different 3-phase voltages can be obtained. Usually the system is 120/208 volts. To use as a 120 volt system, the load is connected as a 4-wire Y, but for a 208 volt system the load is connected as Δ.

The Δ connection for sources also has an advantage in that, if one generator or transformer becomes defective, all three phases are still in operation at reduced output. Figure 14-8 shows how this is possible. The voltage $\mathbf{E}_{AB}$ and $\mathbf{E}_{BC}$ add together to yield the voltage $\mathbf{E}_{CA}$.

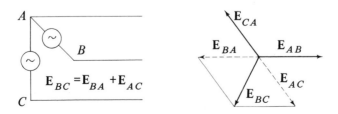

Figure 14-8

14.6   POWER IN BALANCED SYSTEMS

In a balanced 3-phase load, the power in each phase will be the same. Therefore, the total power delivered to the load will always be three times the power delivered to one phase regardless of whether the load is connected in Y or Δ.

$$P_T = 3P_{\text{phase}}$$

$$= 3E_P I_P \cos \phi \qquad (14.3)$$

where

$$E_P = \text{phase voltage}$$
$$I_P = \text{phase current}$$
$$\cos \phi = \text{angle between the phase current and phase voltage}$$

In a Y-connected system

$$E_L = \sqrt{3} \, E_P$$

and

$$I_L = I_P$$

therefore,

$$P_T = 3E_P I_P \cos \phi$$

$$= 3\frac{E_L}{\sqrt{3}} I_L \cos \phi$$

$$= \sqrt{3} \, E_L I_L \cos \phi \qquad (14.4)$$

where

$$E_L = \text{line-to-line voltage}$$
$$I_L = \text{line current}$$
$$\phi = \text{angle between } \textit{phase current and phase voltage}$$
$$\text{(i.e. power factor angle of the load)}$$

With a Δ-connected load

$$E_L = E_P$$

and

$$I_L = \sqrt{3} \, I_P$$

therefore,

$$P_T = 3E_P I_P \cos \phi$$

$$= 3E_L \frac{I_L}{\sqrt{3}} \cos \phi$$

$$= \sqrt{3} \, E_L I_L \cos \phi \qquad (14.5)$$

which is identical to the expression in the case of the Y-connected load. It is, therefore, not necessary to know how the load is connected if the line voltage, line current, and power factor of the load are known.

Measuring power in a balanced 3-phase system is simple since one need only put a wattmeter in one phase and multiply the reading by 3. (See Figure 14-9.) In case the wattmeter cannot be connected in a phase, it can

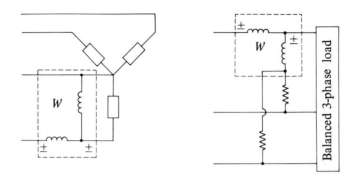

Figure 14-9

be connected with the current coil in one line and the potential coil connected in Y with two resistors having the same impedance as the potential coil.

14.7 UNBALANCED SYSTEMS

Unbalanced 3-phase systems are a little more difficult to handle than balanced systems, yet they appear quite frequently in real life. Fortunately, in most cases the source voltage can be assumed to be balanced. The load, however, is frequently not the same in each phase. With an unbalanced Δ load and assuming the line voltages balanced, one can easily determine each phase current and then use Kirchhoff's current law to find the line currents.

Example (14.3):

Consider a Δ load connected as shown in Figure 14-10. Find the line currents if the line voltages are balanced and equal 100 volts. (Positive sequence.)

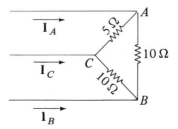

Figure 14-10

Solution:

$$I_{AB} = \frac{V_{AB}}{R_{AB}} = \frac{100\ \underline{/0°}}{10} = 10\ \underline{/0°}$$

$$I_{BC} = \frac{V_{BC}}{R_{BC}} = \frac{100\ \underline{/240°}}{10} = 10\ \underline{/240°}$$

$$I_{CA} = \frac{V_{CA}}{R_{CA}} = \frac{100\ \underline{/120°}}{5} = 20\ \underline{/120°}$$

$$I_A = I_{AB} + I_{AC} = 10\ \underline{/0°} + 20\ \underline{/120°} = 17.3\ \underline{/-90°}$$

$$I_B = I_{BA} + I_{BC} = -10\ \underline{/0°} + 10\ \underline{/240°} = 26.3\ \underline{/220.4°}$$

$$I_C = I_{CA} + I_{CB} = 20\ \underline{/120°} + 10\ \underline{/240°} = 10\ \underline{/180°}$$

In a Y-connected 4-wire load with balanced voltage and unbalanced load, the line currents are simply the phase currents which are found by dividing the phase voltages by the corresponding phase impedances. The current in the neutral is then found by Kirchhoff's current law.

The 3-wire unbalanced Y load creates a more difficult situation since the phase voltages are not known. However, the problem can be solved by writing two mesh equations and one node equation, as shown in the following example.

Example (14.4):

A 3-wire Y-connected load is shown in Figure 14-11. The line voltages are 240 volts. Determine the phase voltages and currents at the load. (Positive sequence.)

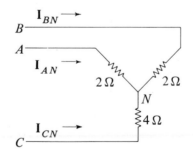

Figure 14-11

Solution:

Writing loop equations around two of the loops, we have

$$E_{AB} = E_{AN} + E_{NB}$$

$$240\ \underline{/0°} = E_{AN} - E_{BN} = 2I_{AN} - 2I_{BN}$$

$$\mathbf{E}_{BC} = \mathbf{E}_{BN} + \mathbf{E}_{NC}$$

$$240 \ \underline{/240°} = \mathbf{E}_{BN} - \mathbf{E}_{CN} = 2\mathbf{I}_{BN} - 4\mathbf{I}_{CN}$$

Kirchhoff's current equation at N is

$$\mathbf{I}_{AN} + \mathbf{I}_{BN} + \mathbf{I}_{CN} = 0$$

If the three equations are rewritten

$$\mathbf{I}_{AN} + \mathbf{I}_{BN} + \mathbf{I}_{CN} = 0$$

$$2\mathbf{I}_{AN} - 2\mathbf{I}_{BN} = 240$$

$$2\mathbf{I}_{BN} - 4\mathbf{I}_{CN} = 240 \ \underline{/240°}$$

These three equations can be solved by determinants to give

$$\mathbf{I}_{AN} = 98.4 \ \underline{/-7.6°}$$

$$\mathbf{I}_{BN} = 52 \ \underline{/210°}$$

$$\mathbf{I}_{CN} = 65.4 \ \underline{/143.4°}$$

The phase voltages are then obtained by multiplying the phase currents by the phase impedances.

$$\mathbf{E}_{AN} = 2\mathbf{I}_{AN} = 196.8 \ \underline{/-7.6°}$$

$$\mathbf{E}_{BN} = 2\mathbf{I}_{BN} = 104 \ \underline{/210°}$$

$$\mathbf{E}_{CN} = 4\mathbf{I}_{CN} = 130.8 \ \underline{/143.4°}$$

Power in unbalanced systems can be measured in one of 2 ways. The simplest that comes to mind is to place wattmeters in each of the 3 phases. The total power will then be the sum of the readings on each meter. Another method that is frequently used is the two-wattmeter method in which a meter is connected in each of 2 of the 3 lines as shown in Figure 14-12. The meter W_1 reads

$$P_1 = V_{AB}I_A \cos (30° + \phi)$$

$$= E_L I_L \cos (30° + \phi) \qquad\qquad (14.6)$$

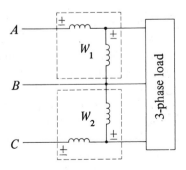

Figure 14-12

while the meter W_2 reads

$$P_2 = V_{CB}I_C \cos (30° - \phi)$$

$$= E_L I_L \cos (30° - \phi) \tag{14.7}$$

and

$$P_1 + P_2 = E_L I_L \cos (30° + \phi) + E_L I_L \cos (30° - \phi)$$

From the trigonometric identities for $A + B$ and $A - B$

$$P_1 + P_2 = 2E_L I_L \cos 30° \cos \phi$$

$$= \sqrt{3} E_L I_L \cos \phi$$

which is the total power in any balanced system.

It is left for the student to show that the total power for an unbalanced system is also given by $P_1 + P_2$. (Problem 19.) By the use of a phasor diagram it can be shown that W_1 will read negative when the power factor angle is greater than 60°.

14.8   SUMMARY

A system in which all of the generated voltages are in phase is called a *single-phase system*. A *polyphase system* is one in which there are two or more generated voltages spaced at equal phase intervals. If the voltages are equal in magnitude it is a balanced system.

Polyphase systems are advantageous because

     1. they deliver a constant power output;

     2. they eliminate the necessity of special starting devices for induction motors;

     3. their rectified output is easier to filter; and

     4. they require less copper than the equivalent single-phase system.

The most common polyphase system is the *three-phase* system in which three voltages are spaced 120° apart from each other.

If voltages $\mathbf{E}_A$, $\mathbf{E}_B$, and $\mathbf{E}_C$ reach their maximum in that order, it is called an *ABC sequence* or *positive sequence*. If the maximums occur in reverse order it is called a *CBA sequence* or *negative sequence*.

Three-phase generators or loads may be connected in *wye* or *delta*.

In a wye connection the line currents and phase currents are the same, but the line voltages are $\sqrt{3}$ times the phase voltages. The line voltages also lead their respective phase voltages by an angle of 30° with positive sequence. For a negative sequence, the line voltages lag their respective phase voltages by 30°.

In a delta connection the line voltages and phase voltages are the same, but the line currents are $\sqrt{3}$ times the phase currents. Line currents lag their respective phase currents by an angle of 30° with a positive sequence and lead their respective phase currents by an angle of 30° for a negative sequence.

Regardless of the manner in which the load is connected, the total power in a balanced three-phase system is given by

$$P_T = 3E_PI_P \cos \phi \qquad (14.3)$$

or

$$P_T = \sqrt{3} E_L I_L \cos \phi \qquad (14.4)$$

A single wattmeter used in one phase of a balanced three-phase system will measure 1/3 the total power. For an unbalanced system it is necessary to use a wattmeter in each phase and take the sum of the readings to obtain the total power, or use the *two-wattmeter* method to determine the power. With the latter method one must be careful to use the algebraic sum to find the total power.

14.9   QUESTIONS AND PROBLEMS

Questions

1. What is a single-phase system? (Introduction)
2. What is a polyphase system? (Introduction)
3. Where might 6-phase be useful? (Introduction)
4. What are the advantages of a polyphase system?   (14.1)
5. What are some disadvantages of a polyphase system?   (14.1)
6. Describe a 2-phase system.   (14.2), (Introduction)
7. Describe a 3-phase system.   (14.2), (Introduction)
8. How are 3-phase voltages generated by one machine?   (14.2)
9. What is meant by "a positive sequence" and "a negative sequence"?   (14.3)
10. Of what importance is the sequence in polyphase?   (14.3)
11. What are line voltages and currents?   (14.3)
12. What are phase voltages and currents?   (14.3)
13. What is a 4-wire Y connection? Why is it used?   (14.3)
14. What is a 3-wire Y connection?   (14.3)
15. What is the relationship between line voltage and phase voltage in a 3-phase balanced Y?   (14.3)
16. What is the relationship between line currents and phase currents in a 3-phase balanced Y?   (14.3)
17. What is a Δ connection?   (14.4)
18. What is the relationship between the line currents and phase currents in a 3-phase balanced Δ ? (14.4)

19. What is the relationship between line voltages and phase voltages in a balanced Δ ? (14.4)

20. Give reasons why you might wish to use a Y or a Δ connection.   (14.5)

21. How is power determined in a 3-phase balanced system?   (14.6)

22. How can a single wattmeter be connected to measure power in a 3-phase system ? (14.6)

23. What type of imbalance is most common in 3-phase systems?   (14.7)

24. How can one solve for the currents and voltages in unbalanced systems?   (14.7)

25. How is the two-wattmeter system used to measure power in an unbalanced system? (14.7)

Problems

1. The line voltages of a balanced 3-phase system are 440 volts. A Y-connected balanced load is connected to the system. Assuming no drop in line voltage, what are the phase voltages? Draw a phasor diagram. Assume a negative sequence.   (14.3)

2. The phase voltages for a balanced Y-connected load are 120 volts. What are the line voltages? Assume a positive sequence and draw a phasor diagram.   (14.3)

3. A 3-phase source is connected to a Y-connected load. The line voltages are 208 volts and the load consists of 20 ohm resistors. What are the phase voltages and line currents?   (14.3)

4. A 3-phase source having a line voltage of 120 volts is connected to a Y-connected load. Each element of the load consists of an inductive reactance of 10 ohms. The voltage $E_{AB} = 120 \; \underline{/10°}$. What are the line voltages, the phase voltages, and the line currents? Draw a phasor diagram.   (14.3)

5. A 3-phase Y-connected load of $Z = 3 + j4$ is connected to a 3-phase source having a line voltage of 208 volts. $E_{AB} = 208 \; \underline{/30°}$. Determine all the line voltages, line currents, and phase voltages. Assume a negative sequence. Draw a phasor diagram. (14.3)

6. Show that the sum of voltage drops around a Δ load is zero.   (14.4)

7. A 25 ohm load is connected in Δ. The line voltages are 225 volts. What are the magnitudes of the line currents and phase currents?   (14.4)

8. Impedances of $5 + j5$ ohms are connected in Δ to a 3-phase source having a line voltage of 220 volts. What are the phase currents and phase voltages? Draw a complete phasor diagram. Assume a positive sequence.   (14.4)

9. If one of the generators in a Δ source becomes inoperative, show how 3-phase is still available.   (14.5)

10. A 3-phase source is connected in Y, while the load is connected in Δ. If the line voltage is 208 volts and the load is 10 ohms, what are the line currents and phase currents in both the source and the load?   (14.5)

11. The phase currents for a balanced load are each 3 amp. The phase voltages are 220 volts. What is the power dissipated in the load if it is a pure resistance?   (14.6)

12. Each load element in a 3-phase has an impedance $Z = 6 + j8$ ohms. The line currents are each 5 amp. If the load is connected in Y, what is the line voltage and the total real power?   (14.6)

13. The line currents in a certain 3-phase system are each 5 amp. The line voltage is 108 volts. If the power factor of the load is 0.8, what is the total real power dissipated? What is the reactive power?   (14.6)

14. The line currents in a certain 3-phase system are each 10 amp. The line voltage is 220 volts. The total real power delivered to the load is 3300 watts. What is the power factor of the load?   (14.6)

15. Determine all the phase currents and line currents in Figure 14-13.   (14.7)

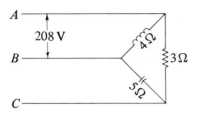

Figure 14-13

16. Determine all the phase voltages and line voltages in Figure 14-14.   (14.7)

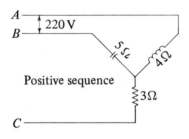

Figure 14-14

17. Determine the reading on each wattmeter in Figure 14-15 and find the total power.

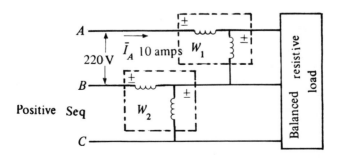

Figure 14-15

18. Repeat Problem 17 for Figure 14-16.   (14.7)

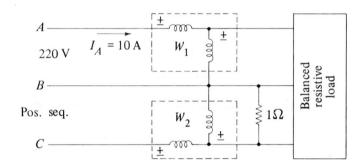

Figure 14-16

19. Show that total power in a 3-phase unbalanced system can be measured by the 2-wattmeter method.   (14.7)
20. Show how you could use 2 wattmeters to measure the reactive power in a 3-phase system. Derive equations to calculate this power from the meter readings.   (14.7)

Section III

Applications

The 91 selected applications of electrical principles given in this section are to be used as references. As such they are presented to show how each application functions and some of their details of construction. Furthermore, they are not necessarily illustrations of commercial practice, as they are only meant to assist the reader in his understanding of principles by giving meaningful representations of a few of the important applications.

15

Voltage Sources

15.1 PRIMARY CELLS

One of the most fundamental voltage sources is the primary cell. The common flashlight battery is a primary cell. A primary cell is not rechargeable. Figures 15-1a through c show the construction of some common primary cells.

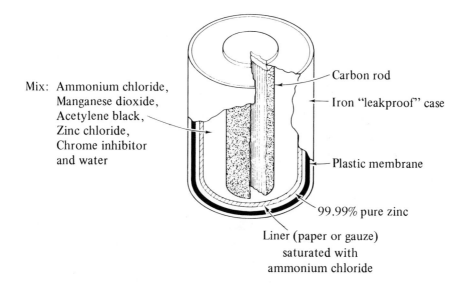

Mix: Ammonium chloride,
Manganese dioxide,
Acetylene black,
Zinc chloride,
Chrome inhibitor
and water

Carbon rod

Iron "leakproof" case

Plastic membrane

99.99% pure zinc

Liner (paper or gauze)
saturated with
ammonium chloride

Figure 15-1a

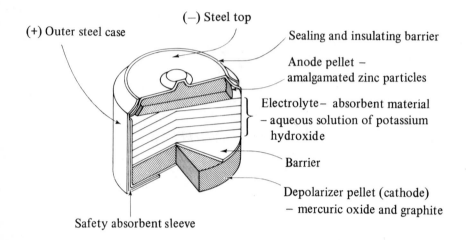

Figure 15-1b

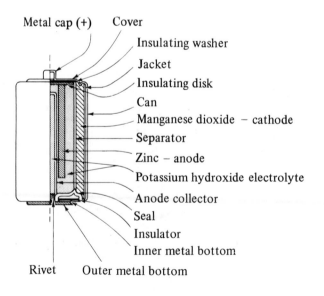

Figure 15-1c

15.2 SECONDARY CELLS

Secondary cells are rechargeable voltage sources. The most common example of the use of secondary cells is in the lead-acid storage battery used in automobiles. Figures 15-2a through c show the construction of some common secondary cells.

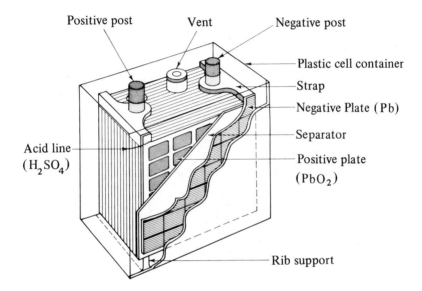

Figure 15-2a

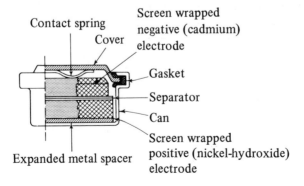

Figure 15-2b

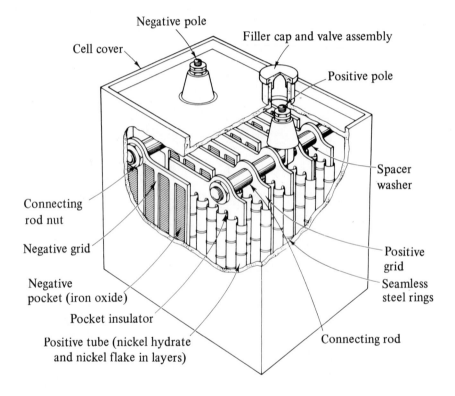

Figure 15-2c

15.3 THERMAL CONVERTERS

Electrical energy can be obtained from heat energy as well as chemical energy. Devices which convert heat energy to electrical energy are called *thermal converters*. The thermocouple illustrated in Figures 15-3a and b is such a converter. It is commonly used to measure temperatures.

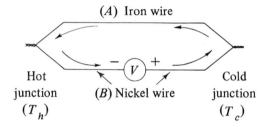

(A) Iron wire

Hot junction (T_h)

(B) Nickel wire

Cold junction (T_c)

Seebeck effect: $dV_{AB} = \alpha_{AB}(T)\, dT$

α = Seebeck coefficient

Thomson effect: in wire A whose length is dx of A, there is a temperature gradient of $\partial T/\partial x$, with a current flow dI, a quantity of heat dQ will be generated.

$$dQ = \gamma_a(T)\, dI \frac{\partial T}{\partial x} dx$$

γ_a = Thomson coefficient.

Peltier effect: when V is replaced with a source of power, the hot junction becomes heated and the cold junction cooled.

$$dQ = \pi_{AB}(T)\, dI$$

π = Peltier coefficient for metals AB

Figure 15-3a

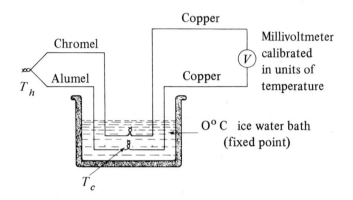

Copper chromel and copper alumel junctions
are at 0°C thus they do not affect the
voltage developed by the heated junction,
T_h. T_c is at a fixed point 0°C.

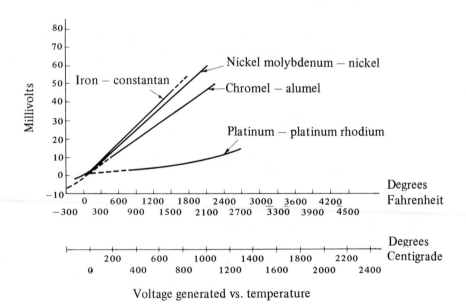

Voltage generated vs. temperature

Figure 15-3b

15.4   ENERGY CELLS

Devices which use up chemical elements or compounds to produce electrical energy are referred to as *energy cells* or *fuel cells*. Figures 15-4a through c illustrate the construction and operation of such cells.

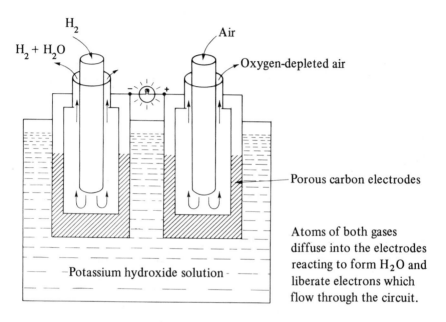

H_2

Air

$H_2 + H_2O$

Oxygen-depleted air

Porous carbon electrodes

Atoms of both gases diffuse into the electrodes reacting to form H_2O and liberate electrons which flow through the circuit.

-Potassium hydroxide solution -

Figure 15-4a

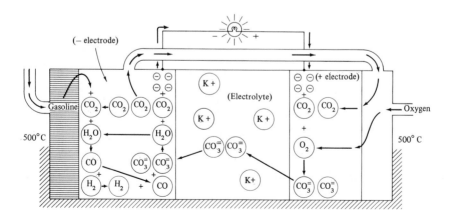

(− electrode)

$500°C$

Gasoline

(+ electrode)

(Electrolyte)

Oxygen

$500°C$

Figure 15-4b

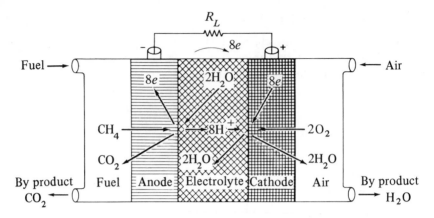

Figure 15-4c

15.5 SOLAR CELLS

Devices which convert radiant light energy to electrical energy are called *solar cells* or *photocells*. Such cells can be connected together to form a solar battery as shown in Figure 15-5b.

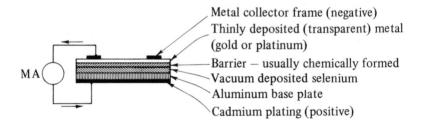

Figure 15-5a

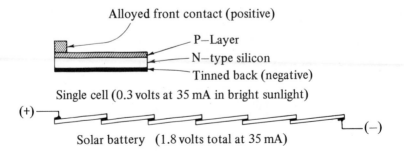

Figure 15-5b

15.6 PIEZOELECTRIC SOURCES

Certain types of crystals produce an electromotive force when subjected to pressure. Such devices are used in microphone pickups, phonograph pickups, and accelerometers. Figures 15-6a and b illustrate two such pressure-actuated devices.

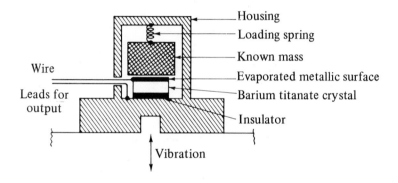

Figure 15-6a

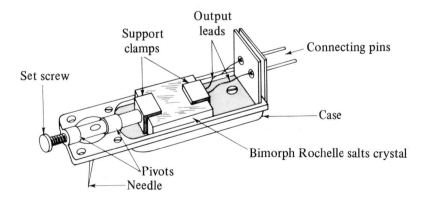

Figure 15-6b

15.7 MAGNETIC CONVERTERS

There are essentially two types of magnetic converters. One type uses a conductor in a changing magnetic field. This type is used in magnetic recording (see Figure 15-7a).

Another way of obtaining voltage from a magnetic field is to use a "hall" device like that shown in Figure 15-7b. A current I_c is applied to the slab of semiconductor material. A voltage V_H proportional to the normal flux density is then produced at opposite ends of the semiconductor.

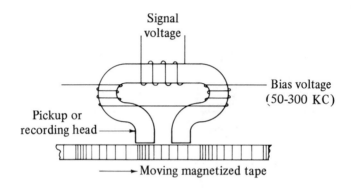

Figure 15-7a

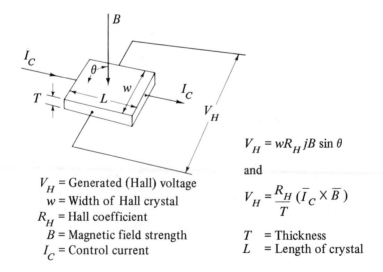

V_H = Generated (Hall) voltage
w = Width of Hall crystal
R_H = Hall coefficient
B = Magnetic field strength
I_C = Control current

$$V_H = w R_H jB \sin \theta$$

and

$$V_H = \frac{R_H}{T} (\overline{I}_C \times \overline{B})$$

T = Thickness
L = Length of crystal

Figure 15-7b

15.8 MECHANICAL CONVERSION

Figures 15a and b show how alternating current and direct current is produced by a single loop of wire rotating in a steady magnetic field. The only difference between the two is the method of picking off the voltage. The alternating-current generator uses continuous slip rings while the direct-current generator has a split slip ring which interchanges the connecting wires to the loop when the current reverses. This produces a unidirectional current or voltage at the output.

Figure 15.8c shows the construction of a single 2-pole direct-current generator.

Figure 15-8d shows the various ways of connecting a direct-current generator. The field may be connected in series with the armature or in parallel with the armature. In some cases there is both a series field and a shunt field. The shunt field may also be connected to a separate source. The generator is then called a *separately excited* generator.

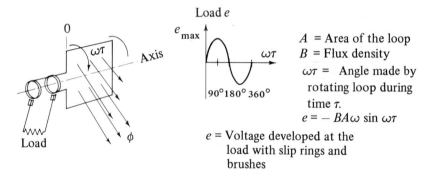

A = Area of the loop
B = Flux density
$\omega\tau$ = Angle made by rotating loop during time τ.
$e = -BA\omega \sin \omega\tau$
e = Voltage developed at the load with slip rings and brushes

Figure 15-8a

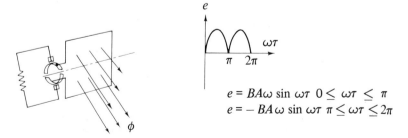

$e = BA\omega \sin \omega\tau \quad 0 \leq \omega\tau \leq \pi$
$e = -BA\omega \sin \omega\tau \quad \pi \leq \omega\tau \leq 2\pi$

Figure 15-8b

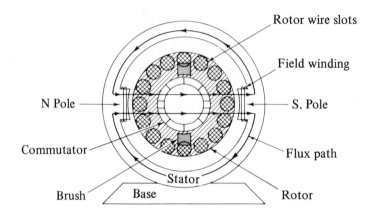

Figure 15-8c

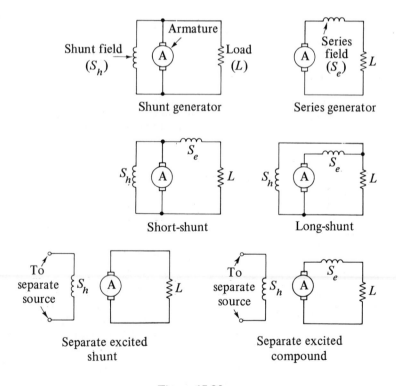

Figure 15-8d

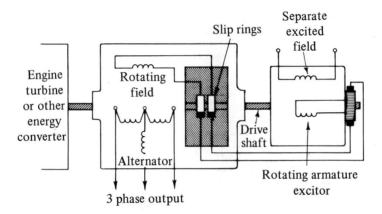

Figure 15-8e

16

Transformers

16.1 TYPES OF TRANSFORMERS

Figures 16-1a through c show some of the various types of construction and symbols used for iron core transformers.

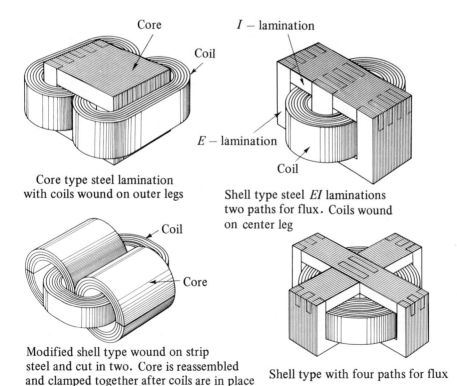

Core type steel lamination
with coils wound on outer legs

Shell type steel *EI* laminations
two paths for flux. Coils wound
on center leg

Modified shell type wound on strip
steel and cut in two. Core is reassembled
and clamped together after coils are in place

Shell type with four paths for flux

Figure 16-1a

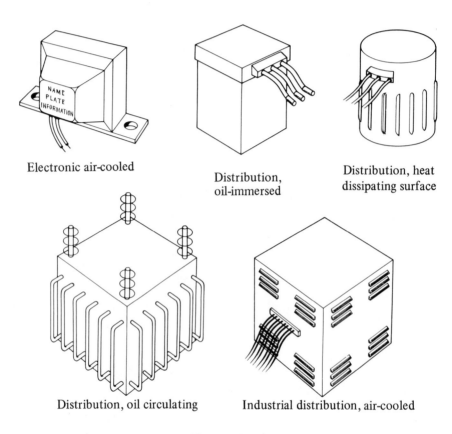

Electronic air-cooled

Distribution,
oil-immersed

Distribution, heat
dissipating surface

Distribution, oil circulating

Industrial distribution, air-cooled

Figure 16-1b

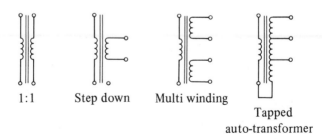

1:1   Step down   Multi winding

Tapped
auto-transformer

Figure 16-1c

16.2 TRANSFORMER MARKINGS

Figures 16-2a and b give conventional terminal markings and lead colors for power transformers.

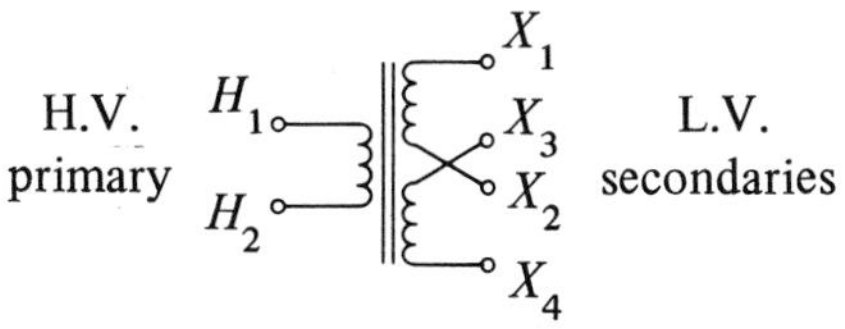

H.V. primary   L.V. secondaries

H_1, H_2 — High voltage side
X — Lower voltages

Note: H_1 is connected opposite of X_1

Figure 16-2a

Primary (not tapped)	Two black leads
Tapped primary	Black common
	Black — red
	Black — yellow (tap)
Secondary (high voltage)	Red
	Red — yellow (tap)
	Red
Secondary (L.V. heaters)	Yellow
	Yellow — blue (tap)
	Yellow
Secondary (heaters)	Green
	Green — yellow (tap)
	Green
Secondary (heaters)	Brown
	Brown — yellow (tap)
	Brown

Figure 16-2b

16.3   IMPEDANCE MATCHING

The figure below shows how transformers are used in electronics for isolation and impedance matching.

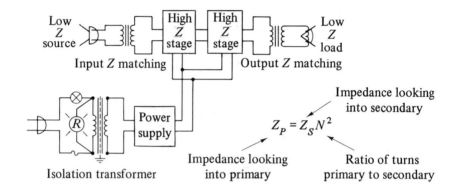

$$Z_P = Z_S N^2$$

Figure 16-3

16.4   POWER DISTRIBUTION

The diagram here is of one section of a typical power distribution system.

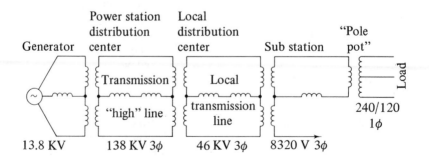

Figure 16-4

16.5 CONNECTIONS

There are a number of ways of connecting transformers in a three-phase system. These connections are shown in Figure 16-5a.

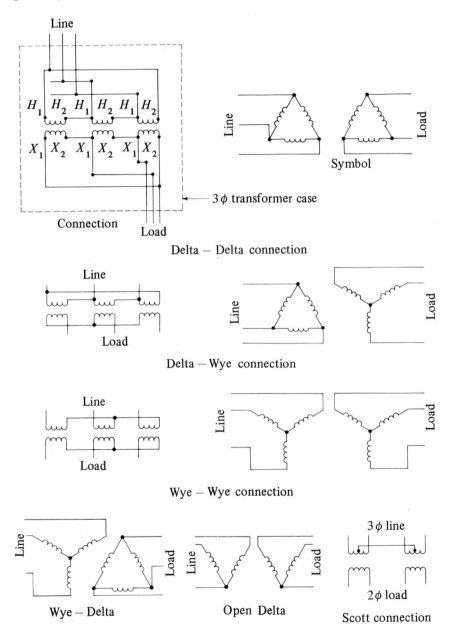

Figure 16-5a

Figure 16-5b shows some miscellaneous transformer connections including a potential transformer and a current transformer. The potential transformer is used to step down high voltage to a safe low voltage for measurement. Likewise, the current transformer is used to step down high current to lower current for measuring purposes.

Figure 16-5c shows how "taps" on a distribution transformer are used to compensate for drops in voltage along a transmission line.

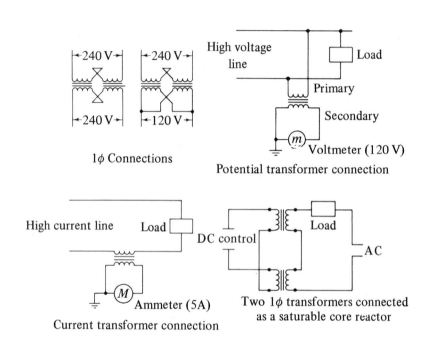

1φ Connections

Potential transformer connection

Current transformer connection

Two 1φ transformers connected as a saturable core reactor

Figure 16-5b

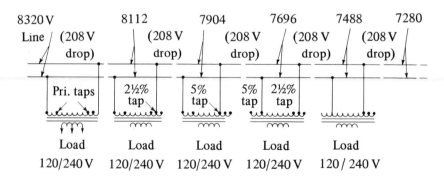

Figure 16-5c

16.6   TESTING TRANSFORMERS

Figures 16-6a through c are wiring diagrams for some of the more important tests used on power transformers. The open-circuit test is used to measure core losses and obtain the core loss resistance and magnetizing inductance for the equivalent circuit. The short-circuit test is used to determine copper losses and the equivalent series resistance and leakage inductance for the transformer.

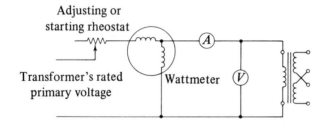

Figure 16-6a

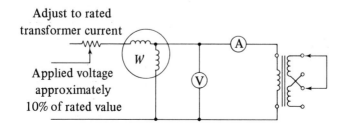

Figure 16-6b

$$R_{pri} = \frac{\text{Wattmeter reading}}{(\text{ammeter reading})^2} \quad \text{and} \quad Z_t = \frac{E}{I}$$

or $Z_t = \sqrt{R_t^2 + X_t^2}$ X_t = Leakage reactance

Figure 16-6c

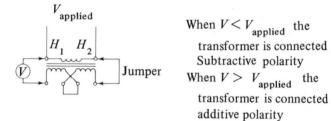

When $V < V_{applied}$ the transformer is connected Subtractive polarity
When $V > V_{applied}$ the transformer is connected additive polarity

Figure 16-6d

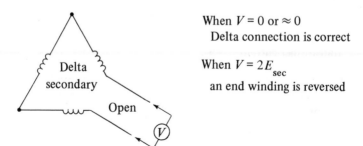

When $V = 0$ or ≈ 0
Delta connection is correct

When $V = 2E_{sec}$
an end winding is reversed

Figure 16-6e

17

Circuit Applications

17.1 SIGNAL CIRCUITS

Figure 17-1 shows the schematic of a simple buzzer system requiring three wires between stations. The buzzer at station A is controlled by the switch at station B and the buzzer at station B is controlled by the switch at station A. The disadvantage of this system is that it requires three wires.

The signal system in Figure 17-1b uses an alternating-current source and two rectifiers (a device that passes current in only one direction). It has the advantage that only two wires are necessary between stations. The light bulbs may be replaced by buzzers if desired.

A wiring diagram for a simple telephone is shown in Figure 17-1c. Ringing current is supplied from the central control station. The receiver and microphone unit are not connected to the line until the receiver is lifted from the hook.

The diagram in Figure 17-1d is for a local telegraph station. The signal between the line and ground controls the relay which switches a circuit controlling the sounder.

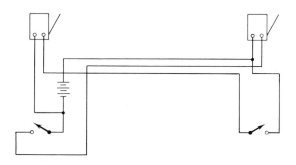

Figure 17-1a

317

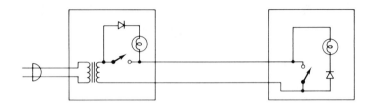

Figure 17-1b

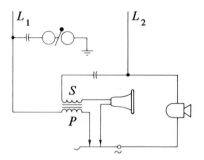

Figure 17-1c

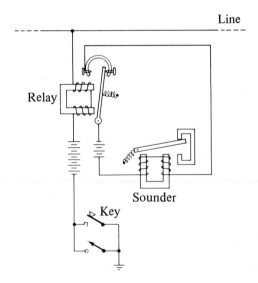

Figure 17-1d

17.2 HOUSE WIRING

The pictorial diagrams in Figures 17-2a through c show some of the typical connections used in house wiring.

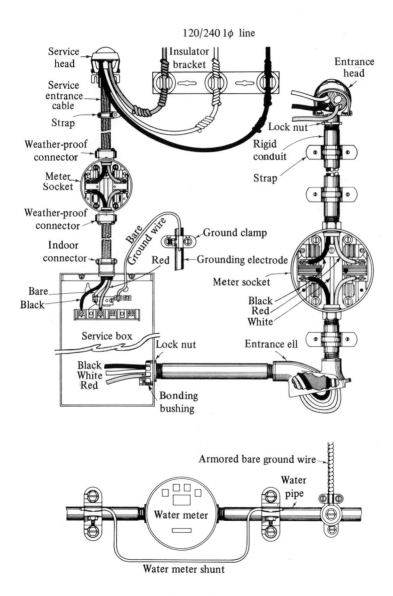

Figure 17-2a

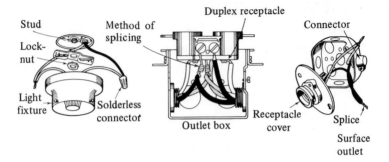

Stud
Lock-nut
Light fixture
Method of splicing
Solderless connector
Duplex receptacle
Outlet box
Receptacle cover
Connector
Splice
Surface outlet

Figure 17-2b

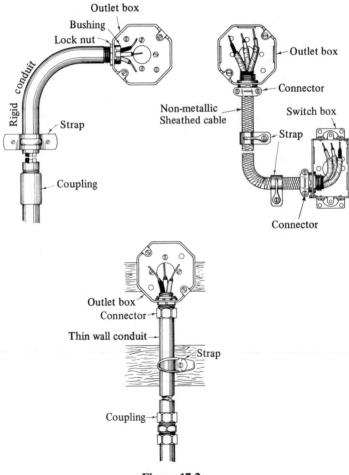

Outlet box
Bushing
Lock nut
Rigid conduit
Strap
Coupling

Outlet box
Connector
Non-metallic Sheathed cable
Switch box
Strap
Connector

Outlet box
Connector
Thin wall conduit
Strap
Coupling

Figure 17-2c

Figure 17-2d shows some schematics for the fluorescent lights. The starter is essentially a switch which is closed when the line voltage is first applied. It supplies current to the filaments in the ends of the fluorescent tube for a duration of time sufficient to let the gas ionize. Once ionized the starter opens and the current in the tube is limited by the inductive reactance of ballast.

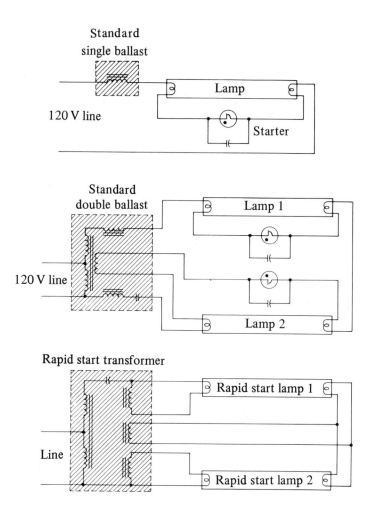

Figure 17-2d

17.3 RELAY WIRING

The electromagnetic relay plays a very important part in the control of many electric circuits. The examples in the figures below are but a few of many relay control circuits. The overcurrent and overvoltages relay circuits are used to disconnect the load from the line at a certain predetermined current or voltage.

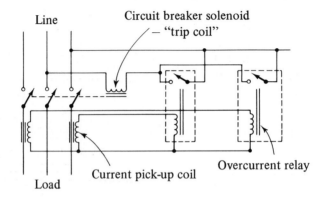

Figure 17-3a

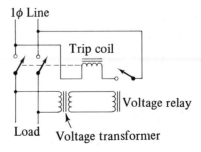

Figure 17-3b

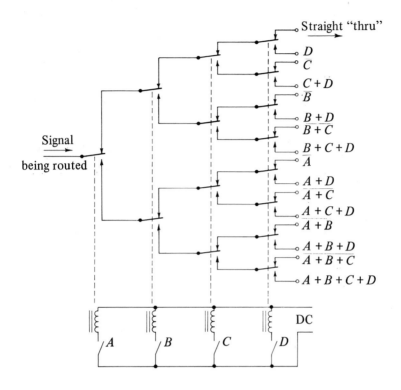

Figure 17-3c

17.4 RECTIFICATION AND FILTERS

A diode is a device which passes current in only one direction. Hence, it can be used to obtain direct current from alternating current. This process is called *rectification*. Figure 17-4a shows some single-phase rectifier circuits which find frequent use in electronic power supplies. The half-wave rectifier passes only one-half of each cycle of alternating current while a full-wave rectifier passes the entire cycle but inverts one-half of the cycle yielding a current in only one direction.

As seen in the figures, the output of the rectifier circuits is not smooth like the output from a battery. Although the output from a three-phase circuit is smoother than that of a single-phase rectifier it is still not as smooth as sometimes required. To make the current more like that from a battery an RC filter like the one shown in Figure 17-4c is used.

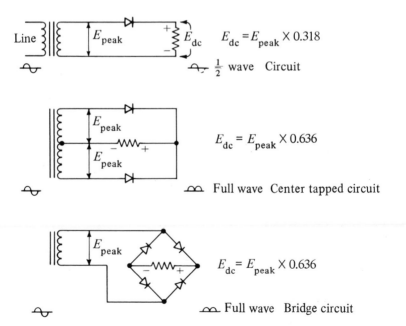

$E_{dc} = E_{peak} \times 0.318$

$\frac{1}{2}$ wave   Circuit

$E_{dc} = E_{peak} \times 0.636$

Full wave Center tapped circuit

$E_{dc} = E_{peak} \times 0.636$

Full wave Bridge circuit

Figure 17-4a

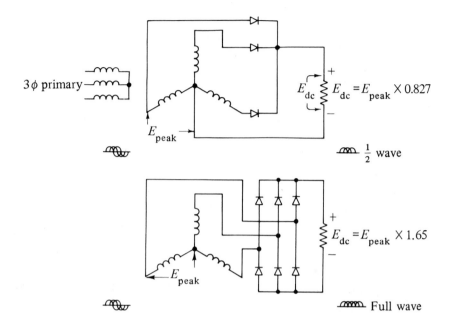

Figure 17-4b

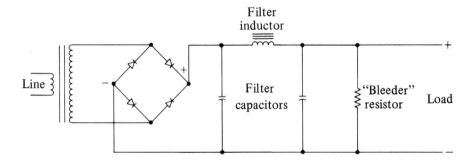

Figure 17-4c

17.5 AUTOMOBILE WIRING

The figure on the next page is a schematic diagram of the electrical wiring in a typical automobile.

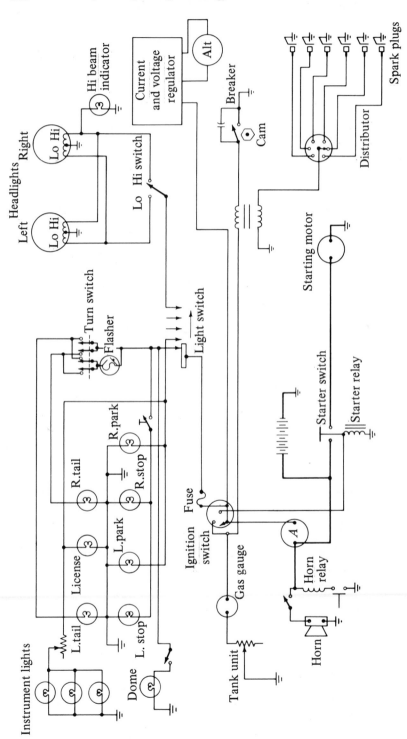

Figure 17-5

18

A-C and D-C Motors

18.1 DEVELOPMENT OF MOTOR FORCES

In an alternating-current motor it is necessary to establish a rotating magnetic field. Figure 18-1a indicates how such a rotating field is obtained with a three-phase voltage and 3 coils spaced 120° apart.

Figure 18-1b shows the development of forces in a simple two-conductor direct-current motor.

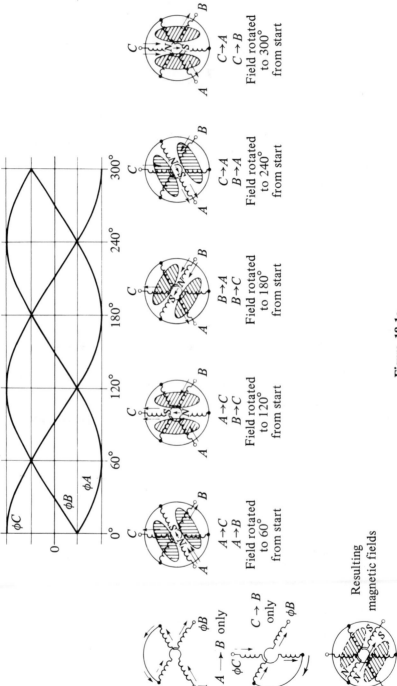

Figure 18-1a

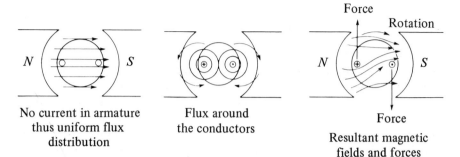

Force

Rotation

N ( ) *S*

No current in armature
thus uniform flux
distribution

Flux around
the conductors

N ( ) *S*

Force

Resultant magnetic
fields and forces

Figure 18-1b

18.2 MOTOR CONVERSION FORMULAS

The table here gives important formulas relating current, voltage, power, and torque for various types of motors.

To Find	Direct Current	Alternating Current		
		Single phase	Two phase†	Three phase
Amperes when Horse Power input is known	$\dfrac{HP \times 746}{E \times \text{EFFiciency}^*}$	$\dfrac{HP \times 746}{E \times E_{ff} \times P.F.}$	$\dfrac{HP \times 746}{E \times 2 \times E_{ff} \times P.F.}$	$\dfrac{HP \times 746}{E \times 1.73 \times E_{ff} \times P.F.}$
Amperes when KW is known	$\dfrac{KW \times 1000}{E}$	$\dfrac{KW \times 1000}{E \times P.F.}$	$\dfrac{KW \times 1000}{E \times 2 \times P.F.}$	$\dfrac{KW \times 1000}{E \times 1.73 \times P.F.}$
Amperes when KVA is known		$\dfrac{KVA \times 1000}{E}$	$\dfrac{KVA \times 1000}{E \times 2}$	$\dfrac{KVA \times 1000}{E \times 1.73}$
Kilowatts	$\dfrac{I \times E}{1000}$	$\dfrac{I \times E \times P.F.}{1000}$	$\dfrac{I \times E \times 2 \times P.F.}{1000}$	$\dfrac{I \times E \times 1.73 \times P.F.}{1000}$
KVA		$\dfrac{I \times E}{1000}$	$\dfrac{I \times E \times 2}{1000}$	$\dfrac{I \times E \times 1.73}{1000}$
Power factor		$\dfrac{\text{Kilowatts}}{\text{KVA}}$	$\dfrac{\text{Kilowatts}}{\text{KVA}}$	$\dfrac{\text{Kilowatts}}{\text{KVA}}$
Horse Power (output)	$\dfrac{I \times E \times E_{ff}}{746}$	$\dfrac{I \times E \times E_{ff} \times P.F.}{746}$	$\dfrac{I \times E \times 2 \times E_{ff} \times P.F.}{746}$	$\dfrac{I \times E \times 1.73 \times E_{ff} \times P.F.}{746}$

Torque (T)
in inch–pounds $T = \dfrac{63000 \times HP}{RPM}$

* EFFiciency or E_{ff} in percent

$\dagger$ Two phase 4 wire given for 2ϕ 3 wire substitute 1.41 for 2

Figure 18-2

18.3   THREE-PHASE MOTORS

The stator of a three-phase motor can be connected in either wye or delta as shown in Figure 18-3a.

In a three-phase induction type motor the rotor may be either of the solid type as in Figure 18-3b or of the wound type shown in Figure 18-3c.

In the synchronous motor, which will only run at one constant speed, the rotor must be wound and supplied with a direct current as shown in Figure 18-3d. The synchronous motor acts as a capacitive load if the current in the rotor is maintained above a certain value and acts as an inductive load if the rotor current is below that value. The synchronous motor may also be used as a generator when driven mechanically.

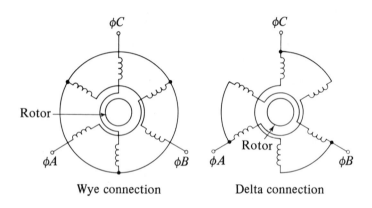

Wye connection   Delta connection

Figure 18-3a

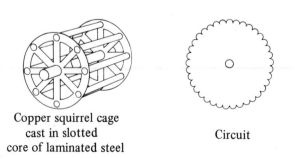

Copper squirrel cage
cast in slotted
core of laminated steel

Circuit

Figure 18-3b

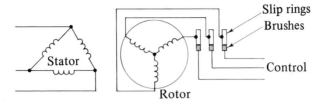

Figure 18-3c

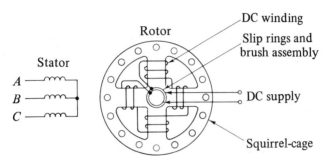

Figure 18-3d

18.4   SINGLE-PHASE MOTORS

A universal motor may be used on either alternating current or direct current and is therefore often called an ac-dc motor. As shown in Figure 18-4a the field and armature are connected in series.

Single-phase motors require some method of starting. Most of these motors are named after the principle used in starting them. Figures 18-4a through g show some common single-phase motor connections.

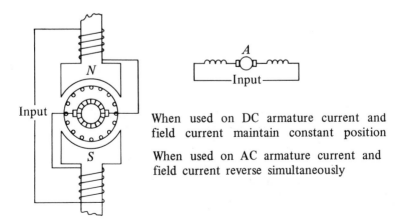

When used on DC armature current and field current maintain constant position

When used on AC armature current and field current reverse simultaneously

Figure 18-4a

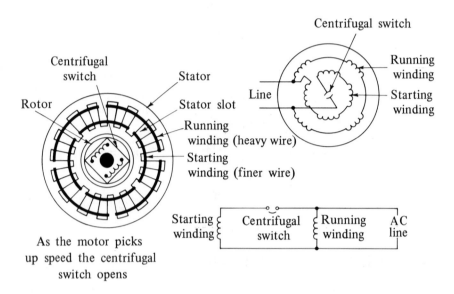

As the motor picks
up speed the centrifugal
switch opens

Figure 18-4b

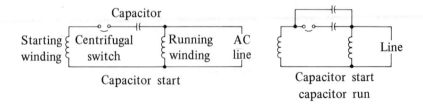

Figure 18-4c

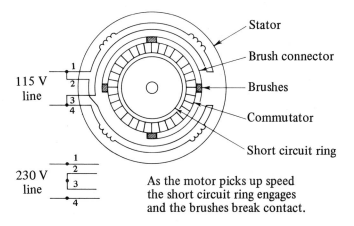

As the motor picks up speed
the short circuit ring engages
and the brushes break contact.

Figure 18-4d

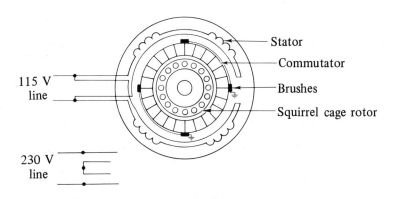

Figure 18-4e

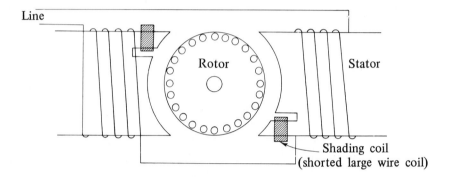

Figure 18-4f

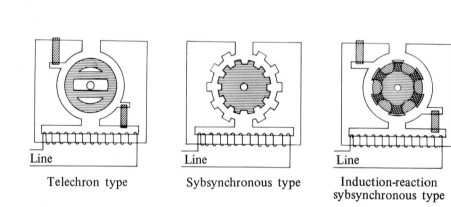

Telechron type   Sybsynchronous type   Induction-reaction
sybsynchronous type

Figure 18-4g

18.5 TWO-PHASE-MOTOR CONNECTIONS

The rotating field in a two-phase motor is produced in the same manner as that in a three-phase motor except that the voltages are 90° out of phase and the windings are spaced 90° apart. Two-phase motors are used primarily in control systems with one winding connected to a reference voltage and the other winding connected to a control voltage.

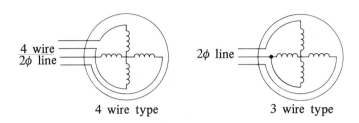

4 wire type   **3 wire type**

Figure 18-5

18.6   SERVOMECHANISMS

Figures 18-6a through e show how motors and generators are used in various types of control systems.

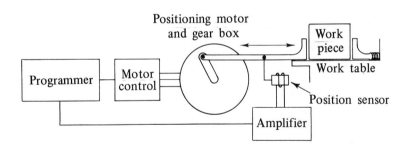

Figure 18-6a

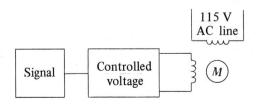

Figure 18-6b

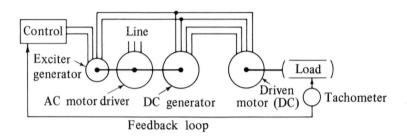

Figure 18-6c

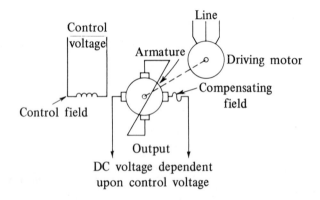

Figure 18-6d

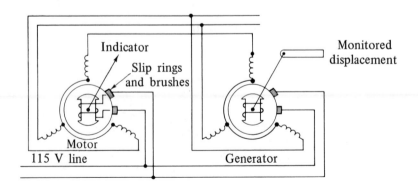

Figure 18-6e

19

Machine Control

19.1 COMPONENTS

Figures 19-1a through c are diagrams of some simple motor starting and reversing switching circuits. A table of symbols used in control circuits is given in Figure 19-1d. The table in Figure 19-1e gives the starter sizes for three-phase motors.

Contactor

Thermal element

Pilot lamp
with yellow lite

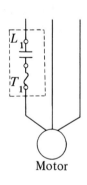

Motor

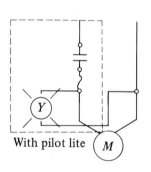

With pilot lite M

Figure 19-1a

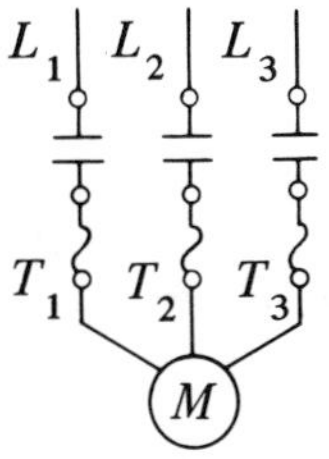

L_1, L_2, L_3 Line connections

T_1, T_2, T_3 Load terminals

Figure 19-1b

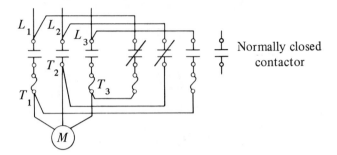

Normally closed contactor

Figure 19-1c

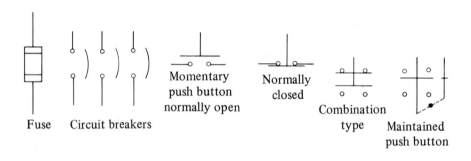

Fuse   Circuit breakers   Momentary push button normally open   Normally closed   Combination type   Maintained push button

Main contactor coil   Forward coil   Reverse coil   Control relay   Under voltage coil   Over voltage coil   Time delay relay

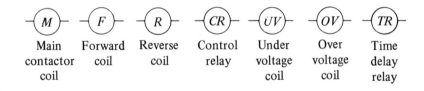

Actuated by main contactor   Over load contact N.C.   Actuated by CR   Plugging switch

Figure 19-1d

3 Phase Horse Power Ratings

Average operating conditions

	110 V	220 V	440 V	$I_{continuous}$	Starter size
	¾	1	1	9	00
	2	3	5	18	0
	3	7½	10	27	1
	7½	15	25	45	2
	15	30	50	90	3
	25	50	100	135	4
	—	100	200	270	5
	—	200	400	540	6
	—	300	600	810	7
	—	450	900	1,215	8
	—	800	1,600	2,250	9

(Horse Power axis at left)

Figure 19-1e

19.2 ACROSS-THE-LINE STARTERS

A simple three-phase starter with a single on button and off button is shown in Figure 19-2a. Figure 19-2b is like that of a except that it has relay control of the direct-current main contactor coil. Figure 19-2c shows a starter circuit with two remote stop-start stations.

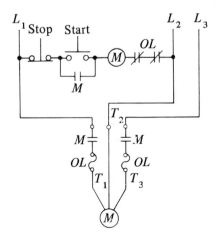

Figure 19-2a

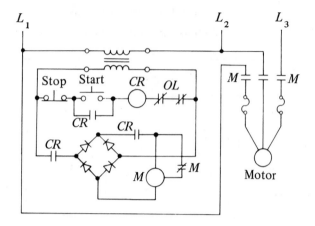

Figure 19-2b

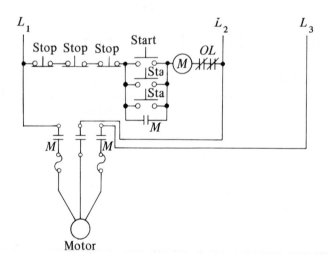

Figure 19-2c

19.3 REVERSING SWITCHES

Figures 19-3a and b are diagrams of typical Forward-Reverse-Stop switches.

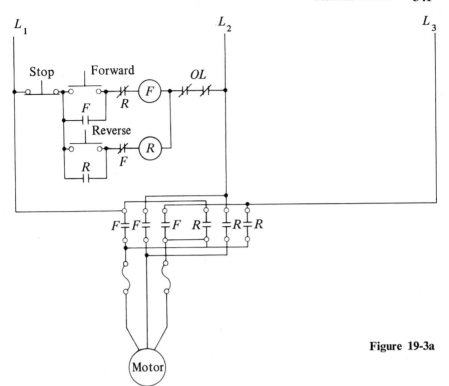

Figure 19-3a

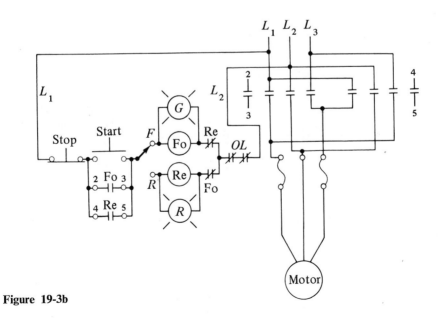

Figure 19-3b

19.4 REDUCED VOLTAGE STARTING

In starting large motors the voltage must be reduced to a point where the starting current is not excessive. The figures below are circuit diagrams of starting circuits that apply reduced voltage for starting.

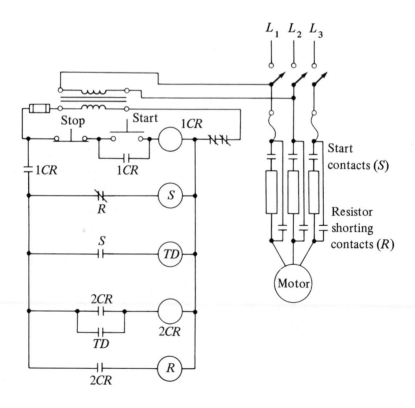

Figure 19-4a

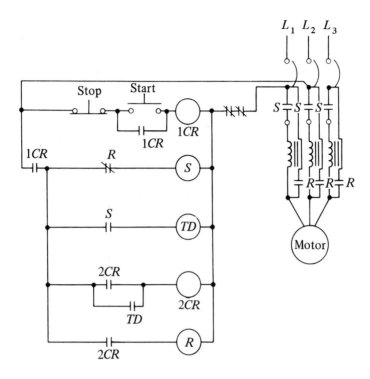

Figure 19-4b

19.5 BRAKING   AND PLUGGING

In certain applications it is necessary to stop and start or reverse quickly. Circuits for this purpose are shown in Figures 19-5a and b.

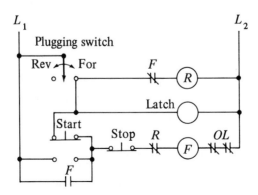

Figure 19-5a

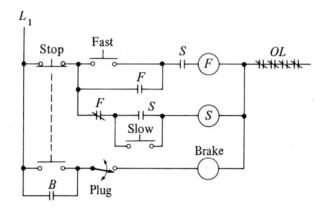

Figure 19-5b

19.6 SPEED CONTROL

It is easier to control the speed of direct-current motors than that of alternating-current motors. Therefore many direct-current motors are used where variable speed control is necessary. Figure 19-6a shows some methods of speed control for direct-current motors. All of these work on the principle of increasing the magnetic field for lower speed and decreasing the magnetic field strength for increased speed. The control is done with a simple rheostat.

Although speed control of alternating-current motors is more difficult, some of the more common methods employed are shown in Figure 19-6b.

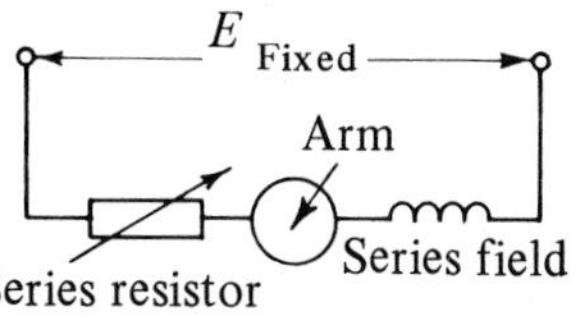

E Fixed

Arm

Series resistor   Series field

$$\text{Speed} \approx K \ \frac{E - I\,(R_A + R_{\text{Arm}} + R_F)}{\phi}$$

$\uparrow R \longrightarrow \downarrow S$

Series motor with field resistor

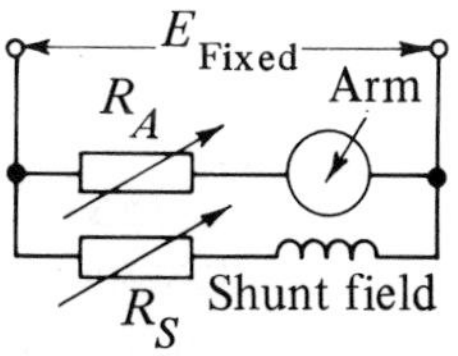

E Fixed   Arm

R_A

R_S Shunt field

$$S \approx K \ \frac{E - I_{\text{Arm}}\,(R_A + R_{\text{Arm}})}{\phi}$$

$\uparrow R_A \longrightarrow \downarrow S$

$\uparrow R_S \longrightarrow \uparrow S$

Shunt motor with field and armature resistors

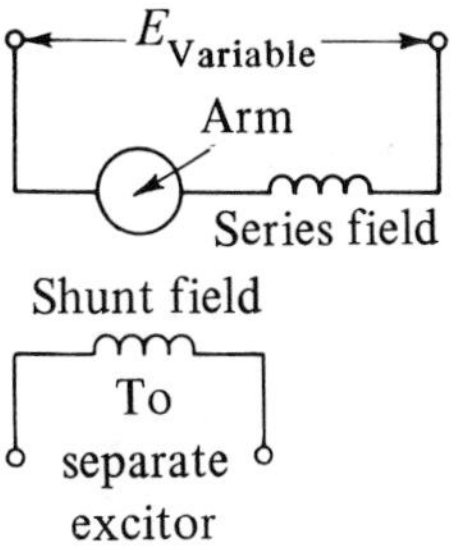

E Variable

Arm

Series field

Shunt field

To separate excitor

$$S \approx K \ \frac{E_{\text{Variable}} - I_{\text{Arm}}\,(R_{\text{Arm}} + R_{SF})}{\phi_{\text{Shunt}} + \phi_{\text{Series}}}$$

$\uparrow E \longrightarrow \uparrow S$

Compound motor with speed controlled by the terminal voltage.

$\uparrow$ Increase in

$\longrightarrow$ Results in

$\downarrow$ Decreasing

S = Speed of armature in RPM

K = Constant

ϕ = Flux/pole

R_F = Field resistance

R_{Arm} = Armature resistance

R = Armature series resistor.

Figure 19-6a

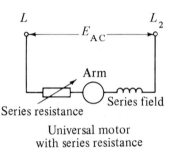

Universal motor
with series resistance

Universal motor
with tapped field.

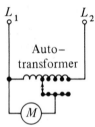

Autotransformer speed control.
Motor may be shaded pole
or perament-split capacitor type.

Other methods include Ward-
Leonard, frequency variation,
rotor voltage adjustment,
brush shift and Kaemer system.

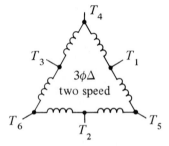

Tapped windings of a
3ϕ motor
(Low : T_1 T_2 T_3 w/T_4 T_5 T_6
tied together
High : T_4 T_5 T_6 w/T_1 T_2 T_3 open)

Figure 19-6b

19.7   SEQUENTIAL   CONTROL

Figures 19-7a and b are wiring diagrams of sequential control circuits like those used in washing machines and on assembly lines.

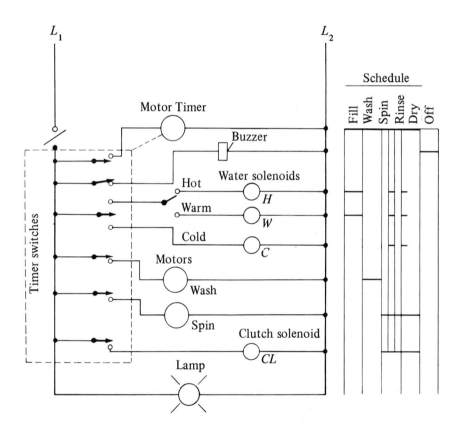

Figure 19-7a

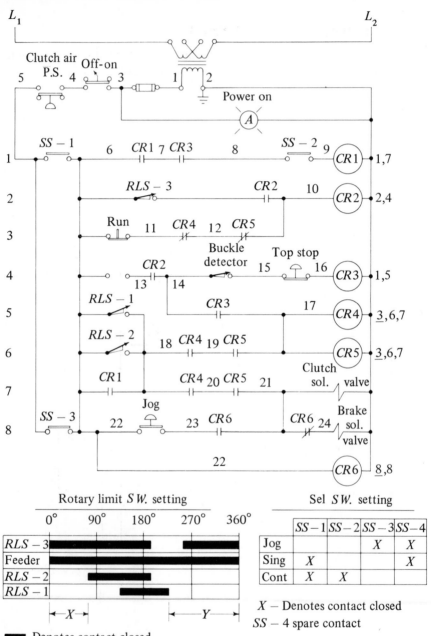

Figure 19-7b

20

Electrical Instruments

20.1 METER MOVEMENTS

One of the most used meter movements is the D'Arsonval movement
shown in Figure 20-1a. The principle for the operation of such a meter is the
same as that for the electric motor. A permanent magnet provides a
magnetic field in which a coil is free to rotate. Current in the proper direction
in the coil produces a torque. The coil then rotates until the counter torque
from a spring prevents it from turning further. The amount of rotation of the
coil is proportional to the average current in the coil. Such a meter responds
only to average current. It is used only to measure direct current.

Figure 20-1b shows another similar movement which uses a moving magnet and fixed coil. It is also for direct current measurement.

A common meter movement for measuring alternating current or direct
current is the iron vane meter shown in Figure 20-1c. It is also more rugged
than the D'Arsonval movement.

If the permanent magnet of a D'Arsonval movement is replaced by
two stationary coils we have an electrodynamic movement like that shown
in Figure 20-1d. By connecting the coils in series it can be used to measure
alternating currents. It can also be connected to measure power, power
factor, and capacitance as shown in Figure 20-1e.

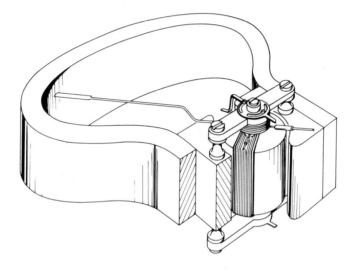

Figure 20-1a

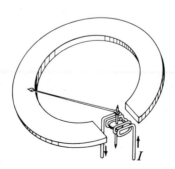

Figure 20-1b

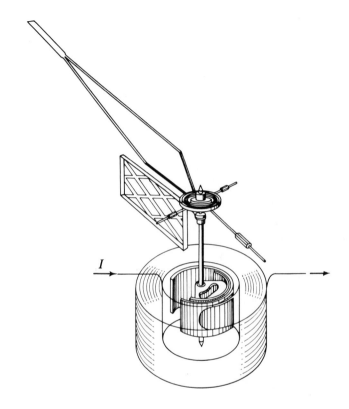

Figure 20-1c

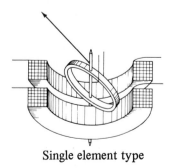

Single element type

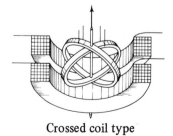

Crossed coil type

Figure 20-1d

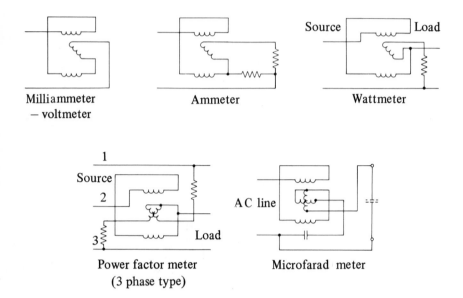

Milliammeter
– voltmeter

Ammeter

Wattmeter

Power factor meter
(3 phase type)

Microfarad meter

Figure 20-1e

20.2 VOLTMETERS AND AMMETERS

All meter movements have a certain amount of internal resistance R_m and require a certain amount of current I_m to read full scale. This means that a voltage of $V_m = I_m R_m$ will deflect the meter to full scale. Any other voltage will deflect it proportionally. Therefore, the meter may be used as a voltmeter. If the basic meter voltage is too small for the voltage to be measured, a series resistor can be added to increase the full-scale rating. The value of the series resistor is determined by the equation in Figure 20-2a. A voltmeter must always be connected across the two points where the voltage is to be determined.

Since the indication on a meter movement is proportional to the current through the coil, the meter can be used to measure current. Such a meter is called an *ammeter*. If the full-scale rating is too small it can be increased by connecting a resistor in shunt with the meter as shown in Figure 20-2b. In order to measure current with an ammeter it is always necessary to open the circuit at the point where the current is desired and connect the ammeter in series with the circuit at that point.

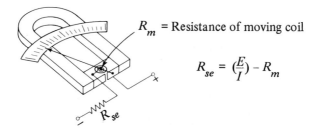

R_m = Resistance of moving coil

$$R_{se} = \left(\frac{E}{I}\right) - R_m$$

Figure 20-2a

$$R_{sh} = \frac{R_m}{(n-1)}$$

n = scale
multiplication factor

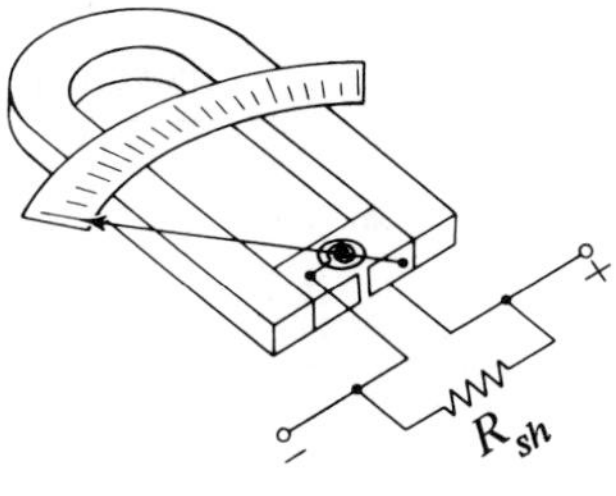

Figure 20-2b

20.3 OHMMETERS

By using a known source and an ammeter or voltmeter it is possible to measure electrical resistance. Such an instrument is called an *ohmmeter*. When measuring resistance with an ohmmeter one should be very careful to remove all power from the circuit being measured. Some circuits for measuring resistance are shown in Figures 20-3a through c.

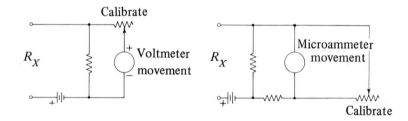

Figure 20-3a

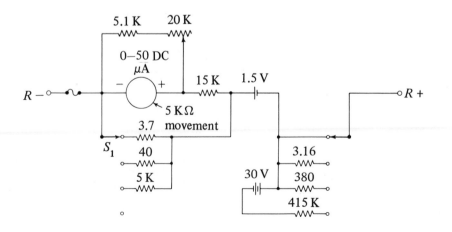

Figure 20-3b

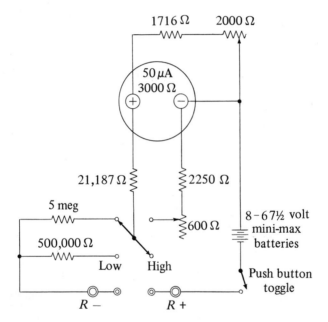

Figure 20-3c

20.4 MULTIMETERS

By special switching arrangements a meter can be used to measure voltage, current, or resistance. Such an instrument is called a *multimeter* or *volt-ohm-meter*. Figures 20-4a through e show the circuits in such an instrument.

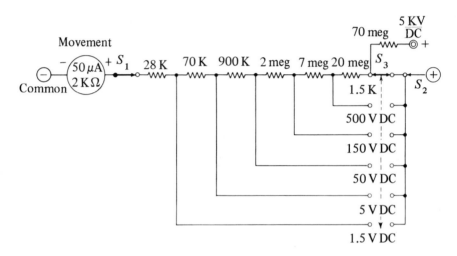

Figure 20-4a

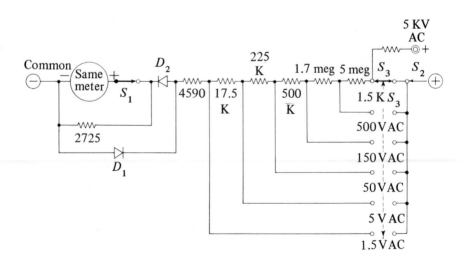

Figure 20-4b

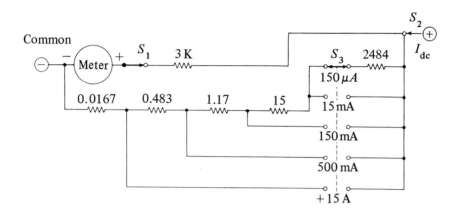

Figure 20-4c

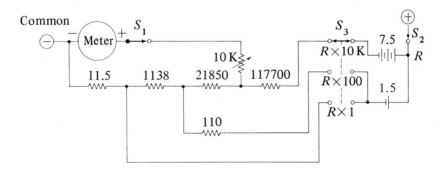

Figure 20-4d

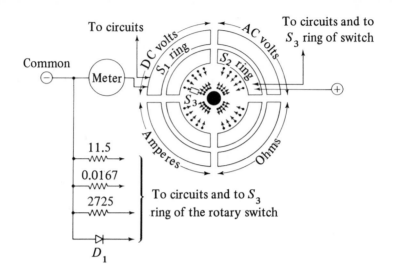

To circuits

Common

Meter

11.5

0.0167

2725

D_1

To circuits and to S_3 ring of switch

To circuits and to S_3 ring of the rotary switch

Figure 20-4e

20.5   OSCILLOSCOPES

The oscilloscope is an instrument for observing waveforms of voltage or current. Its main component is a cathode ray tube similar to the ones used in TV sets. Figures 20-5a and b show the construction of such a tube. The filament heats a cathode to a very high temperature causing it to emit a beam of electrons toward the face of the tube. The electron beam is accelerated and focused by the various plates and grids in the tube. When the beam strikes the chemically treated surface of the tube it produces visible light. The beam may be moved up and down and back and forth by the voltages applied to the vertical and horizontal deflection plates.

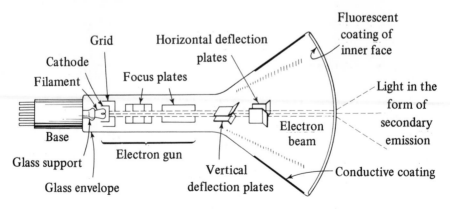

Figure 20-5a

A and B vertical deflection plates
C and D horizontal delection plates

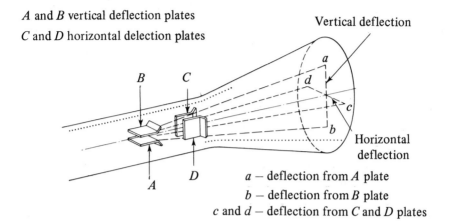

Vertical deflection

Horizontal deflection

a – deflection from A plate
b – deflection from B plate
c and d – deflection from C and D plates

Figure 20-5b

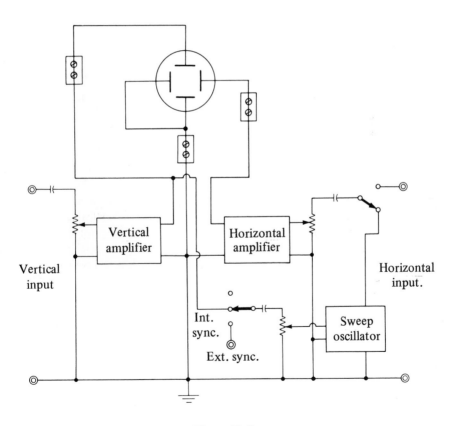

Vertical input

Vertical amplifier

Horizontal amplifier

Horizontal input.

Int. sync.

Ext. sync.

Sweep oscillator

Figure 20-5c

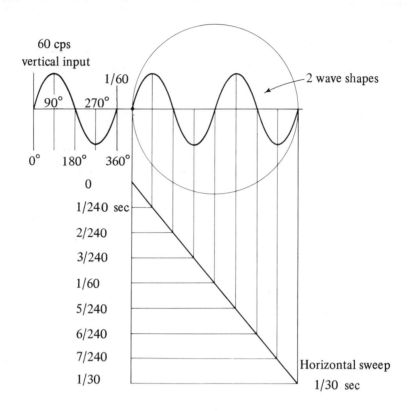

Figure 20-5d

In an oscilloscope a sweep oscillator is connected to the horizontal plates of the cathode ray tube. The sweep oscillator moves the beam across the face of the tube linearly at a given time rate. The signal to be observed is amplified by the vertical amplifier and applied to the vertical deflection plates causing the beam to move up and down to a degree proportional to the amplitude of the signal input. Figure 20-5d shows how the vertical input and the sweep combine to form a pattern which is the waveform of the input signal.

APPENDIX

COMPLEX NUMBERS

Figure A-1 is a view of the *complex plane*. Positive and negative real numbers are plotted along the horizontal axis, which is called the *real axis*. The vertical axis is called the *imaginary axis* and consists of the set of all imaginary numbers.

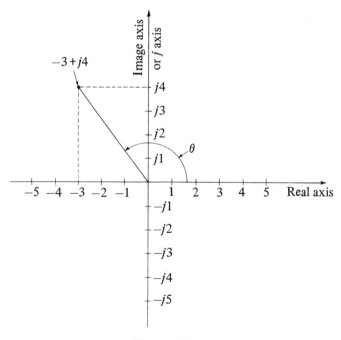

Figure A-1

361

Imaginary numbers are the square roots of the negative real numbers, which can always be expressed as a positive real number times $\sqrt{-1}$. The standard symbol of $\sqrt{-1}$ is i or j. We use j here so that there is no confusion with the symbol for current. Thus, imaginary numbers are expressed as $j1$, $j2$, $j3$, etc.

Any point in the complex plane can be represented by a *complex number*, which consists of a real number part and an imaginary number part. For example, the point 3 units to the left of the origin and 4 units above the origin is written in the form of a complex number as $-3 + j4$. The number 3 is the *real part* and 4 is the *imaginary part*.

When a complex number is expressed as $a + jb$ it is said to be in rectangular form. It may also be expressed in the form of $A \ \underline{/\theta°}$ when A is the straight line distance of the point from the origin, and θ is the angle which a straight line from the origin to the point makes with the real axis. This is called the *polar form*.

Sometimes it is convenient to express a complex number in rectangular form while at other times it is more convenient to express it in polar form. Therefore, it is necessary to be able to convert readily from one form to the other. The right triangle in Figure A-2 shows the relation between the

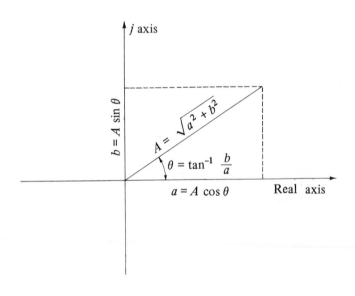

Figure A-2

rectangular form and the polar form. To convert a number, $a + jb$, from rectangular to polar form

$$A = \sqrt{a^2 + b^2}$$

$$\theta = \tan^{-1} \frac{b}{a}$$

or

$$\theta = \cos^{-1} \frac{a}{A}$$

or

$$\theta = \sin^{-1} \frac{b}{A}$$

For example, the number $3 + j4$ is found as follows:

$$A = \sqrt{3^2 + 4^2} = 5$$

$$\theta = \tan^{-1} \frac{4}{3} = 53.1°$$

or

$$\theta = \cos^{-1} \frac{3}{5} = 53.1°$$

or

$$\theta = \sin^{-1} \frac{4}{5} = 53.1°$$

To convert a number, $A\,\underline{/\theta°}$, from polar to rectangular form

$$a = A \cos \theta$$

$$b = A \sin \theta$$

$$a + jb = A (\cos \theta + j \sin \theta)$$

For example, the number $10\,\underline{/30°}$ is converted to rectangular form as follows:

$$a = 10 \cos 30° = 8.66$$

$$b = 10 \sin 30° = 5.0$$

$$a + jb = 8.66 + j5$$

COMPLEX NUMBER REPRESENTATION OF PHASORS OR VECTORS

From the preceding sections it should be clear that the line from the origin to the point can represent a vector or phasor, and thus the complex number used to represent the point can be used to represent the vector or phasor. In the case of a sinusoidal voltage (the same applies to current)

$$e = E_m \sin (\omega t + \theta)$$

The phasor is shown as a line from the origin at an angle of $\theta°$ having a length of E_m units. In the form of a complex number, it can therefore be expressed as

$$\mathbf{E} = E_m \underline{/\theta°}$$

or

$$\mathbf{E} = E_m (\cos \theta° + jE_m \sin \theta°)$$

For example, if

$$e = 10 \sin (377t + 30°)$$

$$\mathbf{E} = 10 \underline{/30°}$$

or

$$\mathbf{E} = 10 \cos 30° + j10 \sin 30°$$

$$= 8.66 + j5$$

It is customary, however, to express voltages and currents as rms phasors. Thus, the voltage in the previous example would be

$$\mathbf{E} = \frac{10}{\sqrt{2}} \underline{/30°} = 7.07 \underline{/30°}$$

THE j OPERATOR

The j operator can be thought of as rotating a phasor or vector counterclockwise by an angle of 90°. It is equal to $\sqrt{-1}$.

$$j = \sqrt{-1} = 1 \underline{/90°}$$

$$j^2 = -1 = 1 \underline{/180°}$$

$$j^3 = -j = -\sqrt{-1} = 1 \underline{/270°} = 1 \underline{/-90°}$$

$$j^4 = 1 \underline{/0°}$$

EQUALITY OF COMPLEX NUMBERS

Two complex numbers are equal when their real parts are equal and their imaginary parts are equal.

$$a_1 + jb_1 = a_2 + jb_2$$

when

$$a_1 = a_2$$

and

$$b_1 = b_2$$

ADDITION OF COMPLEX NUMBERS

The addition of complex numbers is accomplished by adding up all the real parts and then all the imaginary parts.

$$(4 + j3) + (3 - j4) = (4 + 3) + j(4 - 3) = 7 - j1$$

SUBTRACTION

The subtraction of complex numbers is accomplished by subtracting the real parts and then the imaginary parts.

$$(4 + j3) - (3 - j4) = (4 - 3) + j[3 - (- 4)] = 1 + j7$$

MULTIPLICATION

Multiplication may be carried out in both the polar form and the rectangular form.

In rectangular form

$$(4 + j3)(3 - j4) = [(4)(3) - (3)(- 4)] + j[(3)(3) + (4)(- 4)]$$
$$= 24 - j7$$

In polar form

$$(A \underline{/\theta_1{}^\circ})(B \underline{/\theta_2{}^\circ}) = AB \underline{/\theta_1 + \theta_2}$$

$$(5 \underline{/36.9^\circ})(5 \underline{/- 53.1^\circ}) = (5)(5) \underline{/(36.9^\circ) + (- 53.1^\circ)}$$

$$= 25 \underline{/16.2^\circ}$$

DIVISION

Division may be carried out in either the rectangular or polar form. In rectangular form the numerator and denominator must first be multiplied by the conjugate of the denominator. The conjugate is formed by changing sign of the imaginary part

$$\left(\frac{4 + j3}{3 - j4}\right)\left(\frac{3 + j4}{3 - j4}\right) = \frac{[(4)(3) - (3)(4)] + j[(3)(3) - (4)(4)]}{(3)(3) + (4)(4)}$$

$$= \frac{0 - j7}{25}$$

$$= \frac{7}{25}\underline{/- 90^\circ}$$

In polar form

$$\frac{A\ \angle\theta_1}{B\ \angle\theta_2} = \frac{A}{B}\ \angle 0_1 - 0_2$$

$$\frac{5\ \angle 36.9}{5\ \angle -53.1} = \frac{5}{5}\ \angle (36.9) - (53.1)$$

$$= 1\ \angle 90°$$

POWERS

To raise a complex number to the nth power, express it in polar form, take the nth power of the magnitude and multiply the angle by n

$$(A\ \angle\theta°)^n = A^n\ \angle n\theta$$

$$(5\ \angle 36.9°)^2 = 5^2\ \angle 2\,(36.9°)$$

$$= 25\ \angle 73.8°$$

ROOTS

To extract the roots of a complex number, express it in polar form. Then

$$n\sqrt{A\ \angle\theta°} = \sqrt[n]{A}\ \angle \frac{0 + 360(q)}{n}\quad q\ 0, 1, 2, 3, \ldots, n-1$$

$$2\sqrt{5\ \angle 36.9°} = 2\sqrt{5}\ \angle \frac{36.9}{2} = 2.236\ \angle 18.45°$$

and

$$2\sqrt{5}\ \angle \frac{36.9 + 360}{2} = 2.236\ \angle 198.4°$$

Natural Trigonometric Functions For Decimal Fractions of a Degree

Deg.	Sin	Cos	Tan	Cot	Deg.	Deg.	Sin	Cos	Tan	Cot	Deg.
0.0	.00000	1.0000	.00000		90.0	6.0	.10453	0.9945	.10510	9.514	84.0
.1	.00175	1.0000	.00175	573.0	.9	.1	.10626	.9943	.10687	9.357	.9
.2	.00349	1.0000	.00349	286.5	.8	.2	.10800	.9942	.10863	9.205	.8
.3	.00524	1.0000	.00524	191.0	.7	.3	.10973	.9940	.11040	9.058	.7
.4	.00698	1.0000	.00698	143.24	.6	.4	.11147	.9938	.11217	8.915	.6
.5	.00873	1.0000	.00873	114.59	.5	.5	.11320	.9936	.11394	8.777	.5
.6	.01047	0.9999	.01047	95.49	.4	.6	.11494	.9934	.11570	8.643	.4
.7	.01222	.9999	.01222	81.85	.3	.7	.11667	.9932	.11747	8.513	.3
.8	.01396	.9999	.01396	71.62	.2	.8	.11840	.9930	.11924	8.386	2.2
.9	.01571	.9999	.01571	63.66	.1	.9	.12014	.9928	.12101	8.264	.1
1.0	.01745	0.9998	.01746	57.29	89.0	7.0	.12187	0.9925	.12278	8.144	83.0
.1	.01920	.9998	.01920	52.08	.9	.1	.12360	.9923	.12456	8.028	.9
.2	.02094	.9998	.02095	47.74	.8	.2	.12533	.9921	.12633	7.916	.8
.3	.02269	.9997	.02269	44.07	.7	.3	.12706	.9919	.12810	7.806	.7
.4	.02443	.9997	.02444	40.92	.6	.4	.12880	.9917	.12988	7.700	.6
.5	.02618	.9997	.02619	38.19	.5	.5	.13053	.9914	.13165	7.596	.5
.6	.02792	.9996	.02793	35.80	.4	.6	.13226	.9912	.13343	7.495	.4
.7	.02967	.9996	.02968	33.69	.3	.7	.13399	.9910	.13521	7.396	.3
.8	.03141	.9995	.03143	31.82	.2	.8	.13572	.9907	.23698	7.300	.2
.9	.03316	.9995	.03317	30.14	.1	.9	.13744	.9905	.13876	7.207	.1
2.0	.03490	0.9994	.03492	28.64	88.0	8.0	.13917	.9903	.14054	7.115	82.0
.1	.03664	.9993	.03667	27.27	.9	.1	.14090	.9900	.14232	7.026	.9
.2	.03839	.9993	.03842	26.03	.8	.2	.14263	.9898	.14410	6.940	.8
.3	.04013	.9992	.04016	24.90	.7	.3	.14436	.9895	.14588	6.855	.7
.4	.04188	.9991	.04191	23.86	.6	.4	.14608	.9893	.14767	6.772	.6
.5	.04362	.9990	.04366	22.90	.5	.5	.14781	.9890	.14945	6.691	.5
.6	.04536	.9990	.04541	22.02	.4	.6	.14954	.9888	.15124	6.612	.4
.7	.04711	.9989	.04716	21.20	.3	.7	.15126	.9885	.15302	6.535	.3
.8	.04885	.9988	.04891	20.45	.2	.8	.15299	.9882	.15481	6.460	.2
.9	.05059	.9987	.05066	19.74	.1	.9	.15471	.9880	.15660	6.386	.1
3.0	.05234	0.9986	.05241	19.081	87.0	9.0	.15643	0.9877	.15838	6.314	81.0
.1	.05408	.9985	.05416	18.464	.9	.1	.15816	.9874	.16017	6.243	.9
.2	.05582	.9984	.05591	17.886	.8	.2	.15988	.9871	.16196	6.174	.8
.3	.05756	.9983	.05766	17.343	.7	.3	.16160	.9869	.16376	6.107	.7
.4	.05931	.9982	.05941	16.832	.6	.4	.16333	.9866	.16555	6.041	.6
.5	.06105	.9981	.06116	16.350	.5	.5	.16505	.9863	.16734	5.976	.5
.6	.06279	.9980	.06291	15.895	.4	.6	.16677	.9860	.16914	5.912	.4
.7	.06453	.9979	.06467	15.464	.3	.7	.16849	.9857	.17093	5.850	.3
.8	.06627	.9978	.06642	15.056	.2	.8	.17021	.9854	.17273	5.789	.2
.9	.06802	.9977	.06817	14.669	.1	.9	.17193	.9851	.17453	5.730	.1
4.0	.06976	0.9976	.06993	14.301	86.0	10.0	.1736	0.9848	.1763	5.671	80.0
.1	.07150	.9974	.07168	13.951	.9	.1	.1754	.9845	.1781	5.614	.9
.2	.07324	.9973	.07344	13.617	.8	.2	.1771	.9842	.1799	5.558	2.8
.3	.07498	.9972	.07519	13.300	.7	.3	.1788	.9839	.1817	5.503	.7
.4	.07672	.9971	.07695	12.996	.6	.4	.1805	.9836	.1835	5.449	.6
.5	.07846	.9969	.07870	12.706	.5	.5	.1822	.9833	.1853	5.396	.5
.6	.08020	.9968	.08046	12.429	.4	.6	.1840	.9829	.1871	5.343	.4
.7	.08194	.9966	.08221	12.163	.3	.7	.1857	.9826	.1890	5.292	.3
.8	.08368	.9965	.08397	11.909	.2	.8	.1874	.9823	.1908	5.242	.2
.9	.08542	.9963	.08573	11.664	.1	.9	.1891	.9820	.1926	5.193	.1
5.0	.08716	0.9962	.08749	11.430	85.0	11.0	.1908	0.9816	.1944	5.145	79.0
.1	.08889	.9960	.08925	11.205	.9	.1	.1925	.9813	.1962	5.097	.9
.2	.09063	.9959	.09101	10.988	.8	.2	.1942	.9810	.1980	5.050	.8
.3	.09237	.9957	.09277	10.780	.7	.3	.1959	.9806	.1998	5.005	.7
.4	.09411	.9956	.09453	10.579	.6	.4	.1977	.9803	.2016	4.959	.6
.5	.09585	.9954	.09629	10.385	.5	.5	.1994	.9799	.2035	4.915	.5
.6	.09758	.9952	.09805	10.199	.4	.6	.2011	.9796	.2053	4.872	.4
.7	.09932	.9951	.09981	10.019	.3	.7	.2028	.9792	.2071	4.829	.3
.8	.10106	.9949	.10158	9.845	.3	.8	.2045	.9789	.2089	4.787	.2
.9	.10279	.9947	.10334	9.677	.1	.9	.2062	.9785	.2107	4.745	.1
6.0	.10453	0.9945	.10510	9.514	84.0	12.0	.2079	0.9781	.2126	4.705	78.0
Deg.	Sin	Cos	Tan	Cot	Deg.	Deg.	Sin	Cos	Tan	Cot	Deg.

Deg.	Sin	Cos	Tan	Cot	Deg.	Deg.	Sin	Cos	Tan	Cot	Deg.
12.0	0.2079	0.9781	0.2126	4.705	78.0	18.0	0.3090	0.9511	0.3249	3.078	72.0
.1	.2096	.9778	.2144	4.665	.9	.1	.3107	.9505	.3269	3.060	.9
.2	.2113	.9774	.2162	4.625	.8	.2	.3123	.9500	.3288	3.042	.8
.3	.2130	.9770	.2180	4.586	.7	.3	.3140	.9494	.3307	3.024	.7
.4	.2147	.9767	.2199	4.548	.6	.4	.3156	.9489	.3327	3.006	.6
.5	.2164	.9763	.2217	4.511	.5	.5	.3173	.9483	.3346	2.989	.5
.6	.2181	.9759	.2235	4.474	.4	.6	.3190	.9478	.3365	2.971	.4
.7	.2198	.9755	.2254	4.437	.3	.7	.3206	.9472	.3385	2.954	.3
.8	.2215	.9751	.2272	4.402	.2	.8	.3223	.9466	.3404	2.937	.2
.9	.2233	.9748	.2290	4.366	.1	.9	.3239	.9461	.3424	2.921	.1
13.0	0.2250	0.9744	0.2309	4.331	77.0	19.0	0.3256	0.9455	0.3443	2.904	71.0
.1	.2267	.9740	.2327	4.297	.9	.1	.3272	.9449	.3463	2.888	.9
.2	.2284	.9736	.2345	4.264	.8	.2	.3289	.9444	.3482	2.872	.8
.3	.2300	.9732	.2364	4.230	.7	.3	.3305	.9438	.3502	2.856	.7
.4	.2317	.9728	.2382	4.198	.6	.4	.3322	.9432	.3522	2.840	.6
.5	.2334	.9724	.2401	4.165	.5	.5	.3338	.9426	.3541	2.824	.5
.6	.2351	.9720	.2419	4.134	.4	.6	.3355	.9421	.3561	2.808	.4
.7	.2368	.9715	.2438	4.102	.3	.7	.3371	.9415	.3581	2.793	.3
.8	.2385	.9711	.2456	4.071	.2	.8	.3387	.9409	.3600	2.778	.2
.9	.2402	.9707	.2475	4.041	.1	.9	.3404	.9403	.3620	2.762	.1
14.0	0.2419	0.9703	0.2493	4.011	76.0	20.0	0.3420	0.9397	0.3640	2.747	70.0
.1	.2436	.9699	.2512	3.981	.9	.1	.3437	.9391	.3659	2.733	.9
.2	.2453	.9694	.2530	3.952	.8	.2	.3453	.9385	.3679	2.718	.8
.3	.2470	.9690	.2549	3.923	.7	.3	.3469	.9379	.3699	2.703	.7
.4	.2487	.9686	.2568	3.895	.6	.4	.3486	.9373	.3719	2.689	.6
.5	.2504	.9681	.2586	3.867	.5	.5	.3502	.9367	.3739	2.675	.5
.6	.2521	.9677	.2605	3.839	.4	.6	.3518	.9361	.3759	2.660	.4
.7	.2538	.9673	.2623	3.812	.3	.7	.3535	.9354	.3779	2.646	.3
.8	.2554	.9668	.2642	3.785	.2	.8	.3551	.9348	.3799	2.633	.2
.9	.2571	.9664	.2661	3.758	.1	.9	.3567	.9342	.3819	2.619	.1
15.0	0.2588	0.9659	0.2679	3.732	75.0	21.0	0.3584	0.9336	0.3839	2.605	69.0
.1	.2605	.9655	.2698	3.706	.9	.1	.3600	.9330	.3859	2.592	.9
.2	.2622	.9650	.2717	3.681	.8	.2	.3616	.9323	.3879	2.578	.8
.3	.2639	.9646	.2736	3.655	.7	.3	.3633	.9317	.3899	2.565	.7
.4	.2656	.9641	.2754	3.630	.6	.4	.3649	.9311	.3919	2.552	.6
.5	.2672	.9636	.2773	3.606	.5	.5	.3665	.9304	.3939	2.539	.5
.6	.2689	.9632	.2792	3.582	.4	.6	.3681	.9298	.3959	2.526	.4
.7	.2706	.9627	.2811	3.558	.3	.7	.3697	.9291	.3979	2.513	.3
.8	.2723	.9622	.2830	3.534	.2	.8	.3714	.9285	.4000	2.500	.2
.9	.2740	.9617	.2849	3.511	.1	.9	.3730	.9278	.4020	2.488	.1
16.0	0.2756	0.9613	0.2867	3.487	74.0	22.0	0.3746	0.9272	0.4040	2.475	68.0
.1	.2773	.9608	.2886	3.465	.9	.1	.3762	.9265	.4061	2.463	.9
.2	.2790	.9603	.2905	3.442	.8	.2	.3778	.9259	.4081	2.450	.8
.3	.2807	.9598	.2924	3.420	.7	.3	.3795	.9252	.4101	2.438	.7
.4	.2823	.9593	.2943	3.398	.6	.4	.3811	.9245	.4122	2.426	.6
.5	.2840	.9588	.2962	3.376	.5	.5	.3827	.9239	.4142	2.414	.5
.6	.2857	.9583	.2981	3.354	.4	.6	.3843	.9232	.4163	2.402	.4
.7	.2874	.9578	.3000	3.333	.3	.7	.3859	.9225	.4183	2.391	.3
.8	.2890	.9573	.3019	3.312	.2	.8	.3875	.9219	.4204	2.379	.2
.9	.2907	.9568	.3038	3.291	.1	.9	.3891	.9212	.4224	2.367	.1
17.0	0.2924	0.9563	0.3057	3.271	73.0	23.0	0.3907	0.9205	0.4245	2.356	67.0
.1	.2940	.9558	.3076	3.251	.9	.1	.3923	.9198	.4265	2.344	.9
.2	.2957	.9553	.3096	3.230	.8	.2	.3939	.9191	.4286	2.333	.8
.3	.2974	.9548	.3115	3.211	.7	.3	.3955	.9184	.4307	2.322	.7
.4	.2990	.9542	.3134	3.191	.6	.4	.3971	.9178	.4327	2.311	.6
.5	.3007	.9537	.3153	3.172	.5	.5	.3987	.9171	.4348	2.300	.5
.6	.3024	.9532	.3172	3.152	.4	.6	.4003	.9164	.4369	2.289	.4
.7	.3040	.9527	.3191	3.133	.3	.7	.4019	.9157	.4390	2.278	.3
.8	.3057	.9521	.3211	3.115	.2	.8	.4035	.9150	.4411	2.267	.2
.9	.3074	.9516	.3230	3.096	.1	.9	.4051	.9143	.4431	2.257	.1
18.0	0.3090	0.9511	0.3249	3.078	72.0	24.0	0.4067	0.9135	.4452	2.246	66.0
Deg.	Cos	Sin	Cot	Tan	Deg.	Deg.	Cos	Sin	Cot	Tan	Deg.

Deg.	Sin	Cos	Tan	Cot	Deg.	Deg.	Sin	Cos	Tan	Cot	Deg.
24.0	0.4067	0.9135	0.4452	2.246	66.0	30.0	0.5000	0.8660	0.5774	1.7321	60.0
.1	.4083	.9128	.4473	2.236	.9	.1	.5015	8652	.5797	1.7251	.9
.2	.4099	.9121	.4494	2.225	.8	.2	.5030	.8643	.5820	1.7182	.8
.3	.4115	.9114	.4515	2.215	.7	.3	.5045	.8634	.5844	1.7113	.7
.4	.4131	.9107	.4536	2.204	.6	.4	.5060	.8625	.5867	1.7045	.6
.5	.4147	.9100	.4557	2.194	.5	.5	.5075	.8616	.5890	1.6977	.5
.6	.4163	.9092	.4578	2.184	.4	.6	.5090	.8607	.5914	1.6909	.4
.7	.4179	.9085	.4599	2.174	.3	.7	.5105	.8599	.5938	1.6842	.3
.8	.4195	.9078	.4621	2.164	.2	.8	.5120	.8590	.5961	1.6775	.2
.9	.4210	.9070	.4642	2.154	.1	.9	.5135	.8581	.5985	1.6709	.1
25.0	0.4226	0.9063	0.4663	2.145	65.0	31.0	0.5150	0.8572	0.6009	1.6643	59.0
.1	.4242	.9056	.4684	2.135	.9	.1	.5165	.8563	.6032	1.6577	.9
.2	.4258	.9048	.4706	2.125	.8	.2	.5180	.8554	.6056	1.6512	.8
.3	.4274	.9041	.4727	2.116	.7	.3	.5195	.8545	.6080	1.6447	.7
.4	.4289	.9033	.4748	2.106	.6	.4	.5210	.8536	.6104	1.6383	.6
.5	.4305	.9026	.4770	2.097	.5	.5	.5225	.8526	.6128	1.6319	.5
.6	.4321	.9018	.4791	2.087	.4	.6	.5240	.8517	.6152	1.6255	.4
.7	.4337	.9011	.4813	2.078	.3	.7	.5255	.8508	.6176	1.6191	.3
.8	.4352	.9003	.4834	2.069	.2	.8	.5270	.8499	.6200	1.6128	.2
.9	.4368	.8996	.4856	2.059	.1	.9	.5284	.8490	.6224	1.6066	.1
26.0	0.4384	0.8988	0.4877	2.050	64.0	32.0	0.5299	0.8480	0.6249	1.6003	58.0
.1	.4399	.8980	.4899	2.041	.9	.1	.5314	.8471	.6273	1.5941	.9
.2	.4415	.8973	.4921	2.032	.8	.2	.5329	.8462	.6297	1.5880	.8
.3	.4431	.8965	.4942	2.023	.7	.3	.5344	.8453	.6322	1.5818	.7
.4	.4446	.8957	.4964	2.014	.6	.4	.5358	.8443	.6346	1.5757	.6
.5	.4462	.8949	.4986	2.006	.5	.5	.5373	.8434	.6371	1.5697	.5
.6	.4478	.8942	.5008	1.997	.4	.6	.5388	.8425	.6395	1.5637	.4
.7	.4493	.8934	.5029	1.988	.3	.7	.5402	.8415	.6420	1.5577	.3
.8	.4509	.8926	.5051	1.980	.2	.8	.5417	.8406	.6445	1.5517	.2
.9	.4524	.8918	.5073	1.971	.1	.9	.5432	.8396	.6469	1.5458	.1
27.0	0.4540	0.8910	0.5095	1.963	63.0	33.0	0.5446	0.8387	0.6494	1.5399	57.0
.1	.4555	.8902	.5117	1.954	.9	.1	.5461	.8377	.6519	1.5340	.9
.2	.4571	.8894	.5139	1.946	.8	.2	.5476	.8368	.6544	1.5282	.8
.3	.4586	.8886	.5161	1.937	.7	.3	.5490	.8358	.6569	1.5224	.7
.4	.4602	.8878	.5184	1.929	.6	.4	.5505	.8348	.6594	1.5166	.6
.5	.4617	.8870	.5206	1.921	.5	.5	.5519	.8339	.6619	1.5108	.5
.6	.4633	.8862	.5228	1.913	.4	.6	.5534	.8329	.6644	1.5051	.4
.7	.4648	.8854	.5250	1.905	.3	.7	.5548	.8320	.6669	1.4994	.3
.8	.4664	.8846	.5272	1.897	.2	.8	.5563	.8310	.6694	1.4938	.2
.9	.4679	.8838	.5295	1.889	.1	.9	.5577	.8300	.6720	1.4882	.1
28.0	0.4695	0.8829	0.5317	1.881	62.0	34.0	0.5592	0.8290	0.6745	1.4826	56.0
.1	.4710	.8821	.5340	1.873	.9	.1	.5606	.8281	.6771	1.4770	.9
.2	.4726	.8813	.5362	1.865	.8	.2	.5621	.8271	.6796	1.4715	.8
.3	.4741	.8805	.5384	1.857	.7	.3	.5635	.8261	.6822	1.4659	.7
.4	.4756	.8796	.5407	1.849	.6	.4	.5650	.8251	.6847	1.4605	.6
.5	.4772	.8788	.5430	1.842	.5	.5	.5664	.8241	.6873	1.4550	.5
.6	.4787	.8780	.5452	1.834	.4	.6	.5678	.8231	.6899	1.4496	.4
.7	.4802	.8771	.5475	1.827	.3	.7	.5693	.8221	.6924	1.4442	.3
.8	.4818	.8763	.5498	1.819	.2	.8	.5707	.8211	.6950	1.4388	.2
.9	.4833	.8755	.5520	1.811	.1	.9	.5721	.8202	.6976	1.4335	.1
29.0	0.4848	0.8746	0.5543	1.804	61.0	35.0	0.5736	0.8192	0.7002	1.4281	55.0
.1	.4863	.8738	.5566	1.797	.9	.1	.5750	.8181	.7028	1.4229	.9
.2	.4879	.8729	.5589	1.789	.8	.2	.5764	.8171	.7054	1.4176	.8
.3	.4894	.8721	.5612	1.782	.7	.3	.5779	.8161	.7080	1.4124	.7
.4	.4909	.8712	.5635	1.775	.6	.4	.5793	.8151	.7107	1.4071	.6
.5	.4924	.8704	.5658	1.767	.5	.5	.5807	.8141	.7133	1.4019	.5
.6	.4939	.8695	.5681	1.760	.4	.6	.5821	.8131	.7159	1.3968	.4
.7	.4955	.8686	.5704	1.753	.3	.7	.5835	.8121	.7186	1.3916	.3
.8	.4970	.8678	.5727	1.746	.2	.8	.5850	.8111	.7212	1.3865	.2
.9	.4985	.8669	.5750	1.739	.1	.9	.5864	.8100	.7239	1.3814	.1
30.0	0.5000	0.8660	0.5774	1.732	60.0	36.0	0.5878	0.8090	0.7265	1.3764	54.0
Deg.	Cos	Sin	Cot	Tan	Deg.	Deg.	Cos	Sin	Cot	Tan	Deg.

Deg.	Sin	Cos	Tan	Cot	Deg.	Deg.	Sin	Cos	Tan	Cot	Deg.
36.0	0.5878	0.8090	0.7265	1.3764	54.0	40.5	0.6494	0.7604	0.8541	1.1708	49.5
.1	.5892	.8080	.7292	1.3713	.9	.6	.6508	.7593	.8571	1.1667	.4
.2	.5906	.8070	.7319	1.3663	.8	.7	.6521	.7581	.8601	1.1626	.3
.3	.5920	.8059	.7346	1.3613	.7	.8	.6534	.7570	.8632	1.1585	.2
.4	.5934	.8049	.7373	1.3564	.6	.9	.6547	.7559	.8662	1.1544	.1
.5	.5948	.8039	.7400	1.3514	.5	41.0	0.6561	0.7547	0.8693	1.1504	49.0
.6	.5962	.8028	.7427	1.3465	.4	.1	.6574	.7536	.8724	1.1463	.9
.7	.5976	.8018	.7454	1.3416	.3	.2	.6587	.7524	.8754	1.1423	.8
.8	.5990	.8007	.7481	1.3367	.2	.3	.6600	.7513	.8785	1.1383	.7
.9	.6004	.7997	.7508	1.3319	.1	.4	.6613	.7501	.8816	1.1343	.6
37.0	0.6018	0.7986	0.7536	1.3270	53.0	.5	.6626	.7490	.8847	1.1303	.5
.1	.6032	.7976	.7563	1.3222	.9	.6	.6639	.7478	.8878	1.1263	.4
.2	.6046	.7965	.7590	1.3175	.8	.7	.6652	.7466	.8910	1.1224	.3
.3	.6060	.7955	.7618	1.3127	.7	.8	.6665	.7455	.8941	1.1184	.2
.4	.6074	.7944	.7646	1.3079	.6	.9	.6678	.7443	.8972	1.1145	.1
.5	.6088	.7934	.7673	1.3032	.5	42.0	0.6691	0.7431	0.9004	1.1106	48.0
.6	.6101	.7923	.7701	1.2985	.4	.1	.6704	.7420	.9036	1.1067	.9
.7	.6115	.7912	.7729	1.2938	.3	.2	.6717	.7408	.9067	1.1028	.8
.8	.6129	.7902	.7757	1.2892	.2	.3	.6730	.7396	.9099	1.0990	.7
.9	.6143	.7891	.7785	1.2846	.1	.4	.6743	.7385	.9131	1.0951	.6
38.0	0.6157	0.7880	0.7813	1.2799	52.0	.5	.6756	.7373	.9163	1.0913	.5
.1	.6170	.7869	.7841	1.2753	.9	.6	.6769	.7361	.9195	1.0875	.4
.2	.6184	.7859	.7869	1.2708	.8	.7	.6782	.7349	.9228	1.0837	.3
.3	.6198	.7848	.7898	1.2662	.7	.8	.6794	.7337	.9260	1.0799	.2
.4	.6211	.7837	.7926	1.2617	.6	.9	.6807	.7325	.9293	1.0761	.1
.5	.6225	.7826	.7954	1.2572	.5	43.0	0.6820	0.7314	0.9325	1.0724	47.0
.6	.6239	.7815	.7983	1.2527	.4	.1	.6833	.7302	.9358	1.0686	.9
.7	.6252	.7804	.8012	1.2482	.3	.2	.6845	.7290	.9391	1.0649	.8
.8	.6266	.7793	.8040	1.2437	.2	.3	.6858	.7278	.9424	1.0612	.7
.9	.6280	.7782	.8069	1.2393	.1	.4	.6871	.7266	.9457	1.0575	.6
39.0	0.6293	0.7771	0.8098	1.2349	51.0	.5	.6884	.7254	.9490	1.0538	.5
.1	.6307	.7760	.8127	1.2305	.9	.6	.6896	.7242	.9523	1.0501	.4
.2	.6320	.7749	.8156	1.2261	.8	.7	.6909	.7230	.9556	1.0464	.3
.3	.6334	.7738	.8185	1.2218	.7	.8	.6921	.7218	.9590	1.0428	.2
.4	.6347	.7727	.8214	1.2174	.6	.9	.6934	.7206	.9623	1.0392	.1
.5	.6361	.7716	.8243	1.2131	.5	44.0	0.6947	0.7193	0.9657	1.0355	46.0
.6	.6374	.7705	.8273	1.2088	.4	.1	.6959	.7181	.9691	1.0319	.9
.7	.6388	.7694	.8302	1.2045	.3	.2	.6972	.7169	.9725	1.0283	.8
.8	.6401	.7683	.8332	1.2002	.2	.3	.6984	.7157	.9759	1.0247	.7
.9	.6414	.7672	.8361	1.1960	.1	.4	.6997	.7145	.9793	1.0212	.6
40.0	0.6428	0.7660	0.8391	1.1918	50.0	.5	.7009	.7133	.9827	1.0176	.5
.1	.6441	.7649	.8421	1.1875	.9	.6	.7022	.7120	.9861	1.0141	.4
.2	.6455	.7638	.8451	1.1833	.8	.7	.7034	.7108	.9896	1.0105	.3
.3	.6468	.7627	.8481	1.1792	.7	.8	.7046	.7096	.9930	1.0070	.2
.4	.6481	.7615	.8511	1.1750	.6	.9	.7059	.7083	.9965	1.0035	.1
40.5	0.6494	0.7604	0.8541	1.1708	49.5	45.0	0.7071	0.7071	1.0000	1.0000	45.0
Deg.	Cos	Sin	Cot	Tan	Deg.	Deg.	Cos	Sin	Cot	Tan	Deg.

Index